Practice, Practice, Practice: This Psychiatrist's Life

By Daniela V. Gitlin, MD

Published 2020 by Corner Office Books
Printed in the United States of America

ISBN: 978-0-9600085-5-1

Cover art and design by Dwayne Booth
Author Photo Copyright Bonnie J Heath. bonniejheath.com

Copyright/previous publications:

"It's Not Easy Being Green," published in a different form,
Lake Champlain Weekly, October 20-November 4, 2014,
Volume 15, Issue 15.

"There's No Place Like Gnome," published in a different
form, *Psychiatric Times* supplement: "The Patient Who
Made Me a Better Psychiatrist," November 2016.

Dedication

For Kevin and Misha, my beloveds

In memoriam: Sasha, a.k.a. Zen Sage Trapped in a Poodle Body

Author's Note

This book is a memoir of my work and life as a psychiatrist. Only the "journal articles" are fictional; the rest is creative non-fiction.

Maintaining patients' privacy and confidentiality is my core commitment as a therapist, physician, and now, author. All patient names used here are fictitious and any specific information that might publically identify someone has been removed. The patients described are composites of many individuals combined into general character types who illustrate various treatment dilemmas (or life dilemmas). Any resemblance of such a composite character to any actual person is entirely coincidental.

The focus of this book is on the various *situations* I've found myself in with patients (and others) over the years. These actually occurred and have not been changed. I've described what happened as I remember it, or as I've recreated it, in order to make clear what I learned.

Table of Contents

The big talent is persistence. Octavia Butler

A young woman carrying a violin case is lost in midtown Manhattan. She approaches three little old ladies waiting for the light to change at the crosswalk of 50th Street and 7th Avenue. "Excuse me," she says. "How do I get to Carnegie Hall?" The biddies, as one, say, "Practice! Practice. Practice."

Pay attention. Be astonished. Tell about it. Mary Oliver

Introduction

When people find out I'm a psychiatrist, they usually react in one of six ways:

One (while leaning back and holding up crossed index fingers): "Don't analyze me!" To which I smile and say, "Relax. I'm off duty."

Two (with a shudder): "I couldn't listen to all that misery, day after day. How can you stand it?" Are you kidding? It's real and compelling and I can't believe my good fortune. Shadow me here and you'll see why.

Three (with furrowed brow): "What is it you actually *do*? You're just sitting there." I'm listening and thinking about what I'm hearing. I'm problem-solving. I'm living a vivid interior life.

Four (as if rubbernecking an impending crash): "Do you and your husband analyze each other?" No! It's too much work. "What's it like for your kid to have two shrinks for parents?" Our son shrugs at that: we're "just parents."

Five (with disdain): "Why should I pay you to listen to me? That's what friends are for." Well… ask yourself this. Do you have any friends who will give you their full attention for forty-five minutes— Okay, let's be realistic, five minutes— think *only* about what you're saying, and speak *only* to what will be of service to *you*? Me neither.[1]

Six (my favorite): "That is SO cool! Tell me more." Happy to. Read on.

There are many books out there about the exciting and evolving medical aspects of psychiatry, such as the science behind the medications we use and the neurobiology of the brain. This book is not one of them.

People are much more than their illnesses. Certainly insurance companies want to reduce me to a mechanic that prescribes and the patient to a car in need of repair, but that's not how it works. We are two human beings working together to alleviate the patient's suffering in order to live a better life.

Therapy is a process that allows a person, through interacting with a therapist, to learn what gets them into trouble.[2] It takes a while to establish the necessary trust, but sooner or later, and always in the context of a conflict, the patient will behave with me as they do with everybody else.

A martial arts master has to be willing to take some punches from students learning to spar. While the blows a therapist absorbs from a patient aren't physical, the principle applies. I'll react to the patient as anybody else would, but I keep that reaction to myself until I understand

---

[1] My husband, if he's well rested and has nothing distracting him, might give me ten.

[2] This is such hard work that people come in for therapy only when their suffering has become intolerable.

what it's taught me about him or her. How I deliver the feedback makes a difference. If the patient receives it and uses it, that moves the treatment forward.

Maintaining the connection between us is the beating heart of the work and what this book is about. It takes lots of training and practice to facilitate. It's endlessly fascinating, incredibly intimate, and always a privilege.

The work demands so much of a therapist, it's been called the impossible profession. The following is a summary of what's required:[3]

- The basic rule for practicing this art is *the complete concentration of the listener.*
- Nothing of personal importance must be on her mind. She must be free from and undistracted by anxieties as well as desires.
- She must possess a working imagination that is concrete enough to be expressed in words.
- She must be empathic and strong enough to feel the other's experience as if it were her own.
- This empathy is a crucial facet of the capacity for love. To understand another is to love him—not in the erotic sense, but in the sense of reaching out to him and overcoming the fear of losing oneself.
- Understanding and loving are inseparable. *If they are separate, it is a cerebral process and the door to essential understanding remains closed.*

---

[3] Adapted from *The Art of Listening,* by the late psychologist Erich Fromm.

If the patient and I are two circles, where we overlap— the relationship— is a zone of unpredictability. This is where therapy work is done. This is where chance is either my enemy or my friend, depending on my attitude. No amount of practice will ever make perfect. No amount of planning fully protects against the chaos that is intrinsic to as complex an organism as the treatment relationship.[4]

What kind of person voluntarily takes on the challenge? No one, least of all me, would have predicted I'd go to medical school and become a shrink. But as you'll read in The Growing Up Years, the necessary qualities were present early on.

As a physician therapist, carrying life and death responsibility heightened my fear of making a mistake. *What if—* I missed something? *What if—* I over medicated? Used the wrong medicine? Didn't ask the right question? Drew the wrong conclusion?—*and the patient died?* It took me years to accept the weight. I struggled intensely with it during The Training Years.

Long after I finished the residency, an ongoing fear of making mistakes continued to inhibit me from being fully present, disconnecting me from patients. This led to missed opportunities to help, and worse, to burnout. Repeatedly experiencing an electrifying moment of aliveness and connection with patients is, I firmly believe, the antidote. But this requires a tolerance for uncertainty and a willingness to stumble on the edge.[5]

---

[4] Or, really, any relationship.
[5] *Anything worth doing is worth doing badly.* C. K. Chesterton

Increased confidence is the upside of embracing risk instead of running from it. Frequent loss of dignity is the downside. I wish I could be smoother, but it's not possible. When the unexpected reveals itself, you don't know what to do because it's...unexpected. New. The only option is to ad lib, a creative activity that requires trust in myself, the patient, and our bond. Sometimes it goes amazingly well. Sometimes not. There's always something to learn. A sense of humor helps.

Best-selling author Stephen King said, "A little talent is a good thing to have if you want to be a writer. But the only real requirement is the ability to remember every scar." The same can be said of a therapist. The writer mixes memory with craft to induce an experience in the reader. The therapist reviews the past (her own, the patient's, and the patient's treatment history, including the last session) in order to learn from mistakes made there and become more skilled and helpful to patients.

This book combines both agendas. I wrote it to induce the experience of being a therapist in you, the curious reader. I wrote it also for you, my colleagues, to give you a shortcut to bypass my mistakes so you can get straight to your own.

What's my life like? I see lots of patients. I read a lot, professional and otherwise. I think a lot. I run the practice. I'm a wife and a parent. I cook, do laundry, and pay the bills. I pursue my personal interests. The usual working woman's gumbo, seasoned with risk and a hot dash of humor: The Practice Years.

The only interesting thing in any story is how the protagonist deals with trouble, what she learns, and how she, and others, change as a result. This is what keeps me reading. This is what keeps me engaged in session, not to mention in the rest of my life.

On any given day, I know something unexpected will happen in session. (And elsewhere.) I just won't know when or what or with whom. Unfortunately, it might be me. Therapist pratfalls! Patient ambushes! Too many plates up in the air! It's scary. It's embarrassing. It's an adventure.

~If you encounter an unfamiliar term,
look for it in the Appendices, in the Glossary~

The Growing Up Years (1955-1982)

I have walked through many lives,
some of them my own,
and I am not who I was
though some principle of being
abides, from which I struggle
not to stray. […] "The Layers,"
Stanley Kunitz

My First Memory

1958, Santiago, Chile. I am three and a half years old, out for a walk on the city sidewalk with Soyla, the maid, and Bro, eighteen months. Mommy is home with baby Sis. Soyla holds Bro's hand, but I walk free. I am a big girl.

Up ahead in the street, just beside the sidewalk, lies an open cesspool, a concrete-bordered square filled with black water, shiny, flat, fascinating, and dangerous. A gagging stink rises as we approach it.

Cars rumble by, people bustle and chatter, kids yell. It is sweaty hot. A slight breeze wrinkles the surface of the water. A feather, downy and pure white, drifts down over the blackness... very, very slowly.

Bro gasps. I know, with absolute certainty, what will happen next. I feel him before I see him break free. He runs full tilt towards the cesspool, hands reaching. Silence descends. Everything slows down. *He will get hurt!* I strain with all my might to lift my feet— *I have to stop him!*— but they are stuck to the sidewalk. He stumbles on the lip and arms still out stretched— reaching, reaching for the feather— tumbles into the dark stench.

Noise rushes in. People shout and mill about. I stick close to Soyla, who crouches on the concrete edge, screaming his name over and over. She leans out and grabs his shirt, dragging him in. He is a big, chubby little boy with a big chubby face. A man helps her pull him out. He just lies there, soaked and caca-stinky. His face is bloody and strange, and he is not crying. She swings him up on her hip, grabs my wrist tight, and yanks me into running to keep up.

I've been hurtled back into this memory countless times just by glimpsing the long vertical scar splitting Bro's hairline. But what the memory *meant* became clear when I saw Bro, and his scar, at Son's fourth birthday party. *Why! Son's just a baby!* I thought. And at three and a half, *so was I.*

But me-of-the-memory knows she's a big girl. Given that was the oldest and most experienced she had ever been, she *was* a big girl. What had persistently troubled three-and-a-half-year-old-me for so many decades after, the way a tongue probes a sore tooth, was this: she knew what would happen, knew what to do to prevent it, felt the responsibility to enact it, but couldn't.

First Generation American, Four Ways

Nashville. My father is Hungarian (from Budapest), my stepfather Austrian (from Vienna), my stepmother Cuban (from Havana), and my mother Dutch (from Amsterdam). Four parents from four different countries. It was like growing up in a little United Nations, without the mutual benefit and cooperation agreement. English spoken with four different accents and four slightly off syntaxes. It made for close listening.

When I was almost five, my father abandoned Mom, me, Bro (three), and Sis (eighteen months) to marry my stepmother and move to New York City. We were living in Santiago, Chile, where he worked as an economist for the UN. He'd traveled frequently and had been gone for long stretches before. I couldn't understand why he wasn't coming back this time. I cried a lot.

As an adult, I saw some photos of Mom taken right after he left. It was obvious from her stare— over-bright, haunted— that she was untethered from all that she'd assumed, that she hadn't seen it coming, not ever, not even in a nightmare.

The next year, she met and married my stepfather, who became Dad, and he moved us from Santiago to Nashville, Tennessee, where he was a professor of economics at Vanderbilt University. (Two economists:

preference or propinquity?) Dad had given me lots of attention when he was courting Mom, and chocolates in fancy boxes, too. I adored him. After they married, he completely ignored me. *He'd bribed me.* I sealed my shattered six-year-old heart against him. He didn't notice.

I spoke only Spanish at the start of second grade. Thank goodness the nice cafeteria lady wearing a hairnet waved her serving spoon over the pans of food when she asked, in a heavy southern accent, "What you want, honey?" I didn't have enough English to say, so I just pointed. In the bathroom, a blonde girl in my class stopped me on my way out with "Wash your hands! Germs!" *Germs? What was that?* Her tone scared me. One day I couldn't speak or read English, then I could. The interval between remains a fog of fear and confusion.

In third grade, I discovered the school library, where I could check out one book at a time and upon returning it, immediately get another, a nice supplement to the seven I checked out weekly from the public library. That was the year Mom went to the hospital for a couple days and brought home a baby. L'il Sis cooed and stretched her tiny arms out for me and I was smitten. I begged Mom to let me take care of her and she let me. The stinky diapers didn't bother me; L'il Sis always giggled when I cleaned her up.

We grew up without grandparents, aunts, uncles, or cousins around. All were far away, across the Atlantic. Neither Mom nor Dad had a sense of humor (beyond sarcasm) and they fought constantly (in German), as did Bro and Sis (in English). Meals were a trial. Sis was left-handed, I right, and the fixed seating arrangement at the dinner table— Sis to my right, me to her left— meant that we couldn't eat without our dominant hands jostling each other, a constant irritation. We'd squabble. Mom or Dad would snap at us. When I suggested that Sis and I switch seats, Mom said, "Bah! I need you on the end to serve. You're the oldest. Stop it." It didn't make sense. Bro, across from me, sat on the other end. But he wasn't expected to serve or clear, and I knew that was fixed, too.

Very Young Adult

Nashville. Much as I wish otherwise, I have never gotten along with Mom. I was seven when I ran away for the first time, after another stupid argument. I packed my metal lunchbox with the book I was reading, a clean pair of panties, a peanut butter sandwich wrapped in wax paper and a green apple, fastened the clasps, and marched off to my new life.

It was twilight, early summer. The air was humid and warm, heavy with the smells of cut grass and mimosa. Insects buzzed; in the distance, someone mowed their lawn; a car drove by. I walked one block, turned the corner toward Ransom Elementary, walked another.

The houses thinned out and windows lit up. The fireflies came out: a green flash here, another there. Suppertime. I kept walking. No one was out, the drone of the lawn mower was gone and the silence was loud. Something skittered through the scrub. Wind swayed the branches and rustled the leaves of the sycamores. Suddenly, full dark fell.

I'm a little girl, I thought. *Where will I sleep?*

The vastness of the world bore down on me, along with how unprepared I was to make my way in it. I ate the apple on the way home. It wasn't sweet.

Looking at photos of smiling-for-the-camera, growing-up me, you'd never know I was biding my time, preparing to break out. While my brother and sister spent their allowance on comics and candy, I saved mine. They objected to chores; I took on more.

When Son turned seven, I asked myself: What core decision might he already have made— *About us, his parents? About his peers? About the world?* — that was already determining his life's course?

Sniper Attacks

Fifth grade. "I'm king of the hill!" shouted Bro (nine), scrambling up a mound of construction rubble piled by the sidewalk. We were walking home from school. Sis (eight) and I (eleven) dashed up behind him, both shouting: "I'm queen!" Naturally, *I* was queen. I was the oldest.

It rankled that Bro, being younger, could declare himself king. Not because king was the top for boys, like queen was top for girls, but because king topped queen for no apparent reason. It wasn't right. But that's the way it was and there was nothing I could to do about it. There were so many not-right things in the world I couldn't do anything about. Like the anonymous phone calls I'd been getting for months.

Brring brring brring. My chest would contract, stomach plummet, throat thicken— *Please, please, not for me*— "It's for you!" The phone was in the kitchen, where the call would interrupt Mom cooking supper. I took the receiver from her, gave her my back for privacy, and twisted the cord with nail-bitten fingers.

"Hello?"

"Queer!" Girls snickered in the background.

You'd think I'd just hang up, but I always froze, mute, phone to my ear. I almost recognized that voice. *Who was she?*

"Your mother talks funny!" Snorts and hoots. Could I help it my mother had a Dutch accent? She was from

Holland! *I* was American. That didn't matter. The acorn doesn't fall far from the tree. Like mother, like daughter. Guilt by association.

"And she dresses you funny!" Waves of group laughter. I slammed the phone down, hand trembling. There it was. Shaking, I would rush from the kitchen to my room, where I sat on the bed, breathing heavily, hands gripping the bedspread.

Mom *did* dress me funny. I thought of the thrift store jumper I had stripped off yesterday as soon as I got home. A little-girl shift, with a seam running across my flat chest, two quarter-sized gold rings at nipple level. I shuddered with embarrassed loathing.

I'd asked her for penny loafers: "No laces? Impractical!" I'd begged for new clothes, not used (I knew better than to ask for brand name): "Too expensive!" Shamed myself by asking for a training bra: "You don't need one." I *knew* that! She always missed the point. I didn't need to fit into it; I needed it to fit in.

I had tried more than once to explain, but she just scoffed, "Ignore them." I couldn't. They wouldn't let me. I hadn't told her about the calls because I knew what she would say: "Don't let it bother you." If only. It didn't make me feel any better that, at my age, she'd lived through the Nazi occupation of Holland. Hell was hell.

Back to the craggy gravel heap, where I stood atop, Queen of Helpless Rage and Blank Despair, barely seeing my non-domain. Trees. Houses. Streets. To the right of the crossroads stood one of the gazillion Baptist churches that we didn't belong to. Three streets ahead lay home and the phone. To the left, four houses down, lived one of the popular girls, Henri.

Henri wasn't smart, her name was stupid, and her clothes beautiful. Every day she held court at "her" cafeteria table, which I was forced to pass en route to the misfits' table, holding my tray before me as if it were a safety-seeking dowsing rod. I looked straight ahead, so I wouldn't see the glances burning holes in my last-season sweater. But I couldn't not hear the snickers.

To be left alone, that's all I wanted. Well no, I wanted more. I wanted to belong. But not to the likes of them. Never.

The cafeteria scene. The phone voice. The tumblers clicked. The lock opened— Henri. "Time to go," I said to Bro and Sis, who had started tossing gravel at each other.

Over the following weeks, I tracked Henri's voice in the cafeteria, in class, at the lockers. When a call came, I listened even closer: *Did the voices match?* I wasn't sure. I wasn't sure. I couldn't take it any more— "I know it's you, Henri!" Tears streaming, I slammed the phone down.

I hated that I always cried when I stood up for myself. I ran to my room and threw myself face down on the bed. I vowed I would never, ever, be mean to anyone. (I wish I could say I've kept that vow.)

Fast-forward a few years to high school. Henri approached me at my locker—We weren't on speaking terms. *What did she want?*—and confessed, saying she was very, very sorry.

I don't remember accepting her apology. I do remember the astonishment, the pleasure, the relief. I'd called it! It had worried me that I'd blamed her when I wasn't sure. But not much, for after I named her, the calls stopped.

Old Enough To Know

1967, the summer between sixth and seventh grade. That was a time when people dressed up to fly and children were allowed to fly unattended by an adult. Bro (ten), Sis (eight) and I (twelve) flew, all dressed up with me in charge, to New York's LaGuardia Airport to see our father for the first time since he'd left, six years before.

He was not in the crowd of smiling, waving people at the gate. The stewardess escorted us to the airline office, a long walk through the airport that was overwhelmingly noisy, crowded, and huge. We waited for two endless, fidgety hours for him to show up, all breezy and full of good cheer, though no explanation. My stepmother scolded him for picking us up late, which made me feel better, as did watching them joke and laugh with each other and their three young sons (six, four and two), the brothers I'd never met.

Not long after that visit, the recurring nightmare of my teens started up. I am always twelve. I don't know how to drive, yet I am driving the family station wagon and responsible for getting us kids home safely. Bro, Sis and L'il Sis sit in the back. It's dark, the road dips and the car speeds up. To reach the brake, I have to stretch my leg reeeeaaaally far, but no matter how hard I press with the ball of my foot, the car doesn't slow down. Shrieks of laughter blast from the back seat. With deep certainty, I know the station wagon—massive, unwieldy, extremely heavy— will crash. I know it in the way you know the point of no return when you fall: you can't save yourself, you're going to smash into the ground, it's happening in slow motion. The car rushes faster and faster— we're going to die; it's all my fault—I bolt up in bed, sweaty, short of breath, skin crawling, heart pounding out of my chest.

High School: This Too Shall Pass

Seventh grade. In Tennessee, high school begins with seventh grade. Six periods, six different teachers, twenty-five different kids per class. Clanging bells, the din and crush of running *en masse* to the next class at the far end of the school, up and down flights of stairs. Afraid of being late. Not having started puberty. Kids in groups talking mean about me, not to my face, but as I walk by, to my ears. Between my home life and school, I cried a lot, secretly.

One night Mom caught me sobbing in bed, curled to the wall in the dark. She actually sat on the edge of the bed and rubbed my back, asking what was wrong. She always disappointed me when I opened my heart, but hope springs eternal when you're twelve and anguished. I wiped my eyes, rolled onto my back and told her.

"Bah! Why do you let it bother you? You are much too sensitive!" she said, like that was bad and something I could curb, but willfully chose not to. "Just ignore them." She always said that. She was useless.

Later, when I was twenty, one of the most healing things I learned from psychiatrist Dr. Harris, my first therapist, was this: you can't control feelings. It was such a relief to stop trying. They are the natural and automatic response to stimuli— either internal (thoughts) or external (getting bullied). Even as a girl, I knew this intuitively. Each time Mom suggested otherwise, she hurt me on top of the original hurt. Each time, it hurt worse. That night, I gave up on her.

Eighth grade. I couldn't stand sitting alone in the cafeteria anymore. It was like having a sign on my back that said: Mock me. I had to do something.

I spent the rest of the year listening— while walking to classes, to my locker, to the bathroom and cafeteria— and observing that girls in established groups greeted each other and looked out for each other, saving seats at assemblies and in the cafeteria. A pattern emerged: they talked mostly about boys and clothes. Or, for a change, clothes and boys. Over the summer I formulated a plan.

Ninth grade. From day one, I walked with head up in the halls and said hello to anyone who made eye contact with me. When standing in line, if she looked my way, I complimented the clothing of the girl next me. My heart raced, my armpits got damp and my breath short, but I did it.

I got *Who-are-you? Do-I-know-you?* frowns; *How-dare-you?* glares; *Who-me?* raised eyebrows and astonished looks, and after a while, nods and, occasionally, a smile. As the year went on, a few misfit girls clustered around and we sat together in the cafeteria. We had nothing in common, those girls and I, other than being outside looking in. I remember only Lisa, thin and mousy, silent and hovering. I regained the enjoyment of learning, even Algebra I, and scored straight A's. Dad praised me lavishly, "It's about time."

Tenth grade. It was gratifying to have eighth grader Bro observe, as we strolled the hall to our homerooms, "Gee, you know everybody!"

"No, I don't, " I said. "I just greet everybody." It had become obvious, from the amazement and gratitude I got back, how many of us lonely people there were. Lisa and misfits continued to gather around, which was nice at first. But their expectation that I lead the pack quickly dragged me down, a dead weight I didn't know how to unload without hurting them.

Finally I got my period, actually needed a bra, and stopped dreading the gym locker room. I talked cramps like a champ and couldn't believe the boys the fast girls got red-faced and giggly over— smelly, sweaty, rude, loud-mouthed beasts. Yuk. But I kept that to myself, instead asking for more juicy details. Inadvertently, I accessed a law of nature: people love to talk about themselves, especially to someone interested.

I found myself on the periphery of a mixed hippy group. The friendlier I got with them, the more the misfits embarrassed me. The day came that one of the new girls waved to me to sit at her cafeteria table. Lisa, walking with her tray toward "our" table, stopped dead. I broke eye contact, gave her my back, and left her and the others behind. We never had words. I was too ashamed.

I had nothing in common with the new kids. Nobody read. Nobody had an academic parent. Nobody's parents had academic expectations of them. They all drank and smoked in a way I didn't take to. But still, I had fun. Nashville is a music town, and in 1970 one great band after another toured through. The Allman Brothers, Credence

Clearwater, Led Zepplin, Traffic, Janis Joplin, Bob Dylan, Carole King, B.B. King, Aretha Franklin, Jackson Browne. We went to concerts every weekend, something I took completely for granted. Most of the girls had crushes on Paul McCartney. The guys couldn't sit at a table or desk without drumming.

Late fall. It was after a concert that Bobby, a senior and the alpha guy of the group, gave me a ride home. After parking at the top of the driveway, he asked me out. He was slim and slouchy in his jeans and old plaid shirt, love beads dangling a large metal peace sign low to his belt. He wore his long, lank hair parted in the middle and was mild mannered, soft-spoken, and easygoing.

His parents gave him the run of the house, and that's where everyone hung out. He had a massive crush on Grace Slick of the Jefferson Airplane, played air guitar unceasingly and smoked pot constantly. He didn't make me go weak in the knees or anything (not that I knew what that was; I'd only read about it), but most of the girls wanted to go out with him. Now, he'd asked *me* out. I was speechless.

"Do you not want to?" he said, becoming impatient.

"Oh!" I said. "Yes. Sure!" I paused, tentative. "Why me?" *Who asks that? I'm an idiot.*

"You're the only girl who isn't pestering and chasing me."

Overnight I was the alpha girl of the pack. When I wore a jean miniskirt to a piano lesson with my nails painted pink and eyelids shadowed blue, my teacher of many years, Mrs. Ponder, curled her lip, "You look like a floozy." (Up north in New York City, women's lib reigned, but in southern Nashville, it was still deadly for a girl to get a "reputation.") "And, what's that smell?" (Patchouli.) "Don't come to your lesson tarted out like this again. No perfume either."

I quit.

"Why?" Mom cried. "This is the first year it's not painful to listen to you practice!"

"Mrs. Ponder is a ponderous old hag," I said. "I hate her." That got me grounded, but it was worth it.

With Bobby in the picture, my A in geometry was history. By the time I realized what a terrible mistake I'd made letting go of my studies, and the piano, for him, I was too far behind in geometry to catch up. Mom refused to let me resume piano with another teacher: "You'll just quit again." That was outrageous, but I let it go. I knew if I pushed and started again, I'd be stuck. If I did quit again, I'd never hear the end of it. If I wanted to and didn't, it would be a different torture (though probably shorter lived).

Spring. Bobby wasn't actual company, being high most of the time. Then rumors started that he was interested in Katrina, the thirteen-year-old sister of one of the guys. Being fifteen, I took offense instead of seeing that for what it was: he was eighteen going on thirteen. He was always with his friends and the intervals between his calls got longer. I consulted with Julie, my "best" friend, a nice girl perpetually in trouble with her parents over her attraction to bikers. Sweat, motor oil, greasy hair, and danger turned me off, man. But to each her own.

"I don't know what to do," I said. "Have you heard anything more about Bobby and Katrina?"

She shook her head no and pulled her neck into her rounded shoulders.

"Should I break up with him?"

"No!" she said, shocked.

"Why not? He's barely calling me. It's getting humiliating. I don't want to hear through the grapevine he's left me for a seventh grader."

"I couldn't do it," she said.

After waiting two— two!— weeks for him to call, I broke down. "Are we, uh..., still going out?" Silence. I twisted the telephone cord between my fingers and leaned forward in the hard-backed chair, "Is it, uh..., over?"

"Well, uh... yeah, I guess...," he mumbled. That was the first of many times I was disappointed to be right about a guy.

The group dumped me, even Julie. No one made eye contact in the halls. No one saved me a seat in the cafeteria. No one called me. It was all I could do to leave my room for school and meals. Mom scolded, "Come on. Get up. I need you to clean the bathrooms." Dad shrugged, "He was a stupid boy, going nowhere. If you'd wear something besides those baggy jeans and shirts, maybe you'd do better." I lost my temper with both of them frequently.

"Ach!" Mom always said. "You're so fierce!" Like that was a bad thing, something I could curb, but willfully chose not to.

Eleventh grade. In the fall, in art class, I met my first true best friend. Her real name was Margaret, but she called herself Maggitt. She was weird and wonderful and completely herself, without artifice. Her honesty hurt sometimes, but it was a small price to pay. She didn't say things she didn't mean and she did what she said she would do. Her father was Army, something technical, something classified, something super smart. She'd rarely lived in one place longer than a year or two her whole life. She was a brilliant artist and student, straight A's in everything, seemingly without effort. She was going to be an astrophysicist. There was nothing we didn't talk about.

I can still see her standing tall before her easel, brush in one hand, paint-smeared palette in the other; her pock-marked, flat-planed face and straight, shoulder-length brown hair parted in the middle; her dark, alert eyes thoughtfully studying her painting in progress. She was the voice of reason, the sane spot, the life raft that kept me afloat that long, turbulent year.

My parents fought constantly with each other, voices ringing with spite and vitriol. I fought constantly with them. One day late in May, I went too far. Mom stood at the kitchen counter, counting individual blueberries into six bowls, so we'd each get the exact same number. That's the kind of thing she did. Both she and Dad were teens during World War II: she during the Nazi occupation of Holland, he during the annexation of Austria.

The experience had not made either of them kinder, gentler, or more flexible. The Germans brutalized Holland for not collaborating. Mom's brothers disappeared with the Resistance for weeks at a time. A Jewish family her parents had sheltered bolted from the house one night, broken by the terror of waiting to be discovered, and were taken by the Germans outside their front door. At the lowest point of the occupation, the family starved, living on tulip bulbs.

29

We couldn't simply take an apple from the fridge. If one was missing, Mom interrogated us till whoever took it without permission confessed.

The war was long over, we weren't starving, and portioning out individual blueberries was insane. A scream welled up. I snatched the container of blueberries off the counter and threw it across the kitchen, berries flying everywhere. "There! Wasted! And so what! There's plenty more! What's wrong with you?" I shouted.

"Lower your voice. The neighbors will hear," she said. We lived in a three-bedroom suburban house on an acre and a half lot. Even with the windows open, the neighbors weren't going to hear. As usual, her response was beside the point. I blew.

In complete sentences, with impeccable logic and without repeating myself, I ranted about how stupid she was (and why); how she always got things wrong (with examples); how she was suffocating me with her stupid apple and blueberry counting; etc., etc., etc.

I ran to my room and threw myself on the bed, sobbing in dread. It didn't matter that I was right. I had been worse than disrespectful, I'd been cruel. I deserved whatever was coming. Days went by and nothing happened. Finally, broken by the wait, I asked for my punishment.

"Oh, nothing. It was just your period," she said, chopping vegetables at the counter. A sick horror swept up from my belly and I almost threw up. I wasn't an actual person to her, just a body. An incandescent rage followed, cold, bright white and electric, different from anything I'd felt before.

Couple weeks later. Maggitt told me the Army was moving her family the day after school ended and that she wouldn't stay in touch. "I never do. It's just the way I am."

I was devastated. Desperate. How would I survive without her?

"I'm losing my mind! I can't take any more. I have to get out of here."

"Quit talking about it and do it then," she said, exasperated. That jolted me awake. Complaining and whining wasn't a substitute for doing. After my first attempt to run away failed when I was seven because I was too young, I vowed I'd try again when I was older. Since then, I had saved my allowance and babysitting money in preparation. Had the time come? *Yes.* The trapped feeling lifted immediately.

I put together a plan. I stopped fighting with Mom and Dad. I spent more time with my sibs, especially L'il Sis, who was nine. It killed me to leave her, but it was go or drown.

"It's good to see you in a better mood," Mom said in June, about two weeks before school ended, as I folded laundry on her bed, stacking separate piles according to person. Guilt closed my throat, but resolve made me swallow.

The last day of school, Maggitt scrawled that nickname— all vertical lines with one crossbar across the two t's, making a star—across her yearbook photo, obliterating the only physical image I had of her. Tears burned my eyes as I shook my head at her. *I'll never forget you.*

31

The next morning, I hugged L'il Sis hard— "Hey!"— found a reason why Sis shouldn't come with me to the local pool, and walked the mile and a half alone crying, backpack heavy with books, toothbrush, toothpaste, cheese sandwich and a change of clothes. A friend picked me up and took me to the airport. I flew to New York City, to my father, stepmother, and three half brothers. How did I buy the ticket without a credit card or checking account? The same friend had driven me to the airport a couple weeks before, where I bought the ticket with cash.

After that first visit when I was twelve, Bro, Sis, and I spent two weeks every summer with our father, during which he fanned the flames of acrimony between me and Mom. "Come anytime," he'd said, more than once. Yet I didn't call or write I was coming, I suspect for fear he would tell me not to.

I called after I landed at LaGuardia Airport. The phone rang and rang. No answer. I took the bus and then the subway to Manhattan, got off at 42nd Street and walked to the New York Public Library. It was late afternoon, sunny, hot and humid, the street smelling of asphalt, garbage, and urine. I called again from a corner phone booth. No answer. I sat on the dirty concrete steps flanked by the two stone lions, numb. A couple of guys tried to chat me up.

What if they were out of town? I had no Plan B. A few hours later, my father picked up the phone and came to get me. My stepmother wasn't thrilled. My little brothers ran around the apartment living room in circles, loud and exuberant.

"I should call Mom," I said.

"Use the phone in our bedroom," my stepmother said. "It's on the dresser." I lay on my back on their bed, the phone cord stretched to its limit, listening to Mom demand I come home, immediately. I never went back. I was sixteen.

In hindsight, the timing of Maggitt's departure, her refusal to maintain contact, and her exasperation at my empty talk were a gift wrapped in black paper tied with a black satin ribbon. I doubt I would have run away otherwise.

Finally, I Begin My Life

I skipped my last year of high school and started college as a freshman at the New School for Social Research, where my father was a professor of economics in the graduate school. As the school year went on, it became more difficult to sleep on the living room couch. "You need your independence," my father said. "You'll love working and having your own apartment," my stepmother said.

The day after the spring semester ended, I started my first full-time job working for the Girl Scouts in the bowels of their corporate office in mid-town Manhattan, and I moved into my first apartment, a roach-infested, sixth-floor walk-up in the West Village with the bathtub in the kitchen. (It doubled as a counter when covered by a plank.) I placed an ad in the *Village Voice* for a roommate to split the rent. It was heaven.

The joy I took in being on my own and free of parents has, ironically, only been matched by the joy I felt mothering Son the first two years of his life. The expansiveness was marvelous. I didn't clean the apartment for six weeks and learned I preferred the work of keeping it clean to the leisure of living in filth. I loved writing checks to pay the rent, utilities, and phone. I loved going to the laundromat and sliding the quarters in. I loved all the little details of managing my life, including solving the problems and fixing the mistakes.

I cherished my freedom so intensely that I didn't realize for a long time how crushingly lonely I was. My father and stepmother didn't call or visit: "We know you need your space." Dad refused to speak to me. Mom and I had negotiated a tenuous phone détente. L'il Sis, Bro, and Sis weren't chatty when I called. Going to the movies and reading kept me going.

I was an English major. In one class after another, books I had loved when I read them on my own were dissected and killed, in order to figure out— in the most pretentious language imaginable—what made them live. Then there were the many books I loathed from the first few pages but had to read anyway.

Although I had no idea what I wanted to do for work, I decided this: any career that required me to read lots of what I didn't want to read wasn't for me. This critical decision may have steered me away from work that would have come naturally— writing, editing, teaching— yet the result was worth it. Reading for pleasure remains the core of my life.

I drifted into a second major in Fine Art with a focus on marble sculpture, a thoughtful and glacially slow medium if you're not blessed with immense strength. The professor, an established professional with installations all over the City and old enough to be my grandfather, took an interest in me. Though I showed my work in two group shows in SoHo galleries, that didn't fool me into thinking I had a future as a sculptor. I lacked the physical stamina to produce at the rate required and found it impossible to promote myself. When my teacher put the moves on me, I was done.

Meanwhile in Nashville, Bro, 19 and on the Dean's list at Vanderbilt University, suffered a psychotic break from which he never emerged. Schizophrenia is chronic and permanently disabling. The bone-deep loneliness and *Is-this-all-there-is?* I'd suffered in tenth grade came back full bore and stayed, it seemed, forever. The only thing that got me up for work was promising myself I'd go right back to bed as soon as I got home.

Thank God for Dr. Ralph Harris, psychiatrist and psychoanalyst, who saved my life by changing it. The first time we met, I was twenty and he was... old. *What if he dies on me?* "Do you have any questions for me?" he asked kindly.

"Well...," I paused, hesitant.

"Go ahead," he said.

"You're older than I expected. What if you die on me?" *Who asks that? Idiot. Now he'll be mad and that'll be that.*

He smiled broadly, genuinely amused, and chuckled. "It's true I'm old, but my health is good. I'll be around a good while yet." His gaze sharpened a touch. "Provided nothing unexpected happens, of course. I could get hit by a car, for example. Are you OK with that level of random risk?"

Now I smiled, delighted. He understood perfectly. I nodded. An antidepressant lifted the depression and twice weekly therapy sessions helped me put my parents, all four of them, in perspective. (The first iteration anyway. That's a never-ending work in progress.) For the first couple years, I saw him at his Manhattan office, down a few steps on the garden level of a quiet brownstone. And then for three more, after he "retired," in the Bronx at his home, where his schnauzer Otto jumped up on my lap during sessions. When he retired for real, I was ready for it, for I had found my way and had met Hubby.

Two years earlier, holding in my hand the B.A. diploma it had taken me six years to earn while working full time, I thought, *I have to chart a course, have a purpose, do something with myself.* I was 24.

My boyfriend at that time was more adrift than I was, his brother a junkie merchant marine, his mother dead, and his father out of touch. Boyfriend played brilliant classical guitar and whistled full throated like a song bird, with vibrato, range and clarity, each note crisp and soaring— just astonishing— but he was also depressed in a deeply resigned way and refused to go for treatment.

"You're normal," he said. "I'm not. I can't give you what you deserve: marriage, kids, a life. But I'm too weak to leave you. You'll have to do the dirty work. I'm sorry." I cried because I agreed with him. An unwillingness to be self-deluded is an extremely rare and valuable quality in a person.

I was living with several people in a brownstone in Brooklyn. One guy was a law student at NYU whose girlfriend brought bagels when she visited. Another girl was a medical student who spent most of her time studying in her room unless she was with her boyfriend, who beat her. ("Why do you put up with that?" I asked her. She just shrugged.) Joyce was an artist and a friend. For six months, she had grieved over a boyfriend who had disappeared on her—one day they were together, the next he was gone, taking a huge chunk of her heart with him. Then he popped back up.

"He's begging me to take him back," she said, teary. "I don't know what to do. He says he's sorry, he'll never do it again. But how can I believe him?" That she was asking my advice wasn't anything new, nor was she the only one. Everyone in the house told me their troubles. I pondered what she'd told me.

"Why now?" I asked her.

"What?"

"Well, he's been gone six months without a word. What's changed? What's brought him back *now*?"

She stopped crying and went still. Her eyes widened. "That's the question, isn't it. Why now?"

"So, what's he said? Exactly."

We broke it down and she figured out, after eliminating his evasions and her assumptions, that he needed a place to stay.

"God, to think I almost fell for it," she said, aghast. "When he found another bed, he'd just have disappeared again." We contemplated that awful reality. She broke the silence, "You ask really good questions."

A few weeks later, walking home from the subway, I had an *aha!* flash so blinding I stopped cold. *I have a talent. A clarity that cuts right to what matters. I ask good questions. I'll be a therapist.* The conviction was solid.

But how to get there? I discussed it with Dr. Harris, who startled me with his enthusiastic support. Ordinarily, he maintained a neutral, though always compassionate, demeanor.

"You really think I'll be good?"

"Yes."

"Should I become an analyst? I'll have to take the GRE and get a master's. To get a Ph.D., I'll have to write a book."[6]

It was a daunting prospect. "Maybe I should get a social work degree. That would be faster." And easier.

"If you do either of those, you'll always have to defer to a physician."

That sounded good to me. "So?"

"Remember the recurring dream from your teens?"

"You mean the one where I'm twelve and driving with my sibs in the back and the car is going to crash?"

"Yes. When you flew to your father in charge of your younger brother and sister, you carried heavy responsibility without the skills or the authority to manage it. That wasn't the first time, or the last, you were expected to do that. You were a parentified child. If you work as a social worker or psychologist, you'll never have the last word. You'll carry responsibility for a patient without authority. Your childhood trauma will repeat, instead of resolve. Go to medical school and become a psychiatrist. You'll have complete control of the treatment, from meds to therapy."

"But...but..." I sputtered, truly frightened. "I don't have the math and science background!"

"That's easy. Go back to school. Columbia University has a pre-med program for people like you."

"But I'm not smart enough," I moaned.

---

[6] The Ph.D. dissertation is a book-length manuscript often submitted for publication after the degree is awarded.

"Of course you are."

"It'll be so hard!"

"The water's cold, but you'll get used to it," he said, imparting a truth that has served me well since. "You'll be fine."

Dad was supportive too, in his usual way: "Bah. You'll flunk out."

I took out student loans to cover the tuition. Mom surprised me: "I'll help you with living expenses if you agree to be Bro's guardian in the event of my death." I would have done that for nothing.

For two years, including summer semesters, I did my pre-med course work at Columbia's School of General Studies full time, while working part-time as a lab technician in the Black Science building at the uptown medical campus. If you like to suffer, I strongly recommend taking a year's worth of physics over the summer.

It was spring, my last semester of pre-med work and the second of organic chemistry and lab. The lab was three hours twice a week, from six to nine at night, after which I had 90-minute subway ride home to Brooklyn. The ride to work— the medical campus was further north— took longer.

I was half asleep as I stood waiting at the elevator bank to go up to work the morning after a lab, my stuffed book bag on the floor between my feet. A nice baritone voice floated my way, "Come on. It can't be that bad."

It's too early for cornball lines, I thought and looked up into the hazel eyes and smiling face of a very, very cute guy— tall, broad-shouldered, long-legged, and flat-bellied in his pocket tee and jeans. I smiled.

We got on the elevator with a few other people and stood side by side facing the doors, not speaking. He got off at the third floor with a nod, without telling me his name, asking mine, or anything else important such as, "Would you like to go out?" I exited on the fourth floor, bemused.

A few weeks later, we crossed paths in the subway on our respective ways to work. It was hot, smelly, and close on the platform. He was walking from one end, I from the other, so we faced each other as we converged on the stairwell up to the exit. Our eyes met and it was the most natural thing in the world to climb up together, chatting as if we'd always known each other.

In the lobby of the Black Building, on the wall between the two elevators, there was a bulletin board loaded with inked notices on index cards: roommate wanted, bike for sale, volunteers for research needed. I pointed to one seeking volunteers: "The handwriting on this one reminds me of my boss's. She's from Italy."

"My boss wrote that. He's from Italy too. He's setting up a new study. Who do you work for?"

Turns out, his boss and mine were collaborating on that study. We started to run into each other in the building and occasionally had a cup of coffee in the cafeteria on the fly. He was smart, funny, easy to talk to and obviously liked me, so why wasn't he asking me out? My boss, amused, contrived reasons to send me to his lab, where he was head tech. One day, one of the other techs, a large Russian woman with bushy black hair, stomped up to me, much too close, and growled, "He's not here. Can I help you?"

If only I could raise one eyebrow! I shrugged and handed her what my boss had sent me to deliver. *Good luck,* I thought. Maybe he wasn't asking anyone out. Maybe he had a girlfriend. That reminded me of Boyfriend with a pang. I had finally let him go. The ache was constant, a phantom love pain, as though I'd cut off an essential part of myself.

As a résumé-building something-to-do the year I waited to hear from medical schools, I'd applied to Columbia's masters program in biochemical nutrition. If I didn't get in to med school, a science masters would help with the next round of applications. In June, I heard I'd been accepted for September. The program was full time. In August I gave my boss notice.

Turns out Hubby (yes, it was he) was starting that program in the fall, too. The day after my last day at work, he called and asked me out. "What took you so long?" I asked. *Who but me would ask? Idiot.*

"I don't date people from work," he said. Within three months we were living together.

In 1981, one in twenty applicants got in to medical schools in New York state. While my grades and MCAT scores were good, the odds were much better (one in three) if I applied in Tennessee. That's what I did, using Mom's Nashville address. I got my applications in well before the December deadlines. That's how I do things. Meanwhile, Hubby waited until the last minute. That's how he does things. I was astounded to learn he had already applied once and not gotten in, despite stellar credentials, along

43

with tons of lab tech and science work experience. He'd missed the deadlines.

His lab desk was a disaster. His old apartment had smelled like (and looked like) a gym locker room after opposing soccer teams had passed through. He never knew where his keys were. He often left the apartment without money. If I'd known then about Attention Deficit Disorder (ADD), would I have run the other way? Maybe. But probably not. Hubby had that special something that made me want to let him annoy me for the rest of my life.

I got in to the University of Tennessee College of Medicine, Memphis, for August 1982. Hubby, having missed all the deadlines but one, got wait listed at Sackler Medical School, a State University of New York (SUNY) satellite located in Tel Aviv, Israel. His parents wanted him to go. He didn't. They were not happy.

"If you want to come with me to Memphis, we can't live in sin. Memphis is Deep South. We'll have to get married." He didn't want to do that either.

"Your parents don't approve of me living with you, here in everything- goes-New York. It's fine for you, you're a stud. But hardly fine for me, I'm a slut." (Not much has changed about *that* in 2019.) I talked big but really, the idea of medical school without him made my stomach roil. He had saved me in the masters program, which was grueling. The concepts, how and what to study, came naturally to him. Not so for me. Nonetheless, I was the one who wrote the thesis and received the actual diploma. He was ABD, All But Done. "I'll write it soon," he said. I was still innocent and believed him.

"Well, I'm moving in July. Let me know what you decide." You know what he decided. Two weeks after we married and moved, I started medical school. Hubby applied on time to start the following August and got a research tech job at St. Jude's Children's Hospital predicated on finishing his master's thesis. We didn't take a honeymoon. That was a mistake. You're only newlywed once.

At the wedding reception, one of Dad's friends wished us well. "Medical school will break you up. The stats are against you."

The Training Years (1982-1992)
Be careful what you wish for; you might get it.

BEGINNER PRACTICE

Be brave little Piglet.
(adapted from <u>*Winnie the Pooh*</u>, A. A. Milne)

Gross Anatomy

1982, First Month (August), First Year, UT, College of Medicine, Memphis.

Classes were suspended once a month for an exam blitzkrieg in all subjects. The first bombing would start in four days. I was way behind, having wasted time sleeping. Being a creative type not steeped in the sciences had caught up with me. While difficult, the pre-med courses (chemistry, physics, organic chemistry, calculus) had been a feast of logic and reason. By contrast, med school was a glutton's diet of random details untethered from concepts. Especially gross anatomy.

Gross understated the lab. It reeked. A miasma of rot and formaldehyde lay on my skin like plastic wrap. With the first inhalation, legions of my lung cells lay down and died. The first day, a girl ran out of the lab retching. I heard she dropped out. I longed to follow her lead, but no med school, no M.D. I got used to the pickled feeling. Sort of.

Some of the boys coped with pranks. Within the week, they snuck in after hours, cut a strategic slit in the sheet covering their male cadaver and poked a waxy yellow finger through. Next day, muffled snorts erupted around the room. The anatomy professor, Lurch-like in his white-coat, moved his waxy yellow lips regarding the sanctity of the human body, the privilege accorded us, the respect this privilege demanded, etc. In a class of a

49

hundred sixty, only six of us were female. He had to give that waxy yellow speech a few times more as the semester wore on.

We were four to a body. I had a talent for dissection, doing neat work. Each structure had a Latin name, with at least one Latin adjective, usually two or three. While the guys let me dissect fascia from muscle and arteries from nerves, they drove hypothetical exam questions at each other in the spirit of teenaged boys playing chicken in their hot-rods.

"Okay," one quizzed, "if you place an eighteen-bore needle 13.5 centimeters long on the ventral surface of the biceps brachii closest to the axilla, and run it through, medial to the humerus, what structures would it hit, and where would the needle point?"

"At the pizza place across the street?" I wondered. At year's end, there would be a cumulative exam in all courses, not just anatomy. It was unthinkable.

Walking through the modern teaching facility to the anatomy lab to meet my lab mates for a final pre-test round of chicken, my brain ticked off a to-do list. Tonight, we'd finish reviewing the dissection of the arm, the forearm and hand. That left two days to cram the other courses: tomorrow, histology and embryology, and the day after, biochemistry and statistics.

The floor-to-ceiling windows were black with night, the lighting dim. The carpeting muffled my footfalls. The quiet pressed on me, amplifying my exhaustion. I pushed through the double doors into the stench of the older anatomy building.

My steps clattered off the faded, institutional linoleum. Photos of dead anatomists marched down puke-green walls to glass-fronted, dark-wood cases. On the shelves stood jars of mutant fetuses floating in formaldehyde. Goose bumps skittered along my arms from the cranked up air conditioning.

I opened the door to the anatomy lab and my cadaver sat up on his table, swung his legs over the side and shambled toward me. I jumped back— and lost my balance stepping into a bog of corpses, soft, runny, and rotted past the formaldehyde. I thrashed and flailed, yanking my feet up one at a time like frantic pistons, which dug me in deeper even as I pulled myself upright, gasping.

There was a rustling behind me. I jerked my head over my shoulder to look— a blue-uniformed cadaver staggered toward me, cop hat tipped on a skull mangled by student scalpels, one eye socket a dark void, the other dangling an eyeball, teeth bared in a nightmare smile. The suited skeletal arms lifted. The bony hands reached for me.

I twisted, throwing myself to the side— *Please God, let them crash into each other*— sinking to my waist in putrid muck, yanking myself onto my back before my face touched. My cadaver swooped down over me. I looked up at rapidly approaching outstretched arms stripped of skin and fascia, the muscles like rope. *Nice job dissecting out the brachial plexus*, I thought, in that strange calm that comes before disaster strikes. A scream boiled up and my mouth opened. *No! I'll inhale rot!* I woke up on my living room couch.

The relief was immense. So was the greasy formaldehyde stink rising off me. All came clear: lab review, home, sat down, fell asleep. A glance at my wristwatch: I'd lost an hour. Hubby wasn't home. He must still be at work. I showered, scrambled an egg and went into the study. I parked myself at my desk flush against the wall and read the Calvin Coolidge quote tacked to the corkboard right in front of me. I read it every time I sat down.

> *Nothing in the world*
> *can take the place of persistence.*
> *Talent will not do it. Nothing is more common*
> *than an unsuccessful man with talent.*
> *Genius will not. Unrewarded genius is almost a proverb.*
> *Education will not. The world is full of educated derelicts.*
> *Persistence and determination alone are omnipotent.*
> *The slogan— "Press on." —has solved, and will always solve,*
> *the problems of the human race.*

Ignoring the pounding headache, I got to work.

It was my misfortune that my class was the smartest the school had seen in years. The pyramid structure of the program was designed to winnow out the weakest students by the end of the first year. That was the purpose of the comprehensive exam. Ordinarily four or five students failed it and dropped out.

I passed that first anatomy exam but failed the first biochem, a GPA-lowering disaster that would dog me the rest of the year. While I drowned in a tsunami of details, Hubby spent his year suffering a clinical depression as he waited to learn the fate of his application. When he wasn't at work, he lay on the couch, either sleeping or watching TV. In April, he got his acceptance letter.

In May, I learned I wouldn't be allowed to take the comprehensive, even though I had met the minimum overall GPA to take it. I had two options: drop out or repeat the year. I couldn't have felt more humiliated or shattered. If I wasn't a successful student, who was I? If Hubby hadn't been accepted for the fall, it's possible I might have given up. Mom put the cherry on top: "What will I tell my friends?" I hung up on her, a first.

Three weeks went by before she called. "You hung up on me! How rude and unfriendly. Don't do that again," she said, very put out.

"*You* were rude and unfriendly and I'll hang up again if I want to," I said, still reeling from her lack of empathy.

Then Hubby got busted for not writing his master's thesis and almost lost his job. Fortunately he didn't lose it and, even better, his depression lifted. (Did he ever write his thesis? You know the answer.)

As it turned out, being held back against my will was another gift wrapped in black paper. We had July together without school and, once I recovered from the blow to my ego, ecstatic understates how I felt about escaping the comprehensive[7]. Best of all, Hubby and I went through our training years together, well worth two passes through gross anatomy.

---

[7] That year. I had to take it the next. No rest for the stressed.

An Impractical Susceptibility To Beauty

3rd Year Medical School, Emergency Room Rotation.
Beep! Beep! Beep!! Three pagers shrieked in a round. I rolled off the bed, feet already moving toward the door, heart racing. The two other students in the call room shoved me aside, eager and excited, exuding sweat and testosterone. I trailed after them.

In the surgical suite, people in teal scrubs and white surgical masks dashed around a gurney holding the patient: a woman run over in her car by an eighteen-wheeler. Someone shouted. A jet of bright red shot up, glittering in the harsh white light, reaching up up up in a perfect arc....

Everyone but me surged to the table, like metal filings to a magnet. Meanwhile, I backed up against a wall, dumbstruck, tracking first the glowing garnet beauty of the parabola to its peak, then its decay into a vanishing mist of palest pink that fell straight down. I came to with the angry snap of sterile latex gloves peeled off. The attending surgeon announced: "She's gone."

Shame overwhelmed me. I should have tried to help, but the wrong details had grabbed my attention. Not for the first time, I seriously considered dropping out of medical school. Like marriage, however, medicine is easier to get into than get out of. The social shame. The crippling debt. The starting over. I sighed. *At least I hadn't gotten underfoot.*

The shame eased. In fact, "Thank God!" puffed out of my mouth. If I'd done something stupid, the salt of the head surgeon's contempt would have shriveled me like a slug. Having stayed out of the way, no one noticed me in all the excitement. I resolved to study more. How, I didn't know, given that I was already studying every waking hour. How that would help, I didn't know either. It couldn't hurt.

When In Doubt, Take Your Own Pulse

4th Year Medical School, Neurology Rotation.

Five medical students and one attending, we stood in a circle around the patient who writhed on the waxed white linoleum floor, eyes rolling back in his head, a puddle of urine spreading from beneath his jeans. This was the first time I'd witnessed someone seize. It was frightening. I had no idea what to do. That was even more frightening.

The attending in his long white coat impassively pointed out the diagnostic features of a grand mal seizure. Dismay welled up in me. I jammed my hands in the pockets of my short white coat and white-knuckled the small reference book on neurological disorders in the left one and the pharmacology reference in the right. The stethoscope around my neck hung heavy.

While the patient was the subject of the lesson, he suffered unaided. But how else were we to learn? Life was so complicated, so dispassionately cruel, so vast, so... beyond me. My stomach rumbled. I couldn't remember the last time I had eaten. And when I finally did eat, it would be something that had died to fuel me. Why was life set up this way?

My mother heckled me from the peanut gallery in my head: "You're soooo sensitive!" Maybe I was. Once again I asked myself, *Should I become a doctor?*

The attending noticed my abstraction and asked if I was okay.

"No."

Amazingly, he validated that this was normal. "But," he went on, "to be useful to the patient, you must rally."

"How?" I looked at him hopefully.

"When in doubt, take your own pulse."

We all laughed. Nervously.

He looked me in the eye, "I mean it."

A zen koan? My brain vibrated painfully, threatening to blow apart. Please. I didn't have time to work that out. What I needed to do, urgently, was read up on seizure disorders and how to treat them.

This neurologist, a white-coat-draped man-shape whose face I can't see and whose name I can't remember, had just given me the password.

Examinus Interruptus

Last week of medical school.

Yet another snort of laughter disrupted the scritch of No. 2 pencils, the rustle of test booklet pages, and my concentration. Again, I looked up. Again, I saw only heads bent over desks.

Along with my classmates (one of whom was Hubby), I sat for the final time in the tiered lecture hall taking Part Two of Three of the medical licensing exams. If I passed it, in one month I'd start four years of residency training in psychiatry at Albert Einstein College of Medicine/Montefiore Medical Center in the Bronx.

Part One, taken at the end of the second year, covers the basic sciences portion of the curriculum. Part Two covers the clinical portion. Both are multiple-choice exams given in eight, sixty-minute sections over nine hours, in one day. I am not a good test taker. The experience was a ghastly stress, a tedious slog, and Very Serious. Amused snorts didn't fit.

I waited for a few seconds, hoping to catch someone at it. There was a cough behind me near the back, a sigh from the guy two seats over, and the pulsing silence of one hundred fifty-nine brains thinking intensely. I refocused on the next question in this section covering obstetrics and gynecology. The description of a sexually entangled couple was so graphic—

I squirmed and shook my head, hard, to chuck out the image. Wow. Weird. I inhaled and soldiered on: *This position maximizes the likelihood of conception—* Really? I hated when a test question taught me something new— *if the female's cervix is at which angle relative to the flow of semen?* Multiple-choice answers included: *(A) a vector equation, (B) north by northwest, (C) a parabolic trajectory ending at the biscuit-and-gravy diner across the street, (D) the eight ball in the center pocket after bouncing off three sides.* I snorted involuntarily. This had to be a joke.

I looked around the lecture hall, hoping to catch Hubby's or a friend's equally astounded eye. No luck. Everyone had nose to test. I suppressed a giggle surveying my classmates: mostly Bible-study white boys in their early twenties who would blush (or worse) reading this thing.

I flashed back to a clinical cardiology lecture early in the third year. The attending had startled me. "When you put the bell of the stethoscope on the chest of an attractive woman," he had said, "you can't let a sexual fantasy distract you from listening for a heart murmur." He stared out at us as he punched the button of the tape recorder on the podium with an index finger. The *lub-dub, lub-dub* of amplified heartbeats filled the room. I looked at the stethoscope slung around his neck, black against the white coat. *Of course*, I had thought. Having your face a few inches away from a woman's breast *would* be an issue for a young guy.

I re-read the question again. To figure out the answer, I had to imagine myself making love in this position. Again, my brain shut down and my body turned on. Again, I was amazed. How did this little titbit get past the stodgy senior physicians on the licensing board? The doc who wrote it (and sold it) was a prankster of the first order. Had to be. I imagined him: brilliant, early thirties, lithe, with a devilish Van Dyke beard and a twinkle in his eye.

It was even possible this was a real question with a correct answer. That would gild the lily. Too bad I'd never know. I filled in the circle next to (B), for Plan (B). A few rows behind me, someone snorted.

Med School and Residency Training More Alike Than Different, Educator Reveals
By Les Work

July, *Popular Careers*/A Print Media Publication

Wrapping up a series exploring the educational methodologies of several professions, I'll be speaking today about medical training with I.M. Trapt, M.D., psychiatrist and teaching attending. Her recent article in the esteemed journal *Education Hell* makes the counterintuitive point that medical school and residency training are more alike than different.

A lightly edited transcript of the interview follows.

LW: Welcome, Dr. Trapt.

IMT: Thank you for having me.

LW: It was my understanding that medical school is academic, a specialized continuation of college, but that residency training is a hands-on apprenticeship. Straighten us out.

IMT: Well, the similarities are structural, having to do with how the material is taught and tested, which ranks the trainee relative to her peers. The differences are a matter of quantity, rather than quality. Med school is college on steroids. Residency training is med school on steroids. 'Roid rage happens.

LW: Tell us more.

IMT: In college, you take a couple courses a semester in your major, which are demanding, and a couple of electives, which aren't. The first two years of med school continue that format, except that *all* the courses are required, *all* are demanding, and the amount of material you have to master increases with each succeeding semester. It's the cognitive equivalent of walking on a treadmill that keeps speeding up without plateauing. The first semester you walk briskly, the second you jog, the third you run, and eventually you do that carrying a hundred-pound pack while sleeping.

LW: Ouch. That's a lot of pressure. Is that a reasonable way to graduate smart doctors?

IMT: *No*. High grades in med school simply reflect academic mastery of a very narrow type, namely an excellent memory for details coupled with outstanding test-taking skills. You can be at the top of your class and go on to be a lousy doctor.

LW: What! Come on.

IMT: The criteria for acceptance to med school— high grades in math and science, high MCAT scores and technical research experience— don't select for people with the interpersonal savvy required for medical practice in the real world. No one wants to reveal they're vulnerable, especially patients, who, being sick, feel especially vulnerable. Putting people at ease, so they trust you to tell you what's really wrong— that's called taking a good history— is hard and requires emotional finesse. Students get thrown into those choppy relational waters the last two years of med school, which are clinical and hands-on.

LW: That's when they rotate through the basic medical specialties, like internal medicine and pediatrics, correct?

IMT: That's right. Students get a taste of each discipline's work, which helps you decide what kind of doctor you're going to be. At the beginning of the fourth year, you apply to residency training programs in your chosen field. In the last semester, you rotate through electives, such as dermatology or public health or pathology.

LW: How much of a taste are we talking with the basic disciplines?

IMT: Oh…, say, an Indian or Chinese buffet's worth. A lot, but hardly all. During the obstetrics rotation, for example, I delivered a lot of babies— supervised, of course—one to a twelve-year-old girl. During the pediatrics rotation, I looked at lots of broken bones and x-rays, infected ears, and strep throats. In surgery, I assisted at appendectomies, car accident and gunshot surgeries. In the clinic, I lanced boils. In the ER, the surgical residents called me the Suture Queen and let me sew up the facial lacerations of the many drunks that the cops brought in. In retrospect, I think they were just avoiding the vomit and alcohol fumes.

LW: Eeeeww.

IMT: Yeah, medicine is not *Grey's Anatomy* or *House M.D.* You also start doing call during the clinical med school years, which prepares you for residency training.

LW: What's call?

IMT: You're "on call" overnight, meaning you're the one to call for problems on the unit and admissions from the emergency room. You work a full day, are up covering the service that night, and then you work a full day after, 36 hours awake.

LW: Are you on your own? What happens if you don't know what to do?

IMT: As a medical student, you are supervised during the day by the teaching attending and overnight by the resident on call. If the resident is stumped, they wake up the attending to ask for help. Residents are exhausted and disappear to the call room to grab a few *zzzs* whenever possible. I never wanted to wake them up. Most were nice about it, many weren't. I was on my own a lot.

LW: How was that? Did it make you anxious?

IMT: Sure it did. What I learned in class was just one star in the night sky of what I didn't know. I was terrified I'd miss something, make a mistake and kill someone. Still, unlike many of my classmates, I knew when to ask for help, even if it embarrassed me and annoyed the resident or attending.

LW: Are you saying that asking for help got you into trouble?

IMT: Some docs see it as a sign of weakness. You're supposed to know everything already, even though you're a trainee. Don't ask me how that makes sense. And yes, I had to be careful around some attendings and residents. Fortunately, most were happy to teach and reassure me that uncertainty goes with the job.

LW: Tell us how residency training is like med school.

IMT: The structure remains the same as the last two years of med school, just more intense because you're carrying life and death responsibility while totally sleep-deprived. You rotate through your field's subspecialties in blocks, competing with your peers and performing for your attendings, going to lectures and taking tests. Residents work hundred-hour weeks for much of the residency. Anything less felt like a vacation! Still does.

LW: What are these subspecialty blocks? I thought medical students rotated through each specialty.

IMT: Med school exposure is just a broad brushstroke. Each field is huge and subdivided further. Most residencies require a minimum of four years, some more, to cover the basic subspecialties. Psychiatric subspecialties include emergency room psychiatry, consultation-liaison, addiction psychiatry, outpatient and inpatient.

Every psychiatry residency also requires the first year to include at least a three-month rotation through internal medicine, often a full year. In the third year, you apply for post-residency fellowships in specialties not included in the standard residency. For example, child psychiatry requires an additional year of training.

LW: What happens in the fourth year?

IMT: You either do electives in areas of interest or become a Chief Resident on a training service. Chiefs learn how to manage staff and administrate, teach the residents rotating through that service, and provide them backup when on call.

LW: To me, this seems totally hands-on, not at all like med school.

IMT: What's similar is the relentless competition, testing, grading, and jockeying for position at the head of the pack. Becoming a Chief Resident illustrates this best.

LW: Do you apply to become a Chief Resident?

IMT: No. You're chosen. It's considered a great honor. It's all about constantly looking good at morning rounds. You want to be the resident who, after a sleepless night, presents the most *complicated* case. Which, of course, you understand with crystal clarity and present coherently to the attending, using grammatically correct sentences and pulling together all the data you've collected— by interviewing the patient, reading the entire record, calling all relevant family members and affiliated physicians— to support your diagnosis and justify your treatment. Naturally, you leave the attending boggled by your brilliance.

I confess to succumbing to this nonsense myself. Pulling ahead of your peers is addicting, in the same way as gambling. It's not the winning that keeps the cycle going, but the losing. You've done it once; you can do it again; you *have* to do it again or you're a loser.

LW: Who knew!

IMT: Yes, well, for me there was an upside to the madness. I had an academic chip on my shoulder going into my residency, because, you see, I bought the lie that med school grades reflect clinical competence. Learning I could consistently think clearly, use good judgment, and explain my decision-making process while exhausted did my self-esteem a world of good.

On the other hand, some people lose control. One-upping the attending or chief resident is a definite no-no. I've seen a lot of that.

LW: It seems obvious that everyone should work together for the good of the patient.

IMT: You think? Unfortunately, too many guys are run by their egos. And guys run medicine, and the training process. Constant striving to get ahead in the hierarchy of the institution is another thing medical school and residency share.

Once you leave for the outside world, you're on your own without that structure to organize you. Taking care of a patient by yourself is a completely different beast: it's a relationship, not a race to show off yours skills to others. Being a good doctor requires mastery of the database, but it also requires that you help patients cope with the uncertainties of living with a chronic illness, poverty, social stigma, inadequate support, and discouragement that we can't do more.

LW: I'm confused.

IMT: Residency training is not the real world. Being a student is wonderful. You still believe there are Experts out there who know what they're doing, who will give you The Answer. As you approach the end of your training years, you begin to appreciate how much more there is to know and how much guesstimating your attendings are actually doing. It's unnerving.

LW: Thanks for coming in.

IMT: Pleasure.

ADVANCED BEGINNER PRACTICE
Five Uneasy Pieces

Slayer of Dragons

September, First Year Resident, Internal Medicine Rotation, 3:30 a.m.

Nothing had meaning beyond when I would get some sleep. I'd been on call every third night since July 1, the day I started residency training, and it was getting harder, not easier. The third years had lied.

I'd been run off my feet since beginning the previous day at 6 a.m. and all night too, with no end in sight. I hurt all over from walking the waxed linoleum-covered concrete floors of the hospital, my eyes burned with grit, and my head felt too big in a cold-hot way that blocked thinking like fog blocks visibility.

Sitting at the empty nurse's station desk, I finished writing the progress note on the last patient I'd checked on. Maybe after I did the fever workup on the delirious lady in Room 405, I could close my eyes for a few minutes. But that was at least twenty minutes away, not counting the walk to the call room bed and providing everything went perfectly, which it wouldn't because that's the kind of night it was.

A fever workup is a blood draw, made complicated by using sterile technique. First, I had to retrieve the sealed sterile pack— everything needed was in it— from the supply closet, way down the other end of the hall. Then, tear it open and place it just so. After the ritual hand washing, I had to slide the first hand into one glove, just so, without touching the outside, then the other, also just so.

Next, swab the area over the patient's vein with antimicrobial cleanser, surround it with blue-green sterile cloths to isolate the sterile field, prepare the syringe, and stick her, please God only once, if she didn't twitch.

Standing up from the chair required extreme effort: my body wanted to go to ground. My feet throbbed. I lifted the heavy three-ring plastic chart off the desk and filed it back in the chart carousel by room number. I slogged to the supply closet and the pager went off. My legs turned to jelly. I leaned on the wall and pulled the pager out of the pocket of my short white coat. The ER. Another admission. Despair took me. I wouldn't sleep till the end of the coming workday, 9 p.m. at the earliest.

I dragged back to the nurse's station, sat down by the phone and called the ER. A little old lady with a change of mental status, a urinary tract infection (UTI), and probably dehydrated. I'd have to calculate the osmolality of the IV solution she'd need, based on her weight. What was that equation? *What was it?* I drew a complete blank.

Slowing my breathing and willing myself to stay calm, I pulled the thick, spiral-bound pocket reference from a pocket and flipped through the index looking for it: intravenous; osmolality; calculation; equation; UTI, treatment of. Nothing. Tears welled up and, burning, spilled over. I dropped my head on my arms on the desk and sobbed uncontrollably.

I had read about out-of-body experiences reported by people near death: how they left their bodies and watched from high above as they lay in the bed or on the ground, people scurrying around them like ants around crumbs. I hadn't known what to make of those stories. Now it happened to me.

I left my body and, floating up by the ceiling, everything silent, I looked down on myself seated at the desk, head on arms, white-coated shoulders shaking, my dark, French-braided hair surprisingly tidy. I felt no pain, my head was clear, and I watched the scene with interest, as if it were a movie. It was very pleasant.

A hand on my shoulder slammed me back into my body, a visceral, painful thud that hurt through and through. I turned around in shock, my face wet, and saw—Hubby! His sweet face was a mask of concern, his hazel eyes alarmed. "What's wrong! What's happened? Are you OK?"

I grabbed his waist over the chair back, pressed my face into his scrub-covered abs, beyond caring who saw me, and sobbed, "I can't remember the equation!" His arms enclosed me and I burrowed in deeper.

"What equation?"

"How to calculate IV solution osmolality," I wailed looking up at him. "My brain is mush!" Tears streamed down my cheeks.

It's funny now, but it wasn't then. We had no Internet, no smart phone, only the pocket reference manual and memory.

Hubby wrote the equation inside the cover of the reference manual, gave me a hug, and left to take care of his own ER admission. My knight in shining armor. The restorative effect of those ten minutes was better than a nap. Naps don't give you love.

Why Delivering Bad News Can Be A Good Deed

Second Year Resident, Six-Month Rotation, Bronx State Psychiatric Hospital, Long-Term, In-Patient Treatment Unit for Psychotic Disorders.

"No, he'll never work as a doctor again," the attending answered my question about the patient's prognosis. It was morning rounds with her, two fellow residents, the chief resident, and six ward staff, all sitting in beat-up chairs and worn couches along the walls of the meeting room. The sun streamed in through two filthy, insect-encrusted windows.

"You'll have to tell him," she continued. "And his wife too."

My chest squeezed. My stomach ooked. My mouth dried.

Married with two children, Dr. K had suffered a psychotic break shortly after finishing his internal medicine residency; he'd heard voices and was convinced his thoughts could kill his family. Multiple hospitalizations followed. Multiple medications failed to return him to reality. He had been on this teaching ward for three years now with no improvement. What could be worse than permanently losing your mind (for no apparent reason) in young adulthood, while your body chugged along as usual?

He was psychotic in the textbook schizophrenic manner: withdrawn, internally preoccupied with the voices

75

in his head, and delusional. His current delusion was sad: he was on the unit working as a physician.

His wife couldn't understand, let alone accept, what was happening. Every time she came in, several times weekly, she asked the same questions. What was taking so long getting him better? Couldn't I give him a new medicine? When would he return to work? Befuddlement, exasperation, and shame infused all her interactions with him.

I assumed both would take the news badly, which was enough to make me dread delivering it. Being psychotic made Dr. K unpredictable. How would he react when the irresistible force of his delusion met the immovable object of reality? Real fear salted my usual aversion to conflict.

I knew somebody had to give Dr. K the bad news, but why, oh why, couldn't it have been the resident before me? Or the one coming after?

"OK," I said stoically. "Do you have any recommendations for softening the blow?"

"Just tell him. Calmly and matter-of-factly."

"What about his wife?"

"Same."

My stomach sank further. Maybe I'd tell them tomorrow or next week. The attending looked me in the eye: "Report in tomorrow how it went."

Later that day, with a muscular staff guy on tap outside the dingy interview room, I boldly opened with, "So... uh... Dr. K... how are you today?" I leaned forward a little in the armless chair, hands on my knees.

No reaction. He sat hunched across from me on the cracked vinyl couch, a mouse of a man, head angled down, gaze turned in. The voices in his head were obviously louder than mine.

I turned up the volume: "Dr. K!"

He startled, but didn't speak. (He hardly spoke generally and then only in a whisper. He had to be coaxed into session, to meals, to shower, to take medicine.) He sat there mute and frozen, eyes down. I empathized with his wife's exasperation. Ten minutes with him was an endless desert and just as parching. I had to get this over with.

"Dr. K., how do you feel about returning to work?" His gaze hovered over my right shoulder. The silence lengthened. I glanced around the bare room: dingy gray walls, scuffed linoleum floor, banged up metal wastepaper basket, small metal desk with dented edges, fluorescent circle light glaring overhead. When I looked back at Dr. K., he'd resumed staring inside.

"Dr. K, how would you feel about NOT returning to work?"

His eyes tracked vaguely.

"You've been here for over three years now. You probably won't be going back to work." *Oh no!* I suppressed a groan. I had chickened out and hedged. I had to undo that. I couldn't leave him with false hope, for two reasons. I would have to have the conversation with him again and I would be embarrassed at rounds tomorrow.

His head bent down on his neck like a heavy flower. His lips moved silently, talking to the voices in his head. Did they have an opinion about whether he should work or not?

I swallowed and said it. "Dr. K, you'll never work as a doctor again." I tensed. *What would he do?*

He seemed to return from a far distance. His eyes settled on the area around my chin. "No?" he whispered.

"No. I'm sorry." His eyes drifted over my left shoulder.

"OK." He shifted forward on the couch. "Can I go?" He stood up slowly, small and stooped, and shuffled toward the door.

That was it? I studied him closely. Was that slight curve to his lips a smile? Was it possible he was relieved? He quietly opened the door and left the room.

I had assumed the truth would come as a body blow. But that presumed he *wanted* to work. Felt *capable* of working. Maybe he didn't. *Maybe he knew he couldn't.* Maybe I had just delivered good news, not bad.

I flashed back to my internal medicine internship when I felt, always, that I was just one judgment call away from disaster. Plato defined pleasure as the cessation of pain. The relief when I finished that internship was orgasmic. Maybe Dr. K felt something like that now.

The door opened. The aide stuck his head in. "Everything OK?"

I nodded, smiling.

I took a deep, luxurious breath, my rib cage expanding as if a heavy weight had just rolled off it. The world felt much, much roomier. My job was to be open-minded and not assume anything. I saw that his wife, after the initial upset, would be relieved too. After years of waiting for him to recover, she could give up hope and move on to build a new life for herself and her children.

That's why hope was in Pandora's box of the world's evils, I thought. It can trap you in time like an insect in amber.

While it's always uncomfortable to deliver news that banishes hope, doing so frees people to move forward. They may not like it, but you can't do anything about that.

It's patronizing to withhold information people need to make informed choices just because it might upset them (or you). That puts being the agent of someone's upset in perspective and helps me cope with the anxiety that being straight with patients always stirs up.

That people get upset when given bad news is the beginning of a process that needs to play out. That's useful to know and accept. It empowers me to say and do the right thing with anybody, be it a patient, Son, Hubby, a friend, a coworker or an employee. And it's a comfort, in a dark, grown-up sort of way.

The Horror

Third Year Resident, Montefiore Hospital, Bronx, NY, On Call.

I had started at 6 a.m. yesterday. It was now 4:20 a.m. today. Rounds, and the regular workday, would start at 6:00 a.m. and I had yet to sleep. I had been working thirty-six-hour shifts every third or fourth night for over three years. It was killing me. I fell on the call room bed like an axed tree.

Immediately, the recurrent nightmare started up: I was on call. I paced the hospital from one end, where the labs were,[8] to the other, where the patients lay in their beds, needing, needing. Back to the labs for blood work results and then to the clinical floors and back to the labs and more walking endless white halls. Walking. Walking. Sleep, sleep, all I wanted was sleep—

Beep! Beep! Beep! I startled awake, sick to my stomach, heart racing. I thumbed the pager button: the ER. I groaned and my belly clenched. The nurse who answered the phone told me to hustle. A schizophrenic had sliced off his penis with a glass shard, obedient to the voices in his head.

Sitting on the edge of the bed, I couldn't get up. Elbows on my knees, head pressed heavily onto my hands,

---

[8] Remember, no computers. There was no point in calling. The lab techs never picked up the phone.

I saw gouts of blood, heard screams of agony, smelled vomit. *How could he have done that?* My temples throbbed, my eyes burned, my throat swelled. I couldn't cry now. Later.

How will I help him deal with the horror? In the overheated elevator, my teeth chattered against my clenched jaws. Deep inside me a motor thrummed, the tremor extending to my fingertips. Then I heard in my head the voice of my med school neurology attending: *"When in doubt, take your own pulse."* I did it. Taking slow, deep breaths, I walked into the bright white vortex of the ER.

Turned out, the patient was an amiable teddy bear of a man, with an incredibly sweet smile. In no pain at all. *How could that be?* He was cooperative, gentle, and calm. No, he hadn't taken his medicine for many weeks. Sure, he'd take some medicine now. Sure, he'd let the surgeon reattach his penis. The voices hadn't said anything about that. Sure, he'd go up to psych after the surgery.

The interview was crazy in its banality. Nothing could have prepared me for it. I told the story to Hubby, other residents, and my favorite attending. We all marveled at the complexity and mystery of the brain. From the attending, I learned this bizarre absence of pain is fairly common in states of active psychosis.

But the reaction of fellow resident Garth stopped me short: "Haldol.[9] Consult urology. Piece of cake." *Well, duh.* The man had the emotional range of a toothpick. When the urge to smack him passed, envy followed: If only

---

[9] A potent injectable antipsychotic.

I could be so self-satisfied when meeting the minimum standard of competence. I imagined what that would feel like, and decided there was nothing to envy. Compassion and empathy were hardwired into me. I couldn't get rid of those qualities, nor did I want to.

As for the worry that I didn't know enough, that was a good thing. It kept me humble. Still, no matter how much I studied, there would always be something I couldn't anticipate, something I wouldn't know. There was no escape. Just like that, I gave up the idea of leaving medicine. It was too late for me. I was in the gumbo up to my nostrils. I would be a psychiatrist.

Whatever came along, all I could do was my best. That was all I had to offer and it was good enough. It would have to be.

But First, A Little Momba

Early Fourth Year Resident, afternoon session with my therapist at her private office.

"I heard a great joke the other day. Wanna hear it?" I asked Robin, who sat before me in her power chair, shelves packed with books along the wall behind her. I'd been working with her about a year. I cried my way through most of our twice a week, forty-five-minute sessions. The poor woman deserved a laugh.

She looked alert and nodded.

I had brought us coffee from the corner deli and sipped mine (light with milk, no sugar) while she sipped hers (black). Putting the cup down on the end table, between the box of tissues and the lamp casting a warm light through the curtained room, I began.

"Three explorers are lost deep in the Amazon. Suddenly, they find themselves surrounded by fearsome tribal warriors. They are marched to the village, tied together, and left standing in the hot sun for hours. At dusk, the tribal king emerged from a palatial hut.

'For trespassing on our sacred lands, you must be punished,' he intoned.

The explorers made eye contact with each other hopefully. Would they be allowed to live?

'You have two choices. We tear you limb from limb and feed you to the dogs. Or, momba.'

He pointed to one explorer. 'Choose.'

The unlucky explorer swallowed. What was momba? Hoping for the best, he chose it. The king smiled.

Immediately, the warriors grabbed him, skinned him alive, then stomped him till dead. They danced around the corpse, screaming and brandishing their spears.

Turning to the two remaining explorers, who were frozen in horror, the chief intoned, 'For trespassing on our sacred lands, you must be punished. You have two choices. We break all your bones, then stone you to death. Or, momba."

He pointed to one explorer. "Choose."

The explorer agonized. What to do? 'Momba.' The king smiled.

Immediately, the warriors grabbed the explorer, threw him to the ground, stabbed him through the belly and bowels, then set fire to him. They circled around him, dancing, screeching and brandishing their spears.

The king turned to the remaining explorer who was a puddle of terror. 'For trespassing on our sacred lands, you must be punished,' he intoned. 'You have two choices. We tear your heart and entrails out, then throw you to piranhas in river. Or, momba.

'Piranhas!' the poor explorer gasped. The king smiled.

'Good. But first... a little momba.'"

With that I cracked up. I laughed and laughed, in waves, throwing myself around on the nubby couch, eyes tearing. After winding down, I felt excellent, hollowed out and relaxed. I pulled a tissue from the box next to me and wiped my eyes, chuckling and shaking my head, "Ah me." I leaned back, closed my eyes and breathed. God, it felt good to close my eyes.

I felt myself going to sleep and ripped open my Velcro-ed eyelids. I caught Robin in an unguarded moment, gazing at me with a bemused look of… distaste mixed with the struggle to suspend judgment. That cracked me up again.

When I stopped laughing, she said, "I don't get it."

Well, of course she wouldn't. She was a Ph.D. psychoanalyst. So what if she'd written a book to get her degree (I couldn't begin to imagine the research involved, much less the writing). What, besides war, could compete with the misery of residency training, that years-long nightmare of carrying life and death responsibility while utterly sleep deprived? Self-pity salted with moral superiority took me, then shame. What a pain in the ass I was. I had done this to myself. The truth was, I envied her. She had slept regularly while working on her thesis. Well, that was my fantasy anyway.

As a psychoanalyst, Robin was a master of keeping her personal feelings and information to herself. Her job was to keep the focus of treatment on me, the patient. But she had let me in a little. Could I get her to reveal more? How would she handle the challenge? Divulge? Deflect?

My interest in her technique was professional. I was in therapy not just because I needed it (God knows I needed it), but as part of training to become a therapist myself. I had already decided that would be my post-residency focus.

Robin was an excellent analyst, well worth studying. Plus, I loved her. She was totally straight, trustworthy, and kind.

"Admit it," I said. "It's a dark and disgusting joke *and* you think I'm dark and disgusting for finding it hilarious!"

"Well...," she said, smiling wryly. "It's so gruesome. What about it strikes you funny?"

Ha! A compromise: a little self-revelation, then back to the business at hand, me. Very nice.

"It's the perfect metaphor for medical training," I said. "The king is the system and I'm the explorers."

"If you experience the training as that sadistic, I have to ask why you do it."

"Come on. I can't become a psychiatrist otherwise."

"So is it worth it?"

"How would I know? I'm not done." I sighed. "I hope to God it is."

I sighed again and settled deeper into the couch, flashing back to that night on call when, like sirens, the bank of night-black glass doors in the hospital lobby called to me: *Keep walking. Just walk out. Walk into the sunrise and never go back.* The morning before, the guy who pumped my gas refused payment: he had won the lottery! His ecstatic generosity had made me laugh. Walking toward those doors, I realized: *Damn. Winning the lottery won't get me out of this. I have to finish if I'm going to be a shrink.* I crossed the lobby and turned right into the hall that led to the patient floors, away from the call room bed and sleep. *But first, a little momba.*

Danger! Danger! Danger!

Chief Resident, Psychiatric Emergency Room, Jacobi Hospital, Bronx, NY.

The patient was painfully thin, filthy, and jittery. I kept my manner gentle, my voice low, my movements slow. He settled a bit and made tentative eye contact. He was homeless, an IV crank[10] addict so savagely consumed by the addiction, he shot in his neck. Very depressed. Couldn't sleep. Couldn't eat. I continued with the routine interview, asking if he was hearing voices.

Twisting behind himself, he pulled out a huge, cheap kitchen knife, lifting it up high. He stabbed it down, "They tell me to kill! To kill!"

Instantly, I was on my feet, moving toward the door, all the hair on my body standing on end, and stopped. I couldn't get out without passing directly within reach of the knife. How had it come to this?

Becoming Chief Resident in the fourth year of residency was an honor and an acknowledgment by the senior attendings of broad skill as well as teaching and leadership ability. You could put in the request, but in the end, you were chosen. I had wanted the outpatient clinic. Instead, I was offered the psych ER. I was surprised. Proud. Nervous. But not panicked. Since surrendering to the reality that I couldn't know everything in advance,

---

[10] a heroin/ amphetamine mix

unpredictable clinical situations had become opportunities to stretch myself. So far, no one had died on my watch. I accepted the position. It did not occur to me I might be the one at risk.

I supervised the first year residents rotating through during the day and the third years on call at night. I loved the psych ER for many reasons. The pathology was dramatic, the interventions straightforward, and I loved Richie, the night clerk. Richie was a burly black man in his 30s, divorced, with two kids to support. ("Don't have kids if you want any money for yourself," he advised.)

He worked another full-time job during the day, in addition to this gig full-time overnight. I had no idea when he slept, but he was always alert and present. Most important, he always had my back. "You're confident. You know when to ask for help." Me? Confident? And how did that tie together with knowing when to ask for help?

"I've seen more residents pass through here than I can count. Trust me, you're good." I respected Richie. Never look a gift horse in the mouth. Besides, it was nice to hear.

Richie had just started his shift when I had picked up the chart that had *Danger! Danger! Danger!* stamped on it (Yes, three times. In red.) and decided this wasn't an evaluation for a newbie.

The psych ER was a big square. Two attendings and two first years sat at the center island desk doing chart work. In addition to the two interview rooms, down a hall in the back, there was a holding tank for unpredictable patients suffering active psychosis or coming off a bad drug high. Hospital and city police posted there checked these patients for weapons and other contraband.

I had alerted Richie I was going in to interview Mr. *Danger! Danger! Danger!* Stimulant use, especially if chronically injected, can cause extreme paranoia. I had been taught that paranoid patients should sit next to the door, to mitigate the fear. Accordingly, when the security guard escorted the patient in to the exam room, I had offered him the seat by the door. I sat down across him, deeper into the room, started the interview—

And found myself on the balls of my feet, body electric with fear, a psychotic, knife-wielding man between me and the door. What to do? I couldn't think. I couldn't move. The room spun briefly as my eyes tried to look both ways at once.

Freezing proved the right thing. In a moment of clarity, the patient slid the knife across the floor to me, "Take it! Take it!"

I resumed breathing. With a nod, I picked it up by the blade tip with my left hand. He was on my right, by the door. The moment was a bad one when I passed within his reach. But nothing happened. I exited, closing the door behind me.

Where were the cops? *Why hadn't they frisked him?* No one but Richie had looked up. We locked eyes. I lifted up the knife by the blade tip, letting the rest of it swing a little, as if I were holding a dead rat by the tail. He raised his eyebrows: *Oh boy.*

I said loudly to the room at large, "Look at this." The two attendings looked and, as one, stood up from the desk and exited through the door to the medical ER.

I looked at Richie: *What the hell?* He shrugged and slid off his stool to walk toward me. Two cops rushed by, shoving me aside to get into the exam room. "Wait!" I called out. "Medicine first!" They didn't stop.

"Watch," said Richie. "Someone will get hurt." Sure enough, the patient and one of the officers ended up on the medical side.

What did I learn?

1. Never assume the experts know anything. Let a paranoid patient sit by the exit, thus putting myself at risk? The genius that came up with that must have been interviewing patients in an ivory tower.

2. Never assume people are doing their jobs. With the patient's chart stamped *Danger! Danger! Danger!* I should have double-checked that the cops had searched him. A corollary specific to cops: Never assume cops are team players. Though the immediate danger was past and the first order of business was to offer the patient some medication, they took action without consulting with me, the doctor, that resulted in unnecessary injury to the patient and themselves.

3. Never assume leaders will lead.

4. Get to know everyone in the field of battle. You can never predict who will be an ally. It may be a Richie, someone untitled and unacknowledged who blends into the background. It is a rare and beautiful thing to have someone at your back.

5. No one has The Answer(s). To be an adult is to muck about, muddle through, and figure it out for yourself. I was on my own, and had to trust *my* best judgment.

The Practice Years (1992-present)

Sometimes our light goes out but is blown again into flame by an encounter with another human being. Each of us owes the deepest thanks to those who have rekindled this inner light.
Albert Schweitzer

Isn't it a bit unnerving that doctors call what they do practice?
George Carlin

Prologue
1992-1995

After we finished our residencies at Einstein, Hubby and I stayed on as teaching attendings on different services. When Son came along in 1993 and crack vials started showing up in our residential Bronx neighborhood, we looked for houses further north, within an hour's drive. We found we couldn't afford the shabbiest starter-uppers and neither of us is handy.

We had both grown up in suburban neighborhoods where it was safe for kids to bike and play outside without adult supervision. We wanted Son to grow up with that freedom. So we moved even further north, just above the gorgeous Adirondack Park, to an affordable, rural town of 23,000 people desperately in need of psychiatrists. We opened our practice in 1996.

INTERMEDIATE PRACTICE
Education is hanging around until you've caught on.
Robert Frost

There's No Place Like Gnome

January

"Doc, am I a gnome?" Sheldon asked.

What! It was a cuttingly cold, dreary Monday afternoon. We sat in my warm office: sage walls, cream trim, potted peace lily, upholstered couch, matching chair stuffed with Sheldon, bookcase, accordion window shades opaque from the lack of sun, tissue boxes as far as the eye could see.

Silly made a nice change. It'd been hours of patients who were desperately sick, chronically suicidal, resistant to treatment, or just plain miserable.

I wanted to laugh. But I didn't. He was serious. "Uhh… no."

"How do you know?"

"Well… Gnomes are fictional characters."

Sheldon nodded. I waited.

"So, why does my family say I'm a gnome?"

I looked over his unfortunate jug-handled ears, bald dome, glowing eyes, goofy grin, and seventy-year-old, pear-shaped body sagging into the upholstery. It was hard not to giggle. He *was* a little old gnome. There's always a kernel of truth in every delusion (and in every slur or nickname).

This was today's kink in Sheldon's kookiness. Social reassurance ("Your family wouldn't say that!"), while logical as well as true, wouldn't console him. What was the tactful (yet still honest) thing to say? Tact, timing, dosage: that was the challenge for any words that left my lips. I leaned forward.

"Maybe…because you're bald?"

His hands jumped up to his hairless head. "I shaved it myself! But it's not too good in the back." He turned his head so I could see.

Sheldon was the sweetest thing on the planet (when he was stable). An innocent, radiant with wonder, always looking to tell a joke. He'd been a religion teacher at the local Catholic elementary school and a popular performing folk guitarist and raconteur before schizophrenia stole that life. He shifted to face me.

"Doc, do gnomes get erections?" *Here we go.* All aboard the train of Sheldon's sexual delusions. I sighed. It was a familiar slog through gray fog, not interesting but still perilous. First stop: Erections.

I said, "I wouldn't know. I deal only with real creatures." Next stop: Celibacy.

"Doc, how do you define celibate?"

"Well, a celibate person is someone who gives up sexual relations for spiritual reasons." Next stop: Homosexuality.

"Okay. If I'm queer in thought, am I queer in deed?" *Here be dragons. Not going there.*

"You're celibate. So, no." Next stop: V.D.

"The nurse at the doctor's office told me I have a rare form of syphilis. What do you think?"

"I think you don't. Your last blood test was negative." As were the gazillion before. "You're celibate. No sex, no V. D."

Et cetera. More of the same. Can we stop now? The urge to thump my head against a handy wall took me.

Instead, I assessed the data. Psych meds don't get rid of delusions. They help by softening delusions' hard unreasonableness. Maybe. Better meds can't come soon enough. Meanwhile, if Sheldon accepted my reality-based responses and — fingers crossed — suffered less, I'd take it.

Sheldon nodded, "Okay. I believe you Doc."

I smiled. *Hey, this is going well.* I realized I was leaning forward, so lifted his chart off the stack on the ottoman, then scooted back in the chair.

"I was afraid to ask," he said. "I didn't want you to think I was crazy."

A grin escaped me and out popped, "Come on, Shel, we both know you're crazy. That's why you're here." *Oh my God.* I tightened my grip on the chart instead of clapping a hand over my mouth. *I can't believe I said that.*

Our eyes locked. He shrank into the chair and his head retreated into his rounded shoulders, like a scared turtle. The atmosphere in the room darkened, became charged and still, the calm before the storm. *How do I regain his trust?*

My body tingled. My mind sizzled, snapped, and popped in lightning-bolt analysis: I had missed the point and with a heavy hand. I had spoken to the surface question, not to what he was *really* asking, which was: Am I OK as a person? Do you like me, crazy and all?

The clouds parted and the sun came out. I saw the way. I twinkled like mad, maintaining eye contact: *I'm sorry! I didn't mean to hurt you. You are adorable. I love working with you.* He stared, frozen. Would he forgive me? I grounded myself in the quality of the session before this awful moment, in the strength of our years-long bond, and in his sense of humor. I beamed warmth, dialing it up.

He gave me a long, searching look and melted. He dropped his shoulders, lifted his head and smiled. "Good one, Doc."

O! Happy day! I grinned back. *Thank YOU!*

Sheldon gave me a goofy grin, "Wanna hear a joke?"

Wow. He's reaching out. We're good. I was totally engaged. Fascinated. *I LOVE this.*

"Sure. Nothing off-color please."

"Okay. When Cookie Monster was sick, what did he say to his mother?"

"Um…. Don't know."

"I feel crumb-y!"

He laughed freely and so did I.

The session in review: His eye contact was good, mood jovial, and affect broad. Delusional content aside, we'd kept the conversational ball in play continuously for twenty minutes. He let me confront him with reality. He let me console him. He accepted my apology. *Amazing.* A triumph of give and take.

Given he'd required two hospital admissions for terror-loaded paranoia in the last ten years of treatment, one of them on my watch a couple years ago, he was solidly in the maintenance sweet spot. *My cup runneth over.*

I wrote the progress note. Did he need scripts? No. I closed the chart and shifted forward in my seat. "Sheldon, I'm not changing any of your meds today. You're doing great. I'll see you next month."

He glowed and heaved out of the chair. He retrieved his winter coat off the couch and struggled into one sleeve while I held the back and other sleeve forward for him. "Thank you." He wound a striped lime green and white scarf around his neck, then pulled a neon-pink knit cap down over his ears. As he waddled out the door, the bobble wobbled. I had to suppress another giggle. We walked side by side to the checkout window, where we ran into Hubby. Sheldon asked him, "Why should everybody buy a good pair of shoes?"

"Why?" Hubby smiled.

"To save their souls!"

It's so simple, really. What do we all want? To be accepted for our whole selves, from soup to nuts. Especially the nuts.

Sheldon didn't choose his illness. He was disabled, despite treatment. We both had to live with that. I'm competent and full of good will. Still, I screw up. We both had to live with that, too.

One mistake and time stopped. We sized each other up. Sheldon's psychosis, my insensitive gaffe, those fell away. We connected as human beings and found it good. So good, we laughed.

Being an outpatient psychiatrist is a lot like being married.[11] Things go along the same-old for long periods until Hubby and I have a moment. Everything stops and I fall for him again, just like that. Just like the first time. I remember why I love him. Today with Sheldon, I got it,

---

[11] Thirty-eight years as we go to press. Thank you.

just when I needed to, that I love my work. Gnome is where the heart is.

Don I: Treatment, It's Like Peeling An Onion
March.

Don, 48, tall, with long, gray-streaked hair pulled back in a thin rat's tail, sat in the upholstered chair opposite mine, legs out, swollen abdomen stretching his cabled wool sweater, and tried to hide how much pain he was in.

It was a muddy, cold day, though the birds were back, warbling and yakking, and the peace lily by the window had sent up one creamy bud, tightly furled. The special, early spring light glowing through the two shaded, south-facing windows highlighted how miserable Don looked.

It had also been a cold spring day when I met with Don for the first time the first week we'd opened the practice in 1996. He'd presented with symptoms consistent with a clinical depression: low mood; thoughts that went round and round ("they never stop"); restless sleep; poor concentration; constant fatigue; loss of appetite associated with weight loss; lack of interest in friends, family, as well as formerly pleasurable activities.

He was also suffering from severe Crohn's Disease, an autoimmune disorder in which the small and large intestines eat themselves up. The ulcerated tissue can't absorb food properly, resulting in multiple bouts of diarrhea, bloating, and inflammation along the twenty feet of intestine, trouble keeping on weight, and constant hunger coupled with aversion to eating. Who would eat if serious pain always followed? To keep the ulcerative process from spreading and/or flaring, he was prednisone-dependent.

Prednisone is a steroid, a treatment of last resort, for it carries a heavy burden of negative side-effects. The psychiatric ones are significant. Some people become extremely aggressive, others manic, yet others panicked or depressed. I have seen them all.

All of his presenting symptoms could have been caused by depression alone. Or they could be secondary to the Crohn's, or to the prednisone. Or any combination of the three. Was it possible to untangle these threads to find the one at fault? No. Did it matter? No. I was going to give him a trial of an antidepressant regardless.

From the first meeting, it took half a year, give or take a month, to get the dose right, but he responded wonderfully, making us both happy. Me, because antidepressants work less predictably in the presence of a steroid. Don, because he felt himself for the first time in years. Six more months and the Crohn's symptoms had improved so much that his gastroenterologist tapered him off the prednisone. His intestinal and mental well-being held. Now both of us were *really* happy: chronic use of prednisone is always best avoided. And it was summer! He was delighted he could garden, hike, and kayak again.

Once his overall health stabilized, over time Don opened up about other stressors that impacted his mood and Crohn's, namely his wife Jacqueline and their two adult children. He'd married Jackie their last year of high school after she found herself pregnant with their first child, son Evan. She had their second, daughter Jenn, eighteen months later. Then he was drafted into the Vietnam War, leaving her to take care of the children and run the family business alone.

"That was bad for me," he'd said, "but worse for her. These two guys broke into the house in the dead of night while I was overseas and raped her with a knife at her throat, the babies asleep in the next room." He balled his fists and breathed heavily. "They got away, never got caught. The guy with the knife cut her up bad. She's still got the scars."

He'd forced himself to relax, dropping his shoulders. He shook his head, his eyes shiny. "She didn't tell me about it. She said she didn't want me to worry. My parents found her, took care of her, told me. When I got back, she wasn't the woman I married. That woman has never come back. She won't go for treatment, she doesn't sleep, she's jumps at the least little sound, she drinks too much."

On this day in March, now several years further into the treatment, I knew him well enough to tell from his glum silence that she was on his mind. He couldn't get comfortable. He shifted gingerly, stretching his legs again and placing a gentle hand on his round belly. "Jackie's not doing well. Just thinking about it makes me cramp." He looked down and fell silent. There were purple smudges under his eyes and his face drooped in weary sadness.

"It's hard. I can't count on her. She drinks every day now and gets nasty. I stay out of her way till she falls asleep." He sighed.

"She's got a mean mouth." His full lower lip trembled. "That's starting to be a problem with customers. Evan's been taking on more, so our income is holding steady." He paused again. Sighed again. "When she works less, she's underfoot more at the house. I get on her nerves and she tends to go off, which stresses me out. Then I bloat more and go to the bathroom more and hurt more."

"Working from home isn't all it's cracked up to be," I said. He smiled ruefully and shrugged.

"I'm worried about Evan," he said. "He's out every night at the bars. He says he's having a good time, but he's thirty and still doing what he did when he was eighteen. What are the chances he'll meet a nice girl that way and settle down?" He sighed. "He works hard, so that's all right."

He shifted again in the upholstered chair.

"Then there's Jenn. Since she came home from New York, she hasn't done a thing besides go out with Evan and sleep in. She spends the day on the couch. She looks terrible."

Jenn had left home right after she graduated from high school to seek fame and fortune in New York City as an actress. After ten years away, she'd returned to the nest, broke and strung out on coke, pills, and alcohol. She'd given up the coke and pills; obviously she was still drinking.

"I'm sure she's depressed," Don said. I nodded. *No doubt.* "If I can get her to come in, will you see her?"

I groaned to myself. In a small town with too many psychiatrically sick people and too few psychiatrists, seeing multiple family members was the norm. And difficult.

Family loyalty being what it was, if Jenn's treatment went bad (which it might, given her substance abuse history), Don might leave, too. I put that worry aside for now, not having enough data to make a reliable prediction.

"Sure," I said. "Provided it's her idea, not yours." I paused to let this sink in. He nodded. "She has to want help because *she's* sick of being sick, not because you are." I smiled at him. He smiled back and nodded again.

"She'll have to stop drinking in order for me to be of any use to her. AA: 90 meetings in 90 days."

"I know," Don said. "I don't think she's ready for that. Or to see you either."

"Is there anything from your own experience that she might relate to? Maybe you could share how a little medicine helped a lot? Response to medications is genetic, you know. She might do well with what you're taking."

While he thought about that, I groaned to myself again. *Why am I so compulsively helpful?* I was actually encouraging him to send her in. As if the work of treating him wasn't enough. The work of treating two people in relationship with each other—maintaining boundaries and remembering who told me what— made for mind-bending complications.

This scenario would only become more frequent with each year we practiced in this Catholic farming community, where the families were large, had lived here for generations, and were tightly connected to each other through marriage. Hubby and I needed to do a little research, put our heads together, and work out a policy.

For now, if Jenn did come in, I'd have both her and Don agree that, at my discretion, I could share any information that was necessary for each treatment. Everyone, including me, would have to understand and accept there might be fallout to deal with. I groaned to myself again. They hadn't prepared us for this kind of thing in the residency.

"Good idea," Don said. "Thanks. I'll try it."

Pierre and Judy I: A Nice Long Run
June

Pierre was thirty-six years old when he came in with his wife Judy for the intake appointment. It was a surprisingly cool day, more like downstate spring than summer. Then again, when we'd opened the practice in April, it had felt like winter. The overcast morning sky was as dark as dusk from an impending storm, but the light from various lamps made the office cozy.

Pierre had worked since he was twenty-one as a corrections officer (CO) at the state maximum-security prison in the mountains located about thirty minutes west of town. He presented with symptoms consistent with Post Traumatic Stress Disorder (PTSD): nightmares, flashbacks, startling, panic and depression, all of which had started in the wake of several events at the jail, the worst an attack by one inmate on another with a contraband shiv in the exercise yard, on Pierre's shift.

"The blood, Doc, it was a lake. I tried not to throw up, but I couldn't help it. Now the guys hassle me and call me an inmate lover. They won't leave me alone." His eyes filled up. Judy, sitting pressed next to him on the couch, handed him a tissue from the box on the end table and took his hand. They'd been married since their late teens and hadn't wanted children.

"I mean, I know these inmates have done bad things, but they're people! The way it went down, the guy

111

bleeding and screaming, nobody should go through that. I keep seeing it and dreaming it." He tried not to sob. Judy squeezed his hand.

"Tell her about Dolby," she said and shot me a look of concern. Tears rolled down his face.

"My favorite cat. We have two— well, one now. I can't get over the way he died. He was fine, then he started choking like he was hacking up a hair ball." He paused and raised his eyes to look at me. "You know how they do." He looked down. "I didn't think anything of it. Ten minutes later, he was gone. Dead. And I just stood there, doing nothing while he suffered. Just like I did with that inmate." He broke down.

"He has more bad dreams and crying spells over Dolby than all that at the jail," Judy said. He looked at her gratefully. He had wanted her at the intake and he wanted her (as did she) to attend subsequent sessions, which she did. As time went on, that became the norm, having a real benefit.

Pierre had suffered a serious head injury when seventeen—he had taken a corner too fast in the go-kart he was racing and had flown over the hood, no helmet—and now was a poor historian[12]. He had trouble answering questions directly and, instead of reporting something as a narrative, tended to get stuck in the details, repeating them over and over. Then there's the reality that men, in general, are reluctant to disclose their suffering. It's an admission of

---

[12] *Poor historian:* Getting the story, aka the history, from a patient is not as easy as you'd think.

weakness and unmanly. I'm not being sexist. This is simply a fact of gender identity in our male-dominated culture.

Judy helped him, and me, by reporting symptoms he didn't. For the most part, her presence at Pierre's sessions was beneficial. The downside was the loss of privacy: he wouldn't talk about conflicts between them. If they were arguing, she would initiate that discussion.

Two years of twice-a-month sessions later, his trauma symptoms were under control with an effective combination of medications. Pierre became a long-term, medication maintenance patient and remained essentially symptom free for twelve years. Every few years, he and Judy would find themselves stuck in one of their two chronic arguments and come in for a short course of couple's therapy.

Every long-term couple has to accept the fact that there will always be one conflict (or two; any more and the relationship collapses) that will never resolve. The rest tend to be logistical issues that neither party can step back from to see the solution. These are the easiest for me to help with. I am not stuck in their assumptions and the big picture is obvious. Both people are happy to try what I suggest because it doesn't threaten anything essential about themselves or their coupledom.

An example: Pierre hated shoveling their long driveway after a snowfall. On more than one morning he didn't get started early enough, and they were both late to work. Judy nagged him and he resented that. I suggested they hire someone to do it. That hadn't occurred to them. I was a genius.

Not so the irreconcilable issue(s). These cause the therapist to immediately fall from grace. The process is fraught with upset and potholes. The couple fights the work every step—who can blame them?—because they have to make *actual changes,* individually and relative to each other.

Both must accept that: (1) they are different from each other, in a core way, which is the source of the conflict; (2) this difference will not go away; (3) the resulting conflict will not go away either; and (4) they must make peace with that, each in their own way, in order to continue loving each other and stay together.

Pierre and Judy struggled over sex and paperwork. He felt resentful and controlled by her unwillingness to have sex on demand and was dissatisfied with their once-a-week love life. From her side, once a week was more than she wanted but what she could stretch herself to give, and she felt resentful that he didn't appreciate that.

Judy was tall, lean, and neat while Pierre was short, round, and sloppy. He put pressure on her to eat more or exercise less—"Be more womanly! For Christ's sake, get a boob job. Sometimes I feel like I'm having sex with a boy!"— which left her feeling unattractive, rejected, and helpless. His occasional forays into on-line porn devastated her.

"Why am I not enough? If I was curvier, would you stop?" she asked him several summers into the treatment. She was wearing a flowered sundress that flattered her figure while his jeans and beer logo tee shirt insulted his.

Some psycho-educational work helped. Men and women have different sex drives. One partner always wants more sex than the other. Criticizing your sexual partner's looks is never a turn-on. Using porn is like using drugs, all about the high, nothing about the relationship. Sex and making love are two different things: which did they want? No surprise: he wanted sex, she wanted love-making. He didn't know the difference; she did.

"If you kiss me because you want sex, that feels different than if you kiss me because you're happy to see me," she said sadly.

"You understand, Pierre?" I asked.

"Sure, sure" he said, going on to reveal that he didn't. "I just wish you wanted more sex," he said to her. "That's why I want some porn."

"I can't stand the porn! It's like you have another woman, someone you like better than me," she said.

"I'd like you better if you were hotter!" he retorted. *Oh boy.* "And what's the big deal anyway? It's not like I'm cheating."

How to explain it? He *was* cheating *and* putting her down, simultaneously. He couldn't see it from her point of view.

"Pierre, what if you were the one who wanted less sex and Judy used porn on the side? How do you imagine you'd feel?"

He snorted, "Never happen." You'd think a man who broke down over his cat's suffering and inmates' vulnerability to guards' cruelty would be able to put himself in his wife's position. But no.

"Pierre, why don't you try being more affectionate without expecting anything? Do it as an experiment. See if it leads to more sex. But you have to mean it."

"Yeah, I can tell when you're hugging me just because you're horny," Judy said. "Let me initiate, okay?"

"I'll never get any!"

I suppressed a sigh and kept plugging. "Pierre, if Judy doesn't want to and you push, then it's all about you and you're just using her. No one likes being used."

"Okay, okay."

The other area of contention was that Judy managed everything at home, from scheduling repairs, grocery shopping, and paying bills to saving for retirement. She did all the thinking, planning, and worrying about these things, too. And while she didn't mind being in charge, seeing it as her wifely responsibility— "After that go-kart accident, he's never been able to plan ahead or stay on top of paperwork."— she *did* mind his lack of gratitude and co-operation.

"He fights me on everything," she said to me. She turned to face him on the couch. "It's so frustrating you won't admit you can't do it! It's so unfair you're ugly about it." She turned back to me, "Trust me, we'd have nothing if I didn't watch. He can't keep a nickel in his pocket."

He didn't see it that way. "She's a control freak! It's too much trouble to fight her. I can do it, she just won't let me." He jumped up from the stuffed chair, shoved his arms into his leather bomber jacket, and headed for the door.

She looked at me helplessly from the couch and rolled her eyes before saying to his back, "I keep asking you to help me! You won't because you can't. You have no clue." He turned his head and rolled his eyes at her. *Oh boy.*

"Hold up, Pierre. Don't go." He glared at me, hand on doorknob. "Please. Stay. Let's hear more about it from your side." He sat back down, without removing his jacket.

The paperwork issue languished, but as the years unfurled, they made progress sexually. He gave up porn, stopped asking her to get breast implants, told her more often he loved her, hugged and kissed her more often without expecting sex. They began to enjoy their sex life more. He was still frustrated, but less. She still took it personally that his sex drive was stronger than hers, but less. This hard-won *détente*, achieved with multiple courses of intermittent couples therapy over Pierre's dozen PTSD-free years, didn't last.

Bribery Works Better Than Force, Study Reveals

By D. Essem

September, DweebMD, Internet Medical News. A landmark study published last week in the esteemed science journal Family Hell confirms that bribery works better than physical force "to get the little tyrant to do what you want," said I. M. Trapt, M.D., primary researcher and parent.

According to Dr. Trapt, this is the first population-based study to examine the effectiveness of parental persuasion techniques in child-centric households. In such households, parental authority generally goes out the window with the bath water.

What happens to such parents when baby repeatedly spits out prescription antibiotic? "The chumps suffer the anguish of the damned," states Dr. Trapt, "because of a deep-seated need to please." The action takes place on several fronts, she says. Trying to force a spoonful of medicine down an offspring's throat yields outraged screeches and searing glares which cause the parent to cravenly cease and desist. Next comes guilt and, in turn, the negative cognition: "I am a bad parent." Should the child die from untreated bacterial infection, judge and jury will validate this cognition as fact.

However, while possible, such a scenario is improbable. "More likely, the little stinker will just stay sick," Dr. Trapt opines. "If only the parents would lie to the pediatrician—'The dog ate the bottle, Doc, nothing we could do.' But, no, they confess that junior won the Clash of the Cure. Of course, the doc is displeased." Logic dictates, she says, that these honest Abes will feel ashamed and humiliated, "which is enough to unleash the restrained beast in even the nicest."

"It's not that far to go, bullying the little monster," Dr. Trapt says, "And once you're there, very gratifying too, given that you're older, smarter, and bigger."

However, she reports, domination produces nuclear waste that can be stolen and used to make bombs. "One day, in the not too distant future, my son will not only have the desire, but the means, to beat me up. That's what sparked the idea for this study."

Study Highlights:
- Dr. Trapt's eighteen-month-old was tightly strapped into his high chair. A bib embroidered with "My Mommy loves me!" was bow-tied around his neck.
- The goal of the study was to assess which of two parental techniques was more effective in getting the kid to swallow a yucky-tasting antibiotic.
- Coercion Technique: The child's jaws were pried open and a dose shot in with a dropper during the second before the jaws snapped shut. One hand then kept them clamped while the other massaged the throat to force swallowing.
- Bribery Technique: A large piece of chocolate was held just out of the child's reach. The kid was promised he could have it once he voluntarily swallowed a dose of medicine.
- The coercion method failed abysmally (Hazard Ratio for parent: 100%).
- The bribery method succeeded spectacularly (Parental Confidence Interval: 100%).

Clinical Implications:

Dr. Trapt was unimpressed by the failure of the coercion method. "What else would you expect in a house where the chick rules the roost? Duh." She speculates the success of the bribery method had "something to do with the fact that it answers the kid's question: What's in it for me?"

Parents who have ceded authority to their offspring should consider using bribery to get their way, she suggests. "Remember that the brat is getting smarter as he or she ages, while you are getting dumber. The window of opportunity closes quickly. Get the upper hand early."

Encouraged by these results, Dr. Trapt already has preliminary plans in place to expand this research to adults, using her husband as the first test subject.

Don II (Jenn), *eighteen months later...* **What Good Are You?**
April.

Don's daughter Jenn had been coming in since the previous October. It was not going well.

"I've lost my acting career. You can't do anything about that, so what good are you?" Jenn said sourly, slouched in the upholstered chair before me, jeans tucked into mud-encrusted hunting boots, legs crossed, sweatered arms folded across her chest.

When she wore her hair pulled back into a ponytail, I could see the family resemblance, for she was tall and thin like Don, with the same eyes, mouth, and cheekbones. Today, wearing her long, bottle-black hair loose and fluffed with "product," along with a pout, that wasn't as obvious. While she had the elegance of long legs and good posture, I'd been surprised when I first met her at how ordinary her looks were. Maybe she would be more glamorous, if she weren't so unhappy. Or maybe it was preferable for an actress to be a blank canvas that lent itself to paint from any palette.

When she'd come in last fall, she was clean, sober, and depressed. She wasn't a person who looked inside, thought about what she found there, and actively problem-solved. Her comment, not the first of its kind, made me wonder with increasing frequency if she was seeing me just to get Don off her back. Bitterness radiated off her.

The cause of her chronically negative and irritable mood (in combination with other symptoms) might be primary, i.e., a clinical depression. Or it might be secondary to being in recovery; or the result of multiple disappointments and betrayals; or a combination of all these. Regardless, a trial of an antidepressant was justified. She'd been on a "therapeutic" dose of the same one Don was taking for almost six months now and, while she slept better and had more energy, she remained unmotivated and miserable. Depressingly, partial response to one antidepressant alone is common. There are few options and most people in my practice[13] require at least two, and often three, to clear symptoms.[14] Partial response is especially common in the context of prior substance abuse, which alters the brain's baseline chemistry. It was time to consider augmenting her regimen with a second antidepressant from a different class.

"Working in the family business is such a bore," she said, "and Dad is such a nervous nelly. He makes me crazy, hovering over me. Then there's Mom. She's either drunk, nasty, and making mistakes I have to clean up. Or she's impatient and nasty, waiting to get drunk." She frowned

---

[13] The people who respond to one medication (or the first one) prescribed by their general practitioner or gynecologist don't come in to see me, the Crazy Doctor.
[14] Internists struggle similarly when treating high blood pressure, which often requires two or three medications to stabilize.

and broke eye contact, flouncing in the seat as she re-crossed her long legs. Her full lower lip, just like Don's, trembled. I waited. The silence lengthened.

"What's going through your mind?" She came back from far away.

"I was remembering how happy I was when I got the call about my first role, the one that took me to the City." During the fall of her senior year of high school, she and a girl friend had taken the Greyhound bus to New York City to audition for bit parts in soap operas and reality television shows. "I'd forgotten all about the auditions when I finally got a call in early June offering me a part. I was so excited!" Sadness flitted across her face before it settled back into its default put-upon expression. "Mom didn't like that I left right after graduation and she was really mad I was too busy to call her for a couple months."

She'd made a good connection almost immediately and for ten years took all work that came her way, mostly low-budget productions, television commercials, and toward the end, "movies" she wouldn't talk about.

"And nothing to show for it. I'm broke. I'm sick. I'm thirty and have no skills. Thank God for the family business." She paused. "But now I can't leave this armpit town." She scowled and pulled her wool cardigan tighter across her chest with a petulant snort.

"Do you miss it?" *She must*, I thought. The famous people, the excitement, the glamour.

"Not really," she said, shaking her head. "Acting is pretty boring once you get over the thrill of being on camera. I mean, I was just a pretty face really, not a person." She shifted her weight and looked away. "They don't care if you're tired, your feet are killing you, that the pose they stopped you in is impossible to hold. You're just a babe, the girl that makes the leading man look more of a hunk than he is." She paused and considered me in an appraising way. "After work, they just want to fuck you. The director. The producer. Doesn't matter, you're meat."

I took in her utter matter-of-factness, how closely she was watching me, and nodded. Her shoulders drooped.

"Did you make any friends?" She shook her head no and looked down.

"Not one?"

"Nope," she said, talking to her lap, voice low. "You can't imagine the competition. The fear you'll be passed over for someone younger. There's no friendship when you're worrying about your job. Every day that passes is a day you're one day older, the line behind you longer with girls wanting your place." She sighed. "You end up sleeping with these disgusting rich old guys just in self-preservation. Then you have to do coke or whatever to put up with it. Then the drugs take you and it's over."

She sighed again, letting go of her arms to clasp and re-clasp her hands in her lap. There were shadows under her lowered mascara-ed eyelashes, shadows deep in her gaunt cheeks. When she looked up, her dark eyes were shiny and blank.

"I spent most of my free hours in hotel rooms, passed out or getting high or getting laid. You'd think I'd have gone out, seen the sights, but I had no interest. I didn't care. I just wanted not to feel anything."

I felt the horror of her predicament. At first a windfall, a miraculous opportunity to live the dream, it was all casting-couch sexual slavery, the glamour an illusion. Paradoxically, her decline into addiction proved her ticket out. Word got around, she was fired one time too many, and the work dried up.

"Did you call your parents for help?" Again she shook her head no.

"Why not?"

"I thought I could handle it, that it would get better. I was making so much money! But I spent it on coke. It kept my weight down." She fell silent.

"I don't know how ten years got away from me," she said, her voice heavy. "And three more since I'm back in this armpit town."

"Look at me." She sat up, lifted a hand and swept it down her body. "I'm a hag. Old and used up. What man would want me?" She curled her lip. "Not that I want one."

She kicked a booted foot up and down, up and down, the laces clicking, bits of dried mud flaking off.

"Thirty by acting standards may be old Jenn," I said, "but by the standards the rest of us live by, you're young, with most of your life ahead of you."

She gave me a flat look: *Idiot.*

Okay, I got it: her life had started at seventeen, ended at twenty-seven. But, now what? She had way too much time stretching ahead, empty of purpose and meaning. She was at serious risk of a relapse. How committed was she to her recovery?

"How many hours a day are you working for your folks?"

"A few hours in the morning, if I feel like it."

"And if you don't?"

"I sleep in and work a few hours in the afternoon."

"Are they paying you?"

"Oh sure."

"Are they charging you room and board?"

She gave me an incredulous look. "Are you kidding?"

"What else are you doing?"

"Not much. I watch TV. Go out with my brother for a drink." *No!*

I asked quietly, "How often are you doing that?"

She looked down. "Oh, not often."

"Give me a guesstimate. Once a month? Once a week? Every day?"

"Oh… say, couple times a week."

Regular alcohol intake would explain her persistently miserable, low mood. Alcohol disrupts sleep and the breakdown products are depressants, which undo the benefit of antidepressant.

"Are you in touch with your sponsor? Going to AA meetings?"

She shifted uneasily and didn't meet my eyes.

"Are you doing any coke?"

She shook her head no vehemently. "I'm not touching that stuff ever again. Made me crazy paranoid." The coke was another variable working against her. Some people, after exposing their brains to stimulant[15], lose their ability to respond to antidepressants. Okay, she wasn't using coke now. I believed her. The drinking was an issue.

---

[15] Cocaine is a stimulant. Did you know it's also used as an anesthetic by dentists and opthamologists?

"I thought you'd stopped drinking. When did you restart?"

"It's not a problem. Just now and then," she said, not looking at me. This didn't answer the question and revealed a disturbing lack of insight.

"When you do, do you get drunk?"

She shifted uneasily. Still not looking at me, she said, "No."

The clinical rule of thumb when dealing with addicts is to double or triple any number they admit to. She'd said she went out for a drink twice a week. Make that most nights. She'd said no, she wasn't getting drunk. Make that yes, she was. She said she slept in and worked in the afternoon if she didn't feel like getting up. Make that hung over most days. She wasn't doing anything else with her free time. She'd dropped her sponsor and stopped going to AA. She hadn't told me any of this. I'd had to ask. When pressed, she was evasive. Diagnosis: relapse. Well, as the twelve-steppers say, relapse is part of recovery.

She could keep the cycle going indefinitely, as long as her parents carried her, which I knew they would. Her depression was no longer the primary treatment problem. Her drinking was. *Was she willing to address it?*

"Drinking can make you crazy paranoid, too," I said.

She looked surprised. "Really?"

"Sure. It's a powerful brain poison. Some parts of your brain are more vulnerable than others and it's not predictable which part will be affected."

She frowned. "I feel fine." *Sure you do.*

"I know. It takes a while. But regardless, you won't see it when things start to go bad. It creeps up on you. Your ability to notice *that* is also a brain function. If the noticing part is compromised, it won't be able to tell you, and you'll keep thinking you're fine."

"Really? That's interesting," she said intrigued. I saw my opening.

"In fact, it's happening already. You're not seeing that your drinking is a problem. You're barely working, your mood is low, you're not doing much besides going out for a drink and sleeping in."

She glared. "I disagree! You've put me on the wrong medicine. That's what's not working." *Okay. She doesn't want to address her drinking.* I started the search for the crowbar that might open her up to considering it.

"Well, that may be. That's impossible to figure out, though, if you're drinking."

She frowned. "Why?"

"Did you take biology in high school?"

"Yeah." She frowned. "So what?"

"Remember the scientific method? When you set up an experiment to answer a question, you set up two groups that are exactly the same, except for one thing, the variable. You learn what the effect of the variable is by comparing the group with it to the group without it."

Her eyes were glazing over. I hurried.

"When you first came in, you were in recovery. You weren't drinking. You started the antidepressant. But then you added back the drinking." Her eyes sharpened and narrowed.

"Question?"

"I get it. I remember now. We did an experiment in bio where we kept a head of lettuce on the counter for a week and one in the fridge."

"That's interesting. What was question the experiment was supposed to answer?"

"Which one would keep fresh longer. The one in the fridge. Duh."

"Why would that be, do you think?"

"Something about heat and rot, I don't know!" she said, suddenly exasperated, flipping her hair with a snap of her head and crossing her legs the other way. "What's your point?"

I looked her in the eye. "My point is, the only way I can figure out if your medicine is working or not is if it's the only new variable in your life."

"Okay. Okay. Get to the point," she said impatiently.

"Like I said, when you started this antidepressant, you weren't drinking. Now you've added that back. So, that's *two* things that could explain why your mood is low. The alcohol could be making you depressed. Or, the medicine could be ineffective. Which is it? I can't tell. Scientific method: change only one thing at a time to get a reliable answer."

She scowled, fluffed her bangs with a jerky hand, and looked off into the middle distance, as if she were doing time.

"Alcohol breakdown products are depressants," I went on. Her eyes drifted back to me. "They work against the medicine. The only way to figure out what's going on is to remove the alcohol."

She shook her head irritably. "I'm telling you, it's not a problem."

Now *I* felt annoyed. Arguing was pointless. Logic wasn't working. Maybe begging would.

"I'd love to agree with you. But do you see my dilemma? Humor me. Recommit to recovery. Stop drinking. AA, ninety meetings in ninety days. Reconnect with your sponsor. That way I'll be able to figure out if the medicine is working. Or not."

She shrugged and glanced at the clock on the end table beside me. "Isn't this session over yet? I've got to go."

If Only She Could See the Funny
May.

"I'm getting fat!" Sharlie sat in the stuffed chair before me, one arm on the armrest, slim legs turned to the side.

Raising my eyebrows, I suppressed a groan. She glowed with the beauty of young adulthood: taut, flat-bellied, smooth-skinned, and elegant in jeans and a form-fitting tee with a boat neckline. She was finishing up her senior year at the local college. With a double major in accounting and theater, she already had a job lined up doing the books for a small art gallery an hour south. She was in treatment for Obsessive Compulsive Disorder (OCD). Symptoms were acceptably controlled.

The morning light filtering through the shaded window to her right brightened that side of her face and body, casting the left into shadow, a chiaroscuro effect that emphasized her lean dancer's lines, long neck, and the clean planes of her face.

"Look!" She pulled at her non-existent double chin.

"Sharlie. Reality check. That's skin."

"I look just like my mother. She's got a dewlap!"

"The slimness of adolescence is special, the result of rapid growth. Your face is probably just a bit fuller now you're twenty."

"I hate it!"

"Are you still eating Trix for breakfast, Pop Tarts for lunch, and chicken nuggets for dinner?"

"Well, of course. That's all I eat. You know that."

"Are you exercising?"

"I could walk to Burger King, it's so close to my house."

"Do you?"

"No. I drive."

Don III, *six months later...* The Spin
Late October

"She's an adult," Don said calmly, giving me a straightforward look. He sat relaxed in the upholstered chair before me, hands clasped over his belly.

I started to feel better. Maybe Jenn's relapse and departure from treatment hadn't compromised his. I gently stroked my nine-week old puppy, Poodle Oodle, who was curled next to me, asleep. She stirred and nestled closer against my trousered thigh.

"I can't say I'm not worried, though." He paused, looking down. "If she doesn't want to do what you recommend, I can't make her." He looked up. "What *did* you recommend, if you don't mind me asking?" He hunched deeper into the chair, pulling his buffalo plaid flannel shirt askew. He jiggled his foot, sockless in a leather boat shoe, across his knee.

It was blustery and bone-chillingly damp out, the temperature hovering at 33 degrees. I had worn my winter coat to work and turned the heat up to 68, which everyone I'd seen today had appreciated. My toes curled inside their wool socks as I stared at his naked ankles. The locals bragged they didn't wear socks till January. My mind shivered briefly before I dragged it back to business. I gave him a searching look.

"She didn't tell you?"

He shook his head and ran a hand over his face with a slight rasping sound. I didn't want to violate Jenn's confidence by answering directly, but I also needed to know more about what he felt and thought. I asked more questions.

"Did she say anything about why she quit?"

He shifted a little in the seat. "Well," he said, obviously uncomfortable. "She said you kicked her out." He took a breath. "Did you?"

I smiled ruefully. "I'm not surprised that's the spin she put on it. Did she say why?"

Don raised his eyebrows. "Drinking?"

I nodded. "What happened was, I gave her a choice. She could recommit to not drinking, and continue treatment. Or not, and end treatment."

"I can see how she might feel you kicked her out," he said carefully.

"Can you see that I didn't?" I asked, just as carefully. We looked at each other. "*She* chose to leave."

"Looks to me," he said dryly, "that it was your way or the highway."

A few years ago, this challenge would have seduced me into righteous indignation. Me, a tyrant? No way! Having learned the folly of arguing against such covert accusations, I followed poet Robert Frost's wisdom: *The best way out is always through.*

"Well, sure," I said. "That's the agreement from day one."

He frowned, "It is?"

"I'm the expert, right? That's why people come to see me, to get my opinion on the problem and how to treat it. But once I give it, then you have a decision to make. If you agree with my assessment and recommendation and decide to try it, that's treatment. But if you don't, you've rejected it, which means no treatment.

He frowned, "I don't get it."

"Treatment is a relationship in which the patient agrees to do what the doctor recommends."

He nodded, uncertainly.

"Jenn didn't agree with me that drinking was a problem. So she disagreed with my recommendation that she stop, and she left."

"Yeah, okay. I see that." He said, bobbing his head. "But why would she tell me you kicked her out?"

"Well, how did it make you feel when she put it that way?"

He stared off into space for a moment. Sounds from outside seeped into the room: chirping birds, the grinding sound of the garbage truck coming to a stop in the back of the building, a barking dog.

"I felt bad for her," Don said. "I thought you were harsh to kick her out." He paused. "And I was surprised too, because I can't see you being like that."

"Exactly," I said. "Kicked out. Those words imply I was unfair and mean. Interesting, isn't it, that she put it like that? It made you feel sorry for her." I gave him a moment to think that through. When he nodded, I continued.

"She *could* have said I was wrong, for instance, and that she disagreed with me," I continued. "If she'd put it that way, she'd have taken responsibility for her opinion and her decision to leave treatment. Instead, she presented herself as a victim: I kicked her out. I did something *to* her against her will."

Don sighed. "Jenn does that a lot."

I had to agree, if I was understanding him correctly. Just to make sure, I checked.

"What does she do a lot?"

"She blames other people. Nothing is ever her fault. Things just happen to her."

"That's a tough way to go through life," I said. "Always a victim of circumstance, never the captain of your own ship."

He sighed again. "I'm glad you asked how I was doing about her leaving treatment."

"Were you thinking of ending yours?"

He sat up, startled. "No! Why would you think that?"

I smiled. "It's a possibility I had to consider. She *is* your kid. Maybe you'd feel a need to protect her, to take sides."

"You thought I'd leave just because she did?" He gave me a Look. "Come on. I *do* know my daughter, you know. I know how she does things. How she explains things away." The expression that passed across his face was sad but philosophical. "She has to make her own decisions."

He shrugged again. "Evan, too. They're adults." He shrugged again. "If they make bad decisions, what can I do? They're on their own."

We looked at each other.

"I'm afraid you're stuck with me." He smiled.

I smiled back. "Good to know." Poodle Oodle chose that moment to awaken, yawn, and sit up beside me. I looked down at her. She looked up at me, all dark brown eyes and sweetness.

"Gosh, she's cute," Don said approvingly, rising from his seat. He squatted before us, a warm smoke scent from his wood-burning stove wafting off him, and offered her a knuckled fist to sniff. "May I pet her?"

Every Day Is Dog Appreciation Day
By Doodle Poodle, Editor

September, Poodle Times: *By, for, and about the poodle community. "You don't have to be a poodle to love Poodle Times."*

Did you know August 26 was national Dog Appreciation Day? Me neither. Nice, but I don't get it. Your faithful human companion already knows every day is Dog Appreciation Day. And if not, s/he is neither faithful nor human.

All pooches, especially poodles, live to serve. While Mom is no poodle— you can't have everything—she's got the idea. Together, we serve our psychiatric practice. She does the shrinking; I do the loving. I'm a therapy dog, a working dog. You might say I was born to it. From nine weeks on, I've been her right hand at the office.

That's where I learned English, dozing beside her in the magic chair. Where I cut my teeth on that chair's wood base. Where I chased my tail in the waiting room for laughs. Where I got my belly rubs from more humans than you can catch a tossed stick from. Training Mom is hard work, but hardly work when you love it.

So this August 26 was just a regular workday, which goes like this: While she hangs up my leash and stashes her purse in the inner sanctum (the administrative office), I trot ahead to the waiting room, where patients wait to pay their respects.

Mom's patient offers a hand to sniff. Hand lotion! I lick it. "Oh! Kisses!" Sure. Next, I visit Dad's patient, who scratches me under the chin. "Nice to see you!" Naturally. Last, the drug rep, a nice woman whose shoes, shins, and hands smell mysteriously delicious. "Hi there! Smell my horses?" I could have sniffed her all morning, but Mom interrupts. I amble back to her patient, who offers me the other hand to lick. Yes!

When Mom finishes talking with the horse lady and says to her patient, "Come on in," that's my cue to lead the way to her clinical office where I wait at the door— Humans first! After the patient chooses her seat (couch or chair), I choose mine. Sometimes a patient is sad or anxious or upset and needs to give me belly rubs first. Of course, I oblige. That's my job. Sometimes, I just drift off curled next to the patient.

If the patient takes the couch against the wall, I jump on the seat of the matching chair opposite Mom, and vault up onto the top. From there, I survey the property through the bottom of the window not covered by the shade and alert Mom of trespassers at the perimeter, a sideline. If all is quiet, inside and out, I might rest my head on my front paws and my eyes, too. Some days *I'm* needy, and squeeze in next to Mom.

Regardless, I *always* keep my "third ear" open. If the patient weeps or pants, I jump down and mosey over, lean against his ankles or jump up in her lap. No matter what I do, it's always right. That's because I'm a Zen sage trapped in a poodle body.

"Your dog is so good!"

Mom agrees. Good mom!

"Anytime you need a dog sitter, let me know," the adoring human says.

Mom laughs. "I'm afraid you'll have to take a number."

When Mom stirs in the chair and says, "Let me see you in…" that's my cue. I stretch in downward-facing dog, wait by the door as she and the patient rise to their feet, and escort them out. Then I trot to the waiting room to start my rounds anew.

Sometimes I linger there to track down an enticing scent in the wastebasket— empty coffee containers, food wrappers, snot rags— or to deal with an intruder: ants, spiders, the occasional beetle. My bug policy is this: either they go or stop moving, no in-between. "Doodle!" Mom calls out. "Let's go! Time to work!" As if I wasn't working already. Ruff! Ruff!

Love might make the world go round, but getting loved up, nine to five, week after week, can wear a poodle down. That's when I take a mental health day and stay home. When I hear the garage door rumbling at the end of the day, I run to meet Mom at the door. She leans down to fondle my ears and kiss the top of my head: "Patients complained you didn't come in. They said, 'Where's the Doodle?! I didn't come in to see *you*!'" Proves my point: Every day is Dog Appreciation Day. Talk *is* sweet, but how about a treat?

No Patients, No Patience
Early February

My first mistake was sharing my idea with friend Cass, a pediatrician. The second was letting her talk me into presenting it at the Parent Teacher Organization (PTO) meeting at the elementary school, where our sons were in fourth grade.

We walked into the blissfully warm, brightly lit library just before seven o'clock that freezing dark night and snagged the last two seats at the twelve-person table the kids used during the day to browse books and do homework. I stuffed hat, scarf, and gloves into the sleeve of my full-length down coat.

Draping it over chair seat and back, I saw my patient Pamela sitting at the far end of the table, chatting with her neighbor while unwrapping a fireball with a cellophane rustle I could hear over the murmur of conversation. She always snacked through her sessions, too: pretzels, chips, candy, cookies. She'd seen me. We nodded hello as I seated myself. She popped the red ball in her mouth.

Given that our town has only one public elementary school, one middle school, and one high school, it was inevitable— though it had taken seven years— that I would find myself working with an active patient on a community project. It would be more important than ever to navigate by the true north of small town life: unfailing politeness.

She'd married her husband, a high-powered executive at the regional manufacturing site of an international, upscale lighting company, immediately after they both graduated from college. They moved often due to his work and had lived in town only two years. She had never worked outside the home, despite her double major in accounting and business operations. She was in treatment for recurring bouts of depression. Her symptoms had only partially responded to medication. While she wouldn't (or couldn't) acknowledge it, her volatile and controlling husband triggered symptoms regularly. She and their two sons tiptoed around him, perpetually on edge, waiting for the next explosion.

She complained constantly in session, not about him, but about the many women with whom she'd served on committees for local charities or civic organizations. Frequently, she wasn't invited to social events she should have been invited to. Frequently, she wasn't invited to participate on other committees. "They know they need me. I'm the best fundraiser in town. They make me invite myself!" She had no idea why this was so, though I had a hypothesis or two. To help her, I needed more concrete data. Soon, I would have it.

Cass introduced me to everyone at the table. After a round of warm welcomes, I presented my idea for an outdoor Health Day for third to fifth graders, to be held the last Saturday in May, featuring fun physical games and activities of varying degrees of difficulty that would appeal to the entire spectrum of kids: athletes to couch potatoes, boys and girls. The only snacks on offer would be healthy and nutritious.

In the past year, there had been more and more news coverage about the alarming increase in childhood obesity, strongly linked to inactivity and a high sugar diet. Cass bemoaned how many of her patients' young parents (in their late teens and early twenties) were morbidly obese and had already suffered heart attacks or been diagnosed with adult onset diabetes.

"Great idea!" enthused one woman.

"We definitely want to support that a healthy lifestyle can be a fun lifestyle," said another.

"I'm in!" said a third.

While my head was delighted by this response, my heart was not. I am not a group person. Now I was locked into being one for the next four months of weekly meetings. A subcommittee was formed. Cass and I took charge of food, a physical therapist mom and her nurse friend took activities, a couple others marketing and publicity. And Pamela? Obstruction and obfuscation. I went to the March meeting excited to report that two orchards had donated bushels of various apples and a local spring water distributor had donated dozens of cases of twelve-ounce bottles.

Pamela unwrapped a fireball and popped it in her mouth. "That's great, but we need cotton candy, fried dough, and soda vendors too," she said with the air of a matador throwing the first spear into the bull's haunch as it thundered by.

Cass and I sucked in air. A heavy silence descended over the table. I thought about how to respond to this gross power play without compromising the treatment relationship—

"Why?" asked Cass. "That destroys the point of the event." *Thank you, Cass!*

"They're huge moneymakers! Duh." Pamela leaned forward, pushing the edge of the table deep into her belly, her triple chins quivering as she raised her voice stridently. "Besides, the kids love it." She chomped down on the fireball, crushing it between her teeth.

I was horrified. Sugar is addicting, especially when combined with white flour and fat. Addictions are insanely profitable, for obvious reasons. Pamela's own junk food habit was at least part of the reason she was overweight. But now, she had revealed she wasn't just a user but a pusher too. I goggled, speechless, as women around the table started debating whether or not to give our kids access to substances of abuse for the profit of the PTO. Not framed that way, of course.

Cass spoke up again, "This event is about promoting health first and raising money second."

I found my tongue. "It would be a good experiment," I said directly to Pamela, "to see how much money we make without offering the usual fattening, sugary options." I broke eye contact to look at the women who had supported her. "Those vendors don't donate, they just discount. Whereas the vendors I've lined up are donating out of the goodness of their hearts and out of a commitment to our kids' health. (*Are you ashamed yet?*) Selling donated goods is pure profit."

"Yeah," pediatrician Cass said. "Let's see if kids scarf real food after running around." I glanced around the table. Many moms looked alert and interested. Pamela and her soldiers frowned.

"Research suggests kids eat good food as readily as bad," Cass continued. "And that makes sense if you think about it. Kids aren't eating just to fuel, like us adults. They're using food to grow."

"Let's not support addiction eating," I said, all shrink. "Addiction is a brain disorder kindled by exposure, sugar included. Let's not help that genie out of the bottle."

"Well, the PTO is short on money and we have several projects that need funding," Pamela snapped. "We need to think about that, too."

"Yeah! The band needs instruments replaced."

"This library needs more computers."

And so on. She got a surprising amount of support.

The committee bogged down. The debate raged through late March. That Pamela and her allies couldn't (or wouldn't) see there was no place for junk at a *health* day baffled me. Nothing Cass or I said or suggested budged them. The committee was paralyzed, and I was disgusted.

I rarely get impatient with patients' slow rate of improvement. That's because (1) I have no personal agenda or timeline for their healing and (2) the patient empowers me to move the process forward should they get stuck. Whereas, on this committee, the situation was reversed: I had a personal agenda and no authority.

Work was hectic, I was tired, and the evening meetings were cutting into my home life and reading time. And to what end? Social forces outside my control were defeating common sense and reason. Time was running out. The project was in danger of either getting scrapped or betraying its health objective, and most likely the latter.

What's more, I realized Pamela's treatment had run aground. Before our joint participation on this committee, I had seen her at least once a month, often twice. Now, she'd missed appointments, cancelled and rescheduled, cancelled and rescheduled again. I hadn't seen her professionally since February.

Our opposing agendas and public conflict had either (1) backed her into a corner that her need to win wouldn't let her to step away from, which compromised her treatment, or (2) unmasked her dark desire for power over others, which the treatment compromised. If the first, my resigning from the committee might allow her to return to treatment (*and* release me from bondage). If the second, her treatment was already dead and my resignation would only hurt the project. To maintain integrity, I had to find a solution that met *both* commitments, to my patient and to the committee, not one or the other.

What were my choices? Option (1): I could be a drama queen and force the committee to choose: me or junk food. For this to work, my gravitas as a physician had to trump how scary Pamela was. Forget it. Option (2): If the committee decided to sell unhealthy "food," then we should rename the event to remove the health focus. Something like End-of-May Field Day. That ended the hypocrisy and the conflict with Pamela, though it wiped out the reason I'd agreed to participate in the first place. Committee work was torture but another month to fulfill my obligation wouldn't kill me. No way was I helping promote junk, though. I'd transfer to the activities subcommittee.

At the first April meeting, Pamela provoked yet another debate. I scooted forward in my chair and cleared my throat. "Excuse me!" Everyone stared, a few annoyed, others startled, all waiting. "It's ridiculous and hypocritical to sell funnel cake and Kool-aid Slurpees at what we're calling a Health Day." I paused for breath before offering up Option (2).

But the school principal chose that moment to speak. She was a slim, unassuming woman who favored cropped jackets and pencil skirts, soft off-white blouses and low-heeled pumps. She had attended the meetings sporadically and had joined this one late. She had never expressed an opinion either way. She stood behind those sitting across the table from me. The overhead fluorescents cast a shine on her bobbed, silver hair and the rows of wood bookcases behind her fanned out like rays of a halo.

"You have to decide whether you're prioritizing eating or exercising. It's one or the other, not both," she said quietly, looking straight at Pamela, seated on my side of the table. "If you want the kids to run around, you can't tempt them with sweets. That will stop them in their tracks."

A silence ringing with racing thoughts filled the room. Perhaps I wasn't the only one sick of the debate. Perhaps her role as official school leader tipped the undecided and/or intimidated. Perhaps she just struck the right note at the right time. A vote was taken and junk food was removed from the agenda moving forward. Pamela glowered. Her attempts to have it reconsidered at subsequent meetings were shut down.

I finished out the academic year serving on the PTO and saw the Health Day through. It was a great success.

151

The kids had a wonderful time, and we raised a ridiculous amount of money selling donated apples and bottled water, local eggs hard-boiled at home by volunteer moms, chicken kebabs, veggie tacos, and more. It's my pleasure to report these weren't pity purchases. All day, I watched crowds of kids (and their parents) guzzle water and gobble actual food before scampering off to the next thing.

Pamela did not forgive me for "winning." After a few more rescheduled appointments, a no-show, and none of my calls returned, it was soon clear she had dropped out of treatment. Two years later, her husband got a promotion and they moved out of town. In the six months before that move, Cass (now a member of the middle school PTO) reported that Pamela almost single-handedly raised a mammoth amount of money to upgrade the middle school gym floor, stage, and bleachers.

"I sat on those lovely bleachers today and watched the kids up on that beautiful new stage, and it gave me no pleasure," Cass said. We were leaning against our cars in the middle school parking lot, enjoying the sun and chilly spring breeze while we waited for our sons, now seventh-graders, to exit the building after the talent show practice. "I still have nightmares about Pamela's blasting me for not doing enough while ranting she was doing too much. I used to go home from those meetings and cry. To this day, I can barely look donors in the eye, I'm so embarrassed."

"What a shame," I said. "The new gym is spectacular."

That was the first time (but not the last) that I treated someone who was a victim at home and a bully in the community. People resolve conflicts with each other out of one of two paradigms: intimacy or power. The intimacy paradigm presumes mutual respect, a regard for the needs of the other person, and the ability to compromise. Each person gives up something to get something. The power paradigm is a one up/one down, domination/submission structure: winner takes all/loser gets nothing.

Before Pamela, I naïvely assumed that a power-oriented person is either victim or perp. One or the other. She taught me these roles are relative, determined by social context. At home, Pamela was at her husband's feet. In committee, she was at our throats. Either way, she paid a high price: ruined health and social isolation, bitterness and unhappiness, a troubled home life and an abandoned treatment.

In our sessions before the Health Day committee, Pamela had seemed genuinely hurt and puzzled by people's lack of appreciation for her efforts and leadership. After all, she got exceptional results, which gave her great satisfaction. But at what cost? Once she burned through people's goodwill, they found ways to exclude her from projects.

Just when I could have helped her connect those dots, she'd dropped out of treatment. She didn't change her ways on the last project and left town without the consequences catching up with her. May she stay in one place long enough to give treatment a chance.

As for me, I will always be grateful to Pamela for catalyzing such a useful insight about the fluid nature of power relations. It has served me well with other patients.

Did the success of the event inspire me to further community work? I'm sorry, no. I just don't have the patience. Sometimes to grow, you have to push against your limits. Other times, it's best to go with your strengths. I have lots of patience for patients, many of whom are community movers and shakers. I figure it this way: I give at the office.

Don IV (Evan), *three years later...* One-Trick Pony

June

"Evan, if you want to get married and start a family, tomcatting around bars every night isn't the way to go," I said, allowing my exasperation to leak out just a touch.

He sprawled in the upholstered chair before me, legs spread wide to draw the eye to his package, one arm thrown over the chair back, the other relaxed on the armrest, hand dangling off the end, his full lower lip— just like his dad Don's— curled in a habitual subtle sneer. The sum communication of his body parts said, *"Awww, come on, let me off the hook. I'm a bad boy and you love it."*

Evan, in his mid-thirties, formerly slim and still well-proportioned, followed pop trends obsessively and always wore branded clothing. Today, he wore a Tommy Hilfiger white polo with signature logo over his left pec, pleated Calvin Klein khakis, black leather belt with Ferragamo logo buckle and tan L. L. Bean boat shoes. No socks, of course. Every now and then he'd make noises he was going to get photos taken, submit them to an agency and make a killing acting in television commercials.

But he would never follow through. He drank too much, had no idea how to work for something he wanted, and made very good money in the family business. He'd worked for Don since graduating high school and had never taken a college course. He'd presented a year ago last summer with frank symptoms of depression after Don begged me to evaluate him. My spidey sense told me that, just like sister Jenn, who'd dropped out three and a half years ago, he wasn't long for this treatment.

I had seen Jenn again just this morning as I drove to the office. She was striding purposefully along the shoulder of the road, avoiding the wet and muddy grass. She wore a cinched shiny raincoat, wellies[16] with a flower pattern, and a designer tote slung across one shoulder that bounced with each step. She held an open designer umbrella to keep the rain off her moussed, now red hair and heavily made-up face. I saw her walking often, in all weathers, before nine in the morning and after five in the evening. To work, most likely. Exercising to keep her weight down? Lost her license for DUI? Unless Evan or Don told me, I'd never know because I wasn't asking.

I studied Evan thoughtfully. He met my eyes and shifted his weight so that his legs widened more. He just couldn't help himself. His words said he wanted to settle down but his body said otherwise.

"You have to stop drinking, too," I said.

"I'm not doing that," he said, surprising me. This was an about-face from previous sessions. "If I don't go out, I'll be home. Which is boring." The sneer became a leer.

"Well, if you marry and have a baby, you'll be home, won't you? I don't think you want to settle down. I think you want to drink and sleep around."

---

[16] Wellingtons, knee high rubber rain boots

"I don't! I just haven't met anyone special enough to marry."

"You don't go out with anyone long enough to determine that. How long do they last? A couple weeks? A month? You won't meet a family-oriented woman in a bar."

"Yeah, well, if I was a Ph.D.," he said, with obvious envy, "a better class of girl would consider me. But noooo, they all want the prof." I knew the man he was referring to because he brought up this fellow tomcat frequently. Besides the obvious—male cats will always spit and hiss at each other— Evan resented his rival's superior social status because he was one of those people who see the accomplishments of others as undeserved luck rather than the consequence of applied effort. The reality was the reverse: *he* was the lucky one, born into his comfortable living.

I ignored this obvious ploy to distract me.

"Your lifestyle is incompatible with family life," I said. "And nightly drinking is incompatible with good brain health. Your mother is an active alcoholic. Your sister, too. We've talked more than once about how alcohol works against the antidepressant you're taking. And about how the breakdown products are themselves depressants. That's on top of the direct toxic effect on your brain."

I paused. He sat there, silent.

"You've agreed to stop several times. Yet you haven't. Today, you say you won't. You have a drinking problem."

He stretched down in the chair, his body lengthening that much closer to the horizontal. We looked at each other. The silence dragged on. A car swished by outside in the street and rain pattered against the closed windows. It was hot in the office, and the peace lily, luxuriantly dark leafed, obviously enjoyed it. In recent weeks, three new velvety white blooms had appeared, replacing the spent, brown-edged one from April. I felt damp in my linen blouse. We have mild summers here in upstate New York, but the time had come to put in the air conditioner. The floor fan, turned up high, just wasn't enough. It was late June, just past the solstice and the sun wouldn't go down till after 9:30. I glanced at the clock on the end table next to Evan's chair: 7:40. Five more minutes.

I leaned forward to lift his chart off the ottoman, clearing it. He was my last patient of the day. He watched.

I raised my eyebrows, "So?"

"What?" he said.

"You're drinking pretty much every day. You agreed to stop..." I opened the chart and flipped through progress notes, "at last month's session." I flipped some more. "And the month before that and... the month before that." I slapped the two sides of the chart together with a thump. He stared.

"Evan, you're not a kid anymore. It's going to get harder to stop with every year that passes. Your brain won't lay down new pathways, the ones you've got will break down, and you'll get more set in your ways. In the end, you'll lose your ability to stop because of the brain damage." I paused.

He just looked back, giving nothing. Okay then. Time for the old ultimatum. I took a deep breath in, then let it out.

"To stay in treatment, you'll have to stop drinking, go to AA, and outpatient rehab."

"I'm *not* doing that!" He sat up. "Come on! It's not that bad!"

"Yes, it is." I waited. He quirked an eyebrow and gave me an amused smile.

"I'm serious, Evan. You're alcoholic. Functional, yes. But controlled by your drinking nonetheless."

"It's not a problem. I'm not stopping."

"That's your right," I said politely. I slid forward in my seat. "The door is open if you change your mind." I put the chart back on the ottoman, held my hands in my lap and waited.

His expression shifted for the first time into uncertainty. "What?"

"You've rejected my recommendation. That ends treatment."

He gave me a searching look. Paused. Smiled slowly, gazing deep into my eyes and sinking languorously deeper into the chair. All ambient sound shut down, leaving the room muffled.

He dialed up the grin. A fug of male sex hormone and aftershave rose off him, rolled like an ocean wave straight at me, and crashed, molecules spraying like surf against rock. I must have flinched because his grin puckered with satisfaction.

Good grief! He was trying to seduce me. Me! A professional! Older than his mother! I smoothed my face and stilled my body.

He shifted his hips suggestively and his eyes said, *"Aren't you thrilled this young stud thinks you still have it? You lucky, lucky thing you."*

Yuck. So that's how he got them into bed, night after night: A frontal pheromone assault while leaning in too close with a Look: *It's your lucky, lucky night, you cute thing, you.* That would work on the insecurities of many a young woman who had drunk a few too many on his dime. But on me? Come on! I gave him my own Look: *Is that all you've got?*

I flashed back on a much earlier session when he had told me about a traumatic high school experience. Popular with the girls and thoughtless about it, he had been surrounded by five or six infuriated boyfriends behind the school and beaten to a pulp.

"It's not my fault girls like me!" he'd said, with utter lack of insight. "It's not my fault the guys get jealous!"

"There's more to being a man than getting women into bed," I'd commented. "You have to get along with men, too." He'd shrugged. Nothing had happened in subsequent sessions to suggest he'd learned anything. His countless conquests merely kept his ego afloat. He wasn't going to age well. He had no friends. No girlfriend. No real interpersonal skills. Just sex appeal. A one-trick pony. A *desperate* one-trick pony, trying it on me.

I picked up the chart and opened it to the medication sheet, where I documented all the prescriptions I wrote. "We have two options for dealing with your meds. I can give you instructions to safely taper off. Or, I'll write scripts to cover you for three months until you find another psychiatrist or arrange for your primary care doc to write for you."

He didn't move. He didn't speak. He just stared. I waited a couple of beats. Okay. No problem. On a prescription, I wrote a protocol for weaning off. I tore it off the pad and then also wrote scripts to cover him for three months, documenting on the med sheet. All contingencies covered.

I closed the chart and stood. "That's it then."

Disbelief spread across his face.

"Time's up," I said, handing him the scripts, which he took with his eyes glued to mine. I walked past him to stand by the door. Years passed. With obvious reluctance, he stood.

"As I said before, if you change your mind, the door remains open," I said and opened the door. "Don't forget your umbrella."

He stared, his features frozen in shock. I waited. The silence lengthened. He blinked and shook his head, hard. Grabbing his umbrella off the floor, eyes blank and shoulders stiff, finally he exited. (Pursued by a bear?)[17]

I closed the door and exhaled slowly. I'd been holding my breath. Repositioning the fan so it blew directly on me, I sat down, a bit light-headed, and wrote the session progress note. I leaned back, put my feet up on the ottoman and closed my eyes.

---

[17] Shakespeare's most (in)famous stage direction, from *The Winter's Tale*: "(Exit, pursued by a bear.)"

Like many patients, Evan hadn't come in to get better. He'd come in to get credit for *trying*, without any intention of making changes. That's not treatment.

Emotional by temperament, I work hard and continuously to keep my natural reactivity under control, especially with patients. Today, I'd turned a corner professionally. I'd held my ground with complete self-possession, from beginning to end, with a patient determined to dominate me into colluding with his scam.

I rested a few minutes longer, the fan's breeze evaporating away the sheen of sweat on my arms and neck. A good day's work done, and home soon.

Don V, *next month*.... Co-Dependence, the On-Going Saga
July

"I'm afraid both my kids take after their mother," Don said. "Stubborn. Drinkers. Nasty when crossed." He shrugged, tanned shoulders and arms making his white tee shirt pop. He shifted in the chair, stretched his legs out and crossed his ankles, almost losing a flip flop in the process.

"I'm sorry," I said. "I tried. You can lead a horse to water—"

"—but you can't make it drink. I know," he sighed. "I wish there was something I could do."

Here was my chance. I'd been looking for an opening for a while to introduce the idea that he needed to step back from both of them and let them take their lumps. He kept them so comfortable there were no consequences for their poor choices. No pain, no gain.

"Now that you mention it…"

He raised his eyebrows.

"Are both of them home?"

"Evan's been renting an apartment for years. We keep telling him to buy a house for the tax benefits and the savings, but he won't listen. Like I said, stubborn." Exasperated, he still smiled. "Jenn got a job working for a group of lawyers a few years ago. She moved out last year. It's been good for her not to be working with her mother."

He shook his head. "Talk about stubborn. I wish Jackie would drink less. It's too much to ask that she'll stop." A shadow passed over his face and he sighed. Then he brightened.

"Since Jenn's been dating this new guy Gary, *she's* drinking less, so that's good."

"Do you like him?"

"Gary? He's all right. Seems to care for her. That's a nice change from a long string of good-looking, good-for-nothings. Gary's in business for himself, cleans chimneys and such, owns his home. Maybe she's starting to settle down."

He sighed again.

"I'm really worried about Jackie."

"Everyone you love drinks too much, especially your wife."

He shrugged again. "What can I do?"

"Go to Al-Anon?"

He shook his head. "I don't like groups."

"It'll reassure you to learn it's not just you. It's hard living with an alcoholic. You can't plan. You can't count on her."

"It's stressful," he agreed. "But I'm coping. When she's really bad, my Crohn's acts up."

"How's your mood?"

"OK."

"Has your Crohn's flared up with Evan dropping out of treatment?"

He shook his head. "So far, so good. But he's not around much. It's Jackie. Her health is going."

"Consider Al-Anon, Don. You'll meet other husbands in the same position as yourself. You might pick up a few tips. You need the support." I leaned down to the small metal file holder at the foot of my chair, pulled out an information sheet about local Al-Anon meetings— times, places, phone numbers— and handed it to him.

"I know I do," he said, taking it.

Gone Fishing

August

While Hubby was out of town, we enjoyed a torrential rainstorm that flooded the basement and ruined everything. Given the heat, humidity, and lack of air conditioning, it all had to come out pronto— carpet, paneling, the works— to prevent a secondary explosion of black mold and mildew.

Hubby's friend Karl, 62, Karl's nephew Bob, 30, and Son, 11, came to the rescue. When the two-day revels finally ended around eight p.m., we sat down to eat at the picnic table out back. I lit a few citronella candles to keep away the mosquitoes, who were undeterred by our stink.

"Hubby will be devastated he missed out on the fun," I said, taking a bite of my egg salad sandwich.

"Oh yeah, he'll break down and cry," Karl said, and downed some beer.

"The carpet was gross!" Son scrunched his face up in disgust. "Dad lucked out." He inhaled his first PB&J and started his second.

"Yeah, he did. But your Mom did a fine job directing traffic," Karl said, bringing his hand up to his forehead in mock salute. *Uh huh,* I thought, *that's why we're done.*

Bob grinned and poured chips from the bag onto his plate.

"Yeah, I'm bossy," I said, with a tight smile. Hubby, if he were here, would surely quip, *It's a tough job but somebody's gotta do it. And you do it so well!*

"That's true, you are," Son said.

Bob laughed. Karl laughed. I laughed. Son frowned.

"You shouldn't have said that," Bob said to Son.

"I thought agreeing with girls was good," Son said, pulling his eyebrows into a V.

"Sometimes yes. Sometimes no. You gotta read it," Bob said.

"Yeah, unfortunately there's no formula," admitted divorced Karl.

I turned to Son, who looked more befuddled than ever, and smiled, "I was fishing."

"But, Mom," he said, "you don't like to fish."

Good Cop Bad Cop
December

"Uhhh…. You know that appointment I missed last month?" asked my patient Linda, a woman in her mid-fifties originally from Mississippi. She'd moved here with her air force husband thirty years ago. When the base closed, he left but she stayed.

I leaned forward in my seat to retrieve Linda's chart from the top of the stack on the ottoman and checked the last progress note. There it was: *November 14. NS. (No Show.) Reschedule.*

"Uh huh," I said.

It's our office policy to charge for no-shows and appointments cancelled on the day of session. If we didn't, the practice would quickly become insolvent. Been there, almost done that.

She was seated before me in the upholstered chair that matched the couch along the wall of my small office. It was a cold late December afternoon, 4:15 and dark. The table and floor lamps glowed and the electric baseboard radiated warmth. Poodle Oodle, unlicensed mental health assistant, lay on Linda's puffy full-length down coat on the couch. She jumped down, scattering wool hat, gloves, and scarf, to sit at Linda's feet.

When not depressed (which she wasn't right now) Linda was easygoing, with a sly sense of humor, the kind that snuck up on you. She leaned down to fondle Poodle

Oodle, who looked up adoringly and pressed her fourteen pounds against Linda's boot-clad ankles.

"Well... I was wonderin'...," she drawled in her charming southern accent, "Could you.... Would you... be willin' to... to... well, waive the fee?" She glanced up, eyebrows raised in appeal, and stopped petting the pooch, who pawed her hand: *Don't stop! Get back to work.* Linda got back to work.

I hate it when patients ask me that. I hate to say no. "What happened that you missed? Did we make a scheduling error?"

"No, it was mah fault. Your secretary called to remind me of the date and time and wouldn' you know it, I came the day after." She scratched Poodle Oodle's chest.

I flipped back through the past two years' progress notes: many no-shows. Linda was in treatment for depression and Attention Deficit Disorder (ADD). Disorganization, forgetfulness, distractibility: these ADD symptoms had improved with medication, but persisted at a low level nonetheless. At higher doses, she developed side effects. Other meds hadn't been as effective as this one. Pharmacologically, we'd reached the point of maximum gain with minimum pain.

Other patients in the practice with ADD lived with residual symptoms too, yet never or rarely missed appointments. Personality and determination make a difference in how a person manages a chronic condition.

"I always waive the first miss, Linda. I see here you've missed at least five or six more in the last two years.

Knowing myself, I've probably waived a couple of those, too. I just can't this time."

She stopped stroking the pooch and said flatly, "I understan'." Poodle Oodle pawed her shin: *Don't stop! Get back to work.* She got back to work.

Just as tapping the patella with a hammer causes an involuntary knee jerk, her tone of voice triggered an involuntary *Oh-no-she's-mad-I-feel-bad* response in me. Yes, I'm a co-dependent, over-responsible enabler in recovery, for decades. But as the twelve-steppers say, it's one day at a time.

I reminded myself that the only personal need I impose on patients is my need to get paid. Otherwise, it's all about them. Besides, this wasn't a case of financial hardship. This was Linda expecting to be let off the hook because all her life she'd been let off the hook. Saying no would be a therapeutic intervention that might help her become more accountable for the consequences of her actions.

She would surely test my resolve: people like her have radar for people like me. I reviewed the *Don't-Be-A-Wimp* list in my head:

- Just as a chain is only as strong as its weakest link, I am only as professionally effective as my personal limitations.
- Growth can be uncomfortable, even painful work. (For everyone, including me.)
- It's not my job to pad anyone from that discomfort. In fact, it's disrespectful and unhelpful to do so.

- I don't like that she's mad at me. *So what? DO YOUR JOB.*

I resurfaced to the pooch sprawled at Linda's feet, belly up, eyes at half-mast. I smiled.

Linda jackknifed further down, the better to reach the far end of Poodle Oodle's tummy. Keeping her eyes down and lips close to the dog's ear, she whispered sotto voce, "She can't help being a bitch, can she?"

My eyes popped wide. I sucked in air. Sound rushed from the room, leaving a twanging silence behind. Nobody moved. Nobody breathed. I burst out laughing.

Poodle Oodle startled, ears up. Linda guffawed in kind, which made me laugh harder, which cracked her up further....

When we wound down—it took a while—I pulled a tissue from the box on the end table beside me and wiped my eyes. She did the same and smiled ruefully, "I had to give it the old college try, didn't I?"

"Sure." I grinned. "We're even."

She grinned back.

I couldn't have done a better piece of work if I'd planned it—which I hadn't, of course. You can't plan magic.

Linda took a big risk. She tried to shame me: to get her way, to get back at me, or both. If she'd succeeded, my credibility as a trustworthy interpersonal guide would have been riddled with buckshot. Instead, she scored. Making me (the authority) belly laugh, she experienced her own power in the most gratifying and affirming way possible. *And* she got the message. I'm sure she won't ask me again to waive a missed appointment fee.

I scored, too. I hadn't known how far I'd moved beyond co-dependence. It wasn't so long ago that Linda's "joke" would have rankled instead of tickled. Just goes to show: we need each other. Growth is collaborative. Some learning can only occur in the spark of real-time connection, one human to another.

Poodle Oodle rose to her feet and shook herself from head to tail, in a wave. She looked at me: *Are we done?* I nodded: *Well done.*

Holiday Family Gatherings a Contributing Factor to Yearly Winter Flu Epidemic, Study Reports
By D. Essem

December, *DweebMD, Internet Medical News.* A landmark study published last month in the esteemed science journal *Family Hell* asserts that holiday revelry with relatives "is so stressful to the immune system, it collapses like a building seeded with dynamite," says I. M. Trapt, M.D., primary researcher and family member.

"Extensive research has already concluded that baked goods, recreational drugs, and holiday shopping are deleterious to the immune system," Trapt reports. But what happens when family members gather to "enjoy" the holidays? "Nothing good," says Trapt. "Undead grudges, sniper potshots under the influence, Auntie Petunia's tooth-breaker chuck roast, the soup slurper— It all comes back."

Why would we "forget" this? Wishful thinking, she says. What's the cost of hoping for the best? Breached immune defenses and invasion by viral hordes. Expect at least a week of shattering chills, broiling fevers and bodily fluids exiting from multiple portals.

"It's a wonder we don't kill each other. Or keel over," observes Trapt. "That's what gave me the idea for the study."

Study Highlights:

- The study asked: Does avoiding family during the holidays boost immune response, thereby decreasing incidence of flu?
- The researcher's husband and son spent the holidays with both families of origin.
- She stayed home alone, serving as the control group.
- The research period began the Wednesday before Thanksgiving and ended January first, with no time off for good behavior.
- Unlimited e-mailing, texting, and phone contact was allowed between the research participants for three reasons: (1) to maintain family bonding; (2) to maintain verisimilitude of real life; and (3) to prevent nuclear meltdown of Mr. Dr. Trapt and son.
- Mr. Dr. Trapt and son returned home January 2 via emergency medical transport.
- Dr. Trapt remained happy and healthy during the research period, as well as two weeks after, at which point she went down.
- Dr. Trapt's family of origin is no longer speaking to her.

Clinical Implications:

Dr. Trapt was unimpressed that the study validated the holiday-hermit hypothesis. "Less stress, more white blood cells, better immune defense against germ incursion. Duh." As to why the flu struck her down mid-January, she speculates survivor guilt compromised her immune response. "I maxed out keeping Hubby's and Son's pillows fluffed."

"Maxed out nothing," Mr. Dr. Trapt groused. "*I* had to deal with family. She didn't."

"My daughter the doctor, she never texts, she never calls," Sheila Sitsin de Dark, the researcher's mother, said. "Her brother the Nobel Laureate, *he* finds time."

"I feel bad about Mom," Dr. Trapt affirmed. "But I'll get over it."

More research is needed to confirm these findings, she says. Limitations of the study included small sample size, lack of objective measures, and an utter lack of professionalism. Still, the results are encouraging. "Avoid family gatherings over the holidays by all means," she says.

"If you can't and get sick, there are worse things," Trapt says. As in, relatives clustering round. "To make them go away, fib. Say you're contagious," she suggests. Proper timing, she speculates, may make it possible to delegate all holiday responsibilities, avoid everybody, and still capture sympathy and presents. "That's next year's study," she says.

In the meantime, if you don't want to be sick forever, the doc advises, "Pull out the big guns. Nothing kicks viral butt like ginger lemon tea with honey." Chicken soup is also efficacious and delicious, she says. "Kill two bugs with one stone: Beg Mom pretty please to make you hers."

Ginger Lemon Tea
- Bring a spaghetti pot of filtered water to a boil.
- Peel and chunk a palm-sized piece of ginger. Add to boiling water.
- Reduce heat and simmer for an hour with lid askew (to concentrate the tisane). Turn off the heat.
- Wash and slice several lemons into thick coins. Add to the ginger infusion.

- Add honey to taste. Dilute to taste.
- Drink hot till your back teeth float and your family complains they need the bathroom too.
- Stores for at least a week in the fridge.

Don VI, *another three years later....* Around and Around We Go
August

"I have so much good stuff to tell you! For a change." Don gave me a small laugh and a big smile. "All I do when I come in is whine. But not today!" He sat himself down in the stuffed chair before me and pulled a tissue from the box on the end table, wiping his forehead and neck. "Hot out there." He flapped his tee shirt away from his torso, fanning himself. "Sorry I'm so sweaty. I just mowed the lawn and didn't have time to shower."

I shrugged and smiled. "It's just us. *I'm* not reporting those madras shorts to the fashion police."

He grinned back. "Give 'em a few more years, they'll be vintage."

He'd tried Al-Anon, but had let it go after a few months. He'd been holding steady: not doing better, but not worse either. That wouldn't last forever, of course, but I'd take it.

"And, let's get this straight," I said. "You don't whine. You're trying to figure things out. You're talking about stuff you can't with other people. I have big shoulders."

He laughed. He was in a great mood. He leaned forward in the chair, head up, elbows on hairy knees, hands dangling. "Well, you know how Jenn hates it here, how she's always saying it's an armpit town. I've been on edge, like forever, waiting for her to tell me she's moving away to a bigger city somewhere."

I nodded, "Uh huh."

"Well, she's made up her mind. She's staying! She's in love with Gary and he doesn't want to move, having built up his business to a solid place."

"Is this the guy who treats her well?"

"Yup," he nodded with a grin. "They're getting married!" I smiled back. "Even Jackie's pleased," he said, crossing his eyes and scrunching his face up comically.

"That's great! Have they set a date?"

"Yes. Next year. He's from a big family. It's going to be a formal affair, wedding gown, tuxes, flowers, sit-down dinner, the whole shebang. I've never seen her so happy." He leaned back in the chair with a deep sigh of satisfaction.

"And that's not all!" he said.

Not for the first time, I wished I could lift just one eyebrow.[18] I raised both and smiled. "Do tell!"

"Evan's getting married too!"

"You're kidding!" sprang from my mouth, sarcastically. Don didn't notice. *Thank God.* He hadn't mentioned that Evan was dating anyone, much less that it was serious. That was significant news that he'd definitely have brought up. Evan had gotten some poor girl pregnant. Had to be.

"Yes! He met this really nice girl. Quite a bit younger than him, but level-headed. It's been a whirlwind!"

"Was it love at first sight?"

---

[18] I lack the gene that makes that possible.

"That's what she says! She's a gem." Don sparkled with pleasure.

And Evan? Why ask? I knew the answer. Don was so happy, it was impossible not to smile back. "Where'd they meet?"

"At a local bar at one of those speed-dating things young people do now." He rolled his eyes. "It must work! They hit it off. She works as a manager at a discount clothing store."

"How long have they been going out?"

"A couple months."

"And they know already they want to get married?"

"Yes! And here's the best part!" He paused, scooching forward in the chair with excitement.

I nodded: *Go on.*

"I'm going to be a grandpa!"

LATE INTERMEDIATE PRACTICE

Life is not a spectacle or a feast: it is a predicament. Santayana

Pierre and Judy II: It Seemed a Good Idea at the Time

September

Pierre had been free of PTSD symptoms for twelve years the week he turned fifty. The week after, he witnessed his superior officer, a "total asshole," throw an inmate against the wall and kick him viciously in the head while the man was knocked out, and then he, the sergeant, walked away. Pierre got the inmate to sickbay, after which he had a terrible decision to make. The inmate was a pedophile, the most despised of all convicts by both inmates and corrections officers (CO). Pierre would have walked away, too, had the guy not been a distant relation of his.

"*Very* distant, Doc, but still. The sergeant knew we were related. He did it on my watch to stick it to *me,* just because he could. Two for the price of one. He *enjoys* hurting people." He ground his teeth in fury. "The higher ups know all about him. He's not getting away with it this time."

Pierre wrote up an accurate incident report and submitted it. Judy called to cancel his next appointment. He'd suffered an accident at work and needed surgery.

"The sergeant jumped me in the parking lot by my car," he told me when he next came in. "When I stood back up, he shoved me so hard I lost my balance, and fell, dead

183

weight onto my shoulder. He just left me there." That in itself was horrible, but what happened next was worse. A fellow CO, a guy he'd just finished working a shift with, witnessed the assault, got in his car, and drove away. "He gunned it! We're supposed to have each other's backs!"

"Not when you rat somebody out," observed Judy, shaking her head. "I warned you."

He *tsk*ed, outraged. "Everybody knows he's a piece of shit!"

She gave him a look that combined sympathy with exasperation. "Yeah, and so what? Nobody's gonna risk their job backing you against a shark that high up."

He suffered serious injuries: a rotator cuff tear and a compound fracture of the humerus and was out two months after the two surgeries required to repair the damage. After a six-month course of physical therapy, he was cleared before Thanksgiving to return to work, where he found himself shunned by co-workers. No one met his eye, spoke to him, or stayed in his vicinity if they could leave. He was harassed ("Inmate lover!"), shoved into walls, tripped through doors and— "One of the guys tried to close the gate on my hand!" The gate, one foot thick and metal-barred, would have crushed his hand beyond repair.

The day-to-day work in that maximum security prison was physically dangerous, even with a team at his back. Targeted by administration and abandoned by his peers, now themselves a danger, Pierre fell apart.

He suffered a severe recurrence of PTSD. Nightmares and flashbacks of the sergeant assaulting him wrecked his nights and days. He startled. He panicked. He felt deeply humiliated and betrayed, by the sergeant, his peers, and the system. His thoughts darkened further and he slid into a paranoid depression. He was convinced the sergeant had him under surveillance with the intent of getting him fired. He stopped leaving the house for fear of running into someone he worked with. He stopped sleeping.

I took him out of work in January, filled out a mountain of state disability and workers' comp paperwork, and was happy to do it. If we lived in a large metropolitan area with good mental health services, I would have admitted him to an in-patient psychiatric unit. Unfortunately, in our underserved rural area, that wasn't an option because he wasn't suicidal or homicidal, the only symptoms that qualified. Weekly sessions through winter and mud season gave way to bimonthly sessions in late spring and summer. By August, I'd fine-tuned his medications sufficiently to push symptoms into unstable remission.

Although he was under pressure to return to work, just thinking about it would cause a PTSD flare. He considered retiring, but didn't want to: "They'll think I can't cut it." To which I replied, "Where were they when you needed them?"

After another year of several failed attempts to return to work without breakthrough nightmares, panic attacks, and depressive fears, he took early retirement secondary to medical disability the fall he turned fifty-three, with wife Judy's full support. He had always looked forward to retirement— most COs do, it's terrible work— but a year later, when active symptoms had finally settled, the lack of structure and purpose, formerly provided by the job, became a serious problem.

He missed the exercise of walking eight hours a day, the camaraderie of his peers, and bossing prisoners. He was furious he'd been forced to "slink away with my tail between my legs" instead of retiring with "high fives and a bunch of parties."

"He won't do anything," Judy complained, sitting alone on the sofa, Poodle Oodle snoozing on her winter coat where Pierre normally sat. He had chosen to sit in the matching chair. "I'm working full time, he's off all day. I come home and he hasn't made dinner, the laundry's not done, the breakfast dishes are still in the sink, the house is a mess, he's still in pajamas. He sits in front of the computer all day, playing some on-line game."

I looked at him in his baggy sweatpants, sprawled in the chair, one arm thrown over the back. He shrugged. "I reconnected with a high school buddy on Facebook. We play Minecraft and Call of Duty. So what? It's not like it's porn."

She and I grew increasingly worried, and he increasingly dismissive of that worry, as winter snow storms yielded to spring squalls. Then it was summer, the days long and nights hot. He started going out after supper without Judy to bar hop with his "buddy" and play pool. He picked up smoking, then drinking, then one August night he didn't come home. When he showed up in the morning, he was unrepentant.

"It was no big deal, I drank too much. I didn't want to drive, so I spent the night at my buddy's," he said to

Judy in the crisis session that followed, again sprawled on the chair with an arm slung over the back.

"But you should have called!" Judy shouted, leaning forward on the couch, hands gripping her knees. "I was worried sick!"

Jerking himself up in the chair, he snapped "Leave me alone!" when I tried to bring him back to the fact that he was loved, that he mattered, that it wasn't like him to be inconsiderate. His indifference to her suffering was troubling.

"Let's review your meds," I said, and that's when it came out. He'd stopped them a couple months ago, around the time he added pool and booze to his life.

Insight (the mental function that enables you to step back and have perspective) and judgment (the ability to make good decisions) are the first things to go in any systemic illness but especially psychiatric illness, where the affected organ is the brain itself. This makes sense, given how complex these functions are, requiring a massive amount of wiring to network all parts of the brain. They are the last mental capacities to develop in young adulthood and the first to go in dementia.

Off his meds, Pierre lacked insight, his judgment was impaired, his mood irritable, and his behavior unpredictable. Before he retired, his alcohol intake had been negligible: a beer at a restaurant dinner out, a glass of champagne at a wedding. Regular intoxication was ravaging his brain like a California wildfire. It was a relief to have an explanation for the change in his behavior, but the work required to bring him back to baseline was daunting. Inpatient admission wasn't an option. Even if he

187

agreed the drinking was a problem (which he wouldn't), the local outpatient alcohol rehab wouldn't take him if he had gone off his PTSD meds. I was on my own.

What would motivate him to restart his meds and stop drinking?

"How are you sleeping?"

"Horrible," he said. "I can't fall asleep, then I toss and turn. It sucks." *Yay.*

"Why not restart your meds? They'll help you sleep. In a couple weeks, your mood should pick up too."

He shrugged, "Okay."

"Also, no more drinking."

He scowled, "Why?"

"Well, the alcohol in the beer and vodka is disrupting your sleep cycle. The first four hours, while your liver is processing the alcohol, you're relaxed, maybe sleepy." I paused at a sudden thought. "You're not drinking to get to sleep are you?"

He shook his head no.

"Good. After four hours, the breakdown products have the opposite effect: they make you agitated and keep you up. It's actually a mini-alcohol withdrawal. No more drinking."

"Come on!"

"No drinking. Not even one beer. Drinking makes you impulsive, brings you down, works against the medicine. You remember how you were before you retired?" I cocked an eye at him. "Remember how long it took to bring you out? You don't want to go back there."

"Okay, okay."

Things improved over the next three months, and they had a good Thanksgiving. He slept better; he stopped going out at night; he did more around the house. He denied drinking, and I believed him. His eyes were bright and he seemed himself. Judy felt better about him, too.

Then it snowed heavily through December and he stopped leaving the house. While Judy worked, he started on-line gaming again with his buddy, playing deep into the early morning hours. By January, he'd escalated to bar hopping, pool-playing, and smoking.

"Pierre, hanging out in bars is going to lead to drinking."

"No, it won't."

It did. With the January relapse, he blacked out and two days later woke up "on my buddy's couch." Just as Judy was steeling herself to file a missing person report with the police, he returned home hungover, dirty, and wild.

"Doc!" he said from the upholstered chair at the crisis session, "I ran into Ina at the Black Hole! You know, my physical therapist! She helped me with my arm! She lit up when she saw me!"

Pierre raved on about Ina, oblivious to Judy, his eyes beacon bright and his entire manner inappropriately and excessively enthusiastic. Judy sat on the couch like she'd been sucker-punched, speechless, her eyes wide with a mixture of alarm, incredulity, and disgust. Pierre grinned at me. "We talked for hours!"

Judy came to. "What a crock!" she shouted. "You were drunk as a skunk! She wasn't interested— you wouldn't leave her alone! She got the bouncer to kick you and your damn buddy out."

"That's a lie!" he yelled back hotly.

"It's true," she snapped. "While I was worried sick, you were putting the moves on that girl!"

She turned to me, "He won't shut up about her! To *me!* He's been spending hours online trying to find her on Facebook, Twitter, Instagram, I don't know what all. He flipped out the other day— punched the screen of the desktop and broke it!— when some site wouldn't give him her phone number. He's gone crazy."

"No. I. Haven't," he snarled. "You. Don't. Own. Me." Judy looked at him with fury and at me with helplessness.

OMG. He had disconnected from reality and was oblivious to how much he was hurting Judy.

"You've slept with her." Judy said, collapsing into the couch like a popped balloon.

"I haven't! We're just friends!"

She didn't believe him. "What else would explain the way you're behaving?"

Delusion, I thought. He wasn't just infatuated, he'd crossed over the line into psychosis and was probably off his meds, too. When I checked, sure enough, he hadn't been taking them.

Judy demanded he get tested for sexually transmitted diseases and refused to sleep with him despite negative results. She vacillated between disgust ("Drunk out of your mind for everybody in town to see.") and jealousy ("You're two-timing me!").

Once he restarted his meds and they kicked in, an obnoxious entitlement followed his return to reality. ("So I

190

was polluted, so I had a crush, get over it!") Once that receded, a weepy remorse set in that was equally hard to take.

"I'm a piece of shit," he sobbed in March. They were back to sitting next to each other on the couch. He took her hand. She pulled it away.

"Alcohol. It unleashes the beast," I said. "You blacked out. You're alcoholic," I said.

"Come on!"

"You can't control your intake."

"I just wanted to have a little fun!"

"Going on a bender, disappearing for two days, sexually harassing another woman—is that a little fun? Or is it a problem?" I asked, rhetorically.

"Other people can drink without their wives getting on their case. Or their docs," he said, shooting me a barbed look.

Something had changed. There was a nasty edge that hadn't been there before his forced retirement, before the alcohol. What had me really worried was how loose his grip on reality had become. The year before he'd retired, he'd gotten paranoid about his sergeant, convinced the man was stalking him. Now, three and a half years later, against all evidence, he was convinced his former physical therapist was in love with him. What if he started stalking her?

"You know I love you," Judy said sadly. "But I can't live like this. You're sick. Take your meds. No more bars. No more drinking. If you have anything more to do with that girl, I'll ask you for a divorce."

"What!"

She nodded, staring him in the eye, face impassive. That pulled him up short. She had never drawn a line before. She hadn't needed to. He teared up. He agreed to do better, and he did. Between seeing me, outpatient rehab, and AA, he'd cleaned up by June.

Running errands in early September, I drove by the local coffee shop and saw Pierre staring vacantly into space as he sat alone at a sidewalk table with an iced drink before him. Once a vibrant and alert man, at fifty-six, he'd left mid-life behind. He looked as old and faded as his jeans, and lost.

It's Not Easy Being Green
October

"Not so much!" said Hubby, as I served him a beautiful plate of savory grass-fed beef and emerald broccoli over brown rice. Gold sunlight streamed in through the west-facing dining room window, giving the food an even tastier glow.

"Saving yourself for hot dogs and canned baked beans later?" I quipped, knowing full well he was.

"Where's the ketchup?" He was serious.

"This has sauce," said Son, twelve. "You know I like veggies plain."

"You eat the broccoli with brown sauce at the Chinese buffet," I said with a Look: *Eat.*

He shrugged, speared a broccoli floret along with a piece of beef and chewed meditatively. Poodle Oodle sat at attention beside Son's chair, eyes glued to his hand, alert for any food that might fall from the sky.

I took a seat at the head of the table between my two heathens and tucked in. The broccoli was so fresh it talked back.

Oh! I forgot. I jumped up— Poodle dancing around me, *Me! Me! How about me!*— to bring back a bowl of chopped cukes, tomatoes, onion, and parsley in lemon vinaigrette. She sat down at attention beside my chair, eyes darting between my two hands.

"More salad?" cried Hubby. "I'm swimming in salad!"

"I don't hear you complaining you're swimming in bagels, salami, and pretzels," I said drily.

"The Food Sheriff strikes again."

"You're going to leave me a widow. Right about the time I morph into a wrinkled crone."

"Yeah, but you'll be healthy."

"Ha ha. What good will that do me without you?"

Son, mouth full, asked, "What's for dessert?"

I'd been cooking Hubby and Son supper with fresh produce most every day since July, no time off for good behavior or a pizza. It was harvest time at Essex Farm,[19] our CSA.

CSA is short for Community Supported Agriculture. Instead of buying produce (and other staples like eggs, dairy, meat, and flour) from the grocery store, we bought directly from our local farmer. At the supermarket, I paid retail, by the item. As a CSA member, we paid a flat rate up front for a percentage (per person, aka "share") of the farm's yearly production.

During the growing season, once a week, I'd pick up our shares of whatever was on hand. In May, it was chives, spinach, baby radishes, and new carrots. In June, succulent strawberries and spring salad mix. Then it was July, and overnight the harvest took off. Veggie after herb after fruit, the variety and quantity astounded. It was relentless till the fever broke in October, after the first frost.

---

[19] www.essexfarmcsa.com

The farmers kept a three-by-eight-foot chalkboard propped on its short end against a weight-bearing strut of the open air "pavilion" where the bins of produce waited. Weekly announcements for members were written there in colored chalk. For example: *TAKE AS MANY GREEN BEANS AS YOU CAN HANDLE TO PUT UP FOR THE WINTER!*

Truck loads of tangy tomatoes. Mountains of perfumed melons. Springy spinach vaulting *en masse* out the box. Taut purple eggplants big as steroid-swollen bowling pins. Broccoli trees too wide to hug. Leeks long as witch brooms…. My eyes would cloud over, I'd lose my mind, and before I knew it, I would be home, completely overwhelmed, fondling the knife and considering my options.

Most CSAs give members a pre-packed box of that week's yield. Not Essex Farm. They make *me* gauge how much to take for the week. Watch me stand at my kitchen counter, hour after hour, chopping for supper and the freezer. Yes, the abundance takes over my life. I can't help it if my eyes are bigger than my kitchen. So maybe I have a little problem. But I'm *not* a harvest-holic. I can give it up any time.

Seriously, belonging to a CSA is not cheap. If I don't put up the harvest excess, I have two options for winter produce. (1) Buy at the supermarket. Since I've already paid the CSA for a year's supply of premium produce, that's just dumb. Or (2) Go without.

"Option 2!" said Hubby. "Ketchup is a vegetable."

"Ha ha. Not true. Reagan failed to get that by Congress."

Watch me chop chop chop. Stuff stuff stuff ziplock bags. Label label label. Bear all this treasure out to the garage and bury it in whichever of two freezers has room. Yes, two freezers. One was already full of frozen veggies and the season wasn't over yet. Then there was the fact that I cook for six even though we're only three and Hubby always said, "No thanks. We had that yesterday." The second freezer didn't have much space for leftovers. Good thing I'd nailed tonight's meal, cooking just the right amount of beef and broccoli. The remaining rice would start tomorrow's.

I had an extra fridge out in the garage too, filthy with farm dirt and packed with prime produce calling to be cooked, put up, or—

Shut up! I moaned the next evening, pulling open the door. I was *so* tired. I really needed a break. What would be easy and quick? I looked at shelves overflowing with eye-popping greens and reds, oranges and yellows, and waited for inspiration. The rainbow chard gave a little finger wave and jumped into my arms. Okay. Fried rice with sautéed chard, carrots, onion, and curry spices. Toss in eggs scrambled separately. Maybe a few cashews for crunch. I imagined the flavors. *Yum.*

I plodded back into the house and into the kitchen. Hubby moaned, "No. Mercy, please."

Son ran in demanding, "What?" He saw Hubby, my cargo, and his opportunity. "Yeah! Uncle! Uncle!"

Hubby wheedled, "Babe, don't cook tonight. You're working too hard." I felt myself weakening even as I rolled my eyes at him: *I see right through you, mister.*

"Yeah, Mom. Let's order a pizza." Poodle did her part, jumping up and down and around our legs.

"All right. All right. Fine." Like I was doing *them* a favor. Fingers crossed for first frost tonight.

Pierre and Judy III: Cassandra Syndrome

Cassandra was the beautiful daughter of King Priam and Queen Hecuba of ancient Troy. The god Apollo lusted after her and gave her the gift of prophecy as a seduction gift. But Cassandra spurned him. Apollo could have killed her, but instead he spat in her mouth and cursed her: no one would believe her prophecies.

Not again...
August, a year and a half after Pierre's second bender and Judy's first warning.

Bimonthly couple's therapy had appeared to be helping Pierre and Judy regain a tenuous equilibrium until Judy boiled over: "It's the same shit all over again!" she cried from the couch. "You're not taking care of the yard or helping around the house. It's not fair. I'm working! You're not. I can't do everything!"

From the upholstered chair, he shot back: "Well, how long are you going to make me wait for sex?"

"You're still all about that Ina! You made another appointment! One you don't need!"

"I just want her to check my arm!" he said, aggravated.

She shook her head, "I can't."

It takes two.

"When is she going to get over it?" he asked me in our next individual session. After many requests on my part, finally we were meeting without Judy. "I mean, come on, it's been over a year."

Pierre couldn't make the cause-effect connection between his obsession with Ina— even now, with his meds tuned up, it lingered, as delusions so often do— and Judy's current lack of interest. "I kiss her because she wants me to, but then she won't put out," he grumbled sourly.

Put out? That's what teenage boys said. His thirty-six years as a married man seemed to have vanished.

"Pierre, you're stuck on Ina and that pisses Judy off. What's worse is you've got an attitude about it, like she should be okay with it."

"Why shouldn't she be? I'm not cheating on her!"

"You may not be having sex outside the marriage, but Judy knows she's not the only woman on your mind. That makes her feel rejected and jealous and angry. Her willingness to please you has dropped way down her priority list." I studied him, pouting in the chair, his belly bulging over his belt, sporting a tee shirt with an energy drink logo, unclean jeans, and construction boots. *Maybe to the bottom of the list.*

He frowned.

"She wasn't put on this earth to 'put out' as you call it, just because you say so. That's what your hand is for," I said, shocking myself. He *tsked.*

"She's my wife. It's her job to give me sex."

I was incredulous. "Her job? Wouldn't that make her a whore? Is that what you think?" A surreal sensation washed over me. This man sitting in the chair before me might look like Pierre, but he wasn't Pierre.

"Nah. I don't think that," he said, looking sheepish, which reassured me.

"What's her problem anyway? I'm not doing anything with Ina," he said, which didn't.

Your attitude is why, I thought. *It's all about you, you, you. You're into Ina, but she's not into you. You don't get it and your meds aren't working.* I could see what was coming. He'd start drinking, stop his meds, and stalk Ina. Judy would leave him. Then, the bewilderment, the loneliness, the slow decline. He was doomed. *Please. Please let me be wrong.*

Maybe adjusting his anti-psychotic today would help him accept— please God in a few days— that Ina didn't return his feelings. That wouldn't fix his lifestyle, though, which was a whole other problem.

"Pierre, you're going to get into trouble if you don't find something to do with yourself. You need the structure. You could earn serious points with Judy by chipping away at the honey-do list. Who knows what her gratitude might get you!"

"Yeah, right. When hell freezes over."

"How about a part-time job?" He grimaced.

"No? Maybe mentor a kid without a dad? Any ideas? It's good to have people count on you."

He twisted his mouth into a dismissive moue. "I've worked plenty. I'm not working anymore. I'm keeping busy. I'm fine."

He was wrong. It didn't take long, maybe a month. The trees were just turning red at the edges and the nights crisping up when he was back in the bars playing pool with his buddy and smoking. "I'm not drinking! I swear!" he said from the upholstered chair during a couple's session.

I shook my head. "You'll drink. Then you'll stop your meds. Then it's all over," I said.

"Don't put me through it again, Pierre," Judy begged from the couch.

The Tipping Point

He didn't just drink. He added cocaine. Worse, he dropped out of treatment. Over the next five months, he burned through $36,000 of their savings.

"I know he's after Ina. I read in the police report section of the paper that she's filed an order of protection," Judy wept in a February session. She'd continued to come in on her own.

"He calls me at work every day raging for more money. It's never enough! He's going to leave me broke…." She reached for a tissue from the box on the end table.

"…. And the things he's saying to me…," she sobbed. "I feel this small," she said, holding thumb and index finger a fraction apart.

"*He's* the one trashing his rep around town!" I said, appalled. Hurt pride, rage and embarrassment, those I'd expected. Quaking worthlessness? No.

"He can't stand me," she choked a little. "He said I was lucky he hadn't left me for Ina…. He said he wished he had—" she broke down. She grabbed the tissue box and pulled out a wad, emptying the box. Breathing heavily, she forced herself to stop crying, wiped her face and blew her nose.

"All those thongs and padded bras. Eating to put on weight. Well, he can forget the boob job," she said dismally, pitching the ball of used tissue in the wastebasket. She fell silent, staring inside, hands loose in her lap.

"I'm not hot and never will be," she whispered, the tears starting again. "That's what he said," she leaned forward and pressed her face onto her hands, forearms against her chest, shoulders shaking.

"I deserve everything he's dishing out!" she sobbed. "It's payback for all those years I wouldn't give him any. Oh, if only I had! If only I'd been a better wife. None of this would have happened."

Utterly heartbroken, she curled into herself on the couch, head tucked into the cowl neck of her heavy sweater, elbows on her thighs. Poodle Oodle, next to me in the chair, stirred and lifted her head. She'd been so still, I'd forgotten she was with us.

When Judy wound down, I handed her a tissue along with the box from my end table. "Thank you," she said, wiping her wet cheeks, her face slack with sadness. She tossed the used ball in the wastebasket, pulled a few more from the box and sagged into the couch, eyes blank. Poodle Oodle jumped down from our chair, trotted over to the couch, leapt up, and cuddled next to Judy. "Hello baby," she said, stroking her. She leaned back, closed her swollen eyes and rested her head on the couch back.

I grieved for Judy. Any woman, especially after decades of serious devotion to her beloved, would be sliced open to her deepest, most tender and secret self by such contempt. Any woman would be heartsick to be judged so harshly and dismissed. It didn't matter that Ina wanted nothing to do with Pierre or that his behavior was fueled by severe mental illness. These just coated the core truth she was facing: her husband didn't find her desirable.

But to think today's situation could have been avoided if she'd given him sex on demand? No. That would have killed the marriage, too. A healthy and satisfying marriage requires that both partners meet each others' needs with mutual give and take. Yet all too often, women put their needs last, after those of their children, husbands, and aging parents, sending the clear message: *I am less than you. You come first, always.*

"Wait a minute," I said. She came back slowly and focused on me. "Am I understanding you? Having sex against your will would have kept his focus off Ina? Would have prevented him stalking her?" She stared at me for several beats, then blinked.

"No, I guess not," she shook her head. "He's crazy. You know how my brother listens to the police scanner all the time?"

I nodded. This was another popular local hobby. "Well, the police have been over to her place twice in the last two weeks to chase him away. It's only a matter of time before he gets arrested if he doesn't stop." She wailed in anguish, *"Everybody will know* he doesn't want me."

Now I felt deeply sad for Pierre. He had gone too far. Once she'd cried herself out, she'd be done. When he eventually came to his senses, it would be too late. No apology, no weepy remonstrations of regret, nothing he promised, nothing he did would undo this unforgivable breach of man-woman etiquette. It wasn't enough he'd ripped her heart out privately. It didn't matter he was sick.

He'd publicly humiliated her. The marriage was dead, though neither knew it yet.

Lust: *The Great Pretender*

I flashed back to the early phase of Pierre's meltdown the previous September, just before he dropped out of treatment. "Pierre, you have to stop or you'll lose it all, your wife, your home, your cat, your comfort and security, your reputation as a stand-up guy, everything you care about."

"Fuck Judy! Who died and made her my boss?" His eyes had flashed with fury. His expression shifted. "Ina likes me, I know it. She's just shy," he said with sly conviction. Despite the sickening certainty that it was pointless, I kept trying.

"Pierre, she's filed an order of protection against you."

"It's love! She's playing hard to get."

"You're blowing through Judy's money too. It's not right. I'm worried for you."

"Well, don't be. This is the real deal. Ina's mine."

"You're burning your bridges with Judy."

"I don't need her!" he retorted. Meanwhile, Judy was still taking care of his co-pays, the bills, the banking, his retirement and disability paperwork and paying for his residential motel room too. (Of course she'd thrown him out.) I'd adjusted his meds to no avail.

There was something so adolescent about his defiance, as if he was punishing *her*. As if he assumed she would just take it, would always be there for him, would always love him unconditionally. As if she were his mother. Well, she wasn't.

Hell Hath No Fury....

So it came to pass. When the crocuses pushed through the ice-crusted snow, the cops arrested him for harassing Ina one time too many. He crawled back to Judy after she posted his bail and got him a lawyer, crying his sad song of remorse. She refused him. She changed the locks, packed up his clothes, and left the boxes on the porch. But she kept covering the bill at his by-the-week motel.

He called me, begging, "Come on, Doc, almost twenty years, have a heart."

"Only if you clean up, go for outpatient rehab and AA, take your meds as prescribed. And, listen to me, Pierre, only this one time. The next time you quit treatment is the last."

"Okay, sure, whatever you say, Doc. You gotta help me." Clean and sober, and taking his meds as prescribed, his Ina delusion slowly receded as the months passed, in the same way the paranoia about his sergeant had.

He wept through his twice-a-month sessions: with regret, with sorrow, with bewilderment. He cried through the snow of April, the mud of May, and the trees' yellow-green leaf-burst in June. He persisted in asking Judy to take him back; she persisted in refusing. He made a payment plan with her to refund the savings he'd blown through.

"She lets me go to the house when she's not there, to see the cat and do my laundry," he said in July. "She won't let me come over when she's there."

Another year passed, as did his contrition. "How much longer is this shit going to go on? How many times am I going to say I'm sorry before she lets me come home?" He shifted in the seat. He'd gained weight since the breakup. His shirt strained at the armpits, pulled against the buttons, and looked like he'd slept in it. Judy hadn't attended his sessions since I'd taken him back. He was on his own.

Judy had continued to come in for herself, about once a month. I flashed back on our last session. She didn't feel guilty any longer for not wanting to reconcile. "I feel free," she'd said. "It feels good to put myself first. To not have to worry about him wanting sex. To not worry about him taking his meds." I'd nodded.

"And," she'd said with a big smile, sitting up in the chair, "I'm tap dancing again! I danced all through elementary school into high school. I stopped in tenth grade when I started dating Pierre. He didn't like how the practices took time away from him. It feels great!" Poodle Oodle, sitting next to her, pressed in and looked up. Judy looked down and laughed, then pulled Poodle in closer. "You cuddle bug."

I returned from that session with Judy when Pierre *tsk*ed with irritation and shifted in the seat again. "Well?"

"Pierre," I said patiently, "it'll take as long as it takes."

"How long? I mean, come on. I've got needs."

He just didn't get it. I suspected he never would.

"It's not about your needs Pierre. It's about how you really, really hurt her."

"Okay, I'm sorry! How long is she going to punish me for?"

Should I explain that he'd done so much damage to their bond that she might let it break, and let him go? That she might *not* be punishing him? Because if she was, that would mean she still cared? No, too subtle. Best to simply point the way.

"You have to make things right between you. What are you doing about *that*?"

"What do you mean?"

I suppressed a sigh. "Ask yourself: how can I court Judy? Make her want me back?"

"Like what?"

"How about the house? Are you helping with repairs and maintenance?"

He gave me a look both incredulous and put-upon. "I'm not working on the damn house! I'm not living there."

I gave it one more shot. "Women appreciate men who make their lives easier. That's a big turn on."

He threw one arm across the back of the upholstered chair, lifted one jean-clad leg and rested the ankle on the other knee. He shook his head, twisted his lips and *tsk*ed.

Break-In! Or Why I Didn't Call the Cops
Late September

A kid sprawled dead asleep on the patient couch. My eyes bulged. My jaw unhinged. I blinked— a few times— but it was no good. He was still there. Dirty sneakers on my nice upholstery, throw pillow over his eyes to block the sun, drool glittering on his chin.

It was a brisk, blue-sky, Sunday morning. A fiery quilt of yellow, red, orange and green leaves lay over the lawns and streets. I had driven to the office with Son, sixteen. The plan had been: drop off Son outside to rake the property, drop off toilet paper inside for the patient bathroom, bolt home. Hubby was out of town for the weekend. The house would be mine for the blissful hour Son was raking. Well, scrap that.

Questions: Is He Dangerous? Should I Call the Cops?

The Kid continued to mouth breathe rankly. The air was low on oxygen and high on alcohol-stink. I sniffed deeply and diagnostically: no trace of anything nastier.[20] I took my first calculated risk.

"Hey!" Nothing.

---

[20] People who smoke crack and/or meth give off a distinct chemical odor.

I took a second, bigger, calculated risk. Picking up a book from the chair-side table, I poked a fleshy shin: "HEY YOU! WAKE UP!"

He startled, the pillow sliding off his face. Struggling against gravity, he negotiated the no-man's land between sitting and standing— barely.

"Who are you?"

He swayed, eyelids drooping.

"WHAT ARE YOU DOING HERE?" I barked.

He almost lost his balance. "Huh?"

I pegged him for a soft college boy sleeping off a Saturday night spent at one of the downtown bars. The Black Hole probably, just a couple of blocks away. For once, I was under no professional obligation to be therapeutic. I let it rip, the outraged homeowner: "WHO THE HELL ARE YOU? WHAT ARE YOU DOING HERE? HOW DID YOU GET IN?"

He cringed. "I don't... girl... uhh... oh god...." He swallowed and looked queasy.

Answers: Not Dangerous. No Cops.

The building was a gracious 1830s Victorian, formerly a single-family home. Now our offices took up the main floor. My eyes zeroed in on the glass-paned door at the far end of the room that accessed the wrap-around porch. It stood ajar, a chunk of frame splintered off, with slider lock attached. The peace lily usually parked in front of it was pushed to the side, dirt spilled on the floor. One glance, I knew. The kid had given that door one solid kick, shoved it open, and gone to ground on the couch.

"LOOK AT THAT DOOR! YOU BROKE IN!"

"No... no...."

"YES!"

"Some girl... I didn't... I don't—"

"GIRL? YOU HAD A GIRL WITH YOU?!"

I looked at the couch. I looked at him. I screeched, "You didn't... YOU DIDN'T HAVE SEX ON MY COUCH, DID YOU?!!"

"No! I would never...!"

"DID YOU PUKE ANYWHERE? PEE ANYWHERE?"

Dashing out into the hall, I bumped into Son, who was avidly eavesdropping.

"Why aren't you raking?"

"Rake broke."

"Oh. Did you hear?" He nodded.

"Check the rest of the office for puddles." I shuddered. "GO!"

Son ambled off.

Should I Call the Cops Just Because He Broke in?

I turned back to The Kid. His eyes were open but nobody was home.

"I SHOULD CALL THE POLICE!"

He grabbed the sides of his head in alarm. "No! Please!" His bloodshot eyes drifted, then focused on me with increasing bewilderment. He dropped his arms to his sides. "Uh.... Where am I?"

Taking pity on him, I lowered the volume. "This is my office. I see patients here. I am a doctor. A psychiatrist."

He looked utterly befuddled.

"You went on a bender last night downtown, didn't you?"

He nodded, head bowed.

"And you picked up some girl. Who's long gone. You kicked that door in." I pointed at it.

"No, no…."

"You don't remember a thing, do you?"

He shook his head.

"What's your name?" I asked, picking up a scratch pad and pen from an end table.

"Uh…. Uh…. Da…. Danny."

"Last name?" He gave it.

"Address?" He gave a dorm address. *Yes! A college boy.*

"Phone number?" He gave it, stammering.

I Commit Myself, with Doubt

"Here's the deal, Danny. You get a free pass on jail this time." I ripped the paper with my name and number off the pad and handed it to him. "I will get an estimate. You will be paying for the repairs."

"Okay," he whispered.

"Get out of here. Call me Monday. That's tomorrow. Don't disappoint me."

From the front door, I watched him stumble down the walkway leading to the sidewalk, tail between his legs.

I turned to Son, who had been at my back for a while.

"You OK, Mom?"

"Sure," I said, exhaling. " Let's go."

"What's for lunch?"

Revisiting My Decision at Home, Cup of Tea in Hand...

Danny Boy.... Danny Boy had that doted-upon, only-child aura. He looked about nineteen. Only three years older than Son.... This wouldn't be his first pratfall under the influence, just the first with consequences.

In my mind's eye, I shadowed him shambling dorm-ward through the leaves piled high on the sidewalk. One glowing, red-hot skewer burning through his temples from left to right. Another boring through the middle of his forehead to the back. Eyeballs pulsing. Tongue swollen, parched as the Sahara. The pain flaring up worse, if that was possible, remembering. Hauled up from the deep, not knowing where he was, blinded by sun, a deranged female (that would be me) in his face barking, barking, barking.

"YOU'VE COMMITTED A FELONY," I'd shouted. He'd cowered.

"You call me Monday. Don't disappoint me," I'd hissed, the Mother from Hell, showing my teeth, staring into his glazed and frightened eyes. And read there: *What if my parents find out? Oh god, oh god.*

Justifying Myself to Hubby Sunday Night

"I can't believe you didn't call the cops!"

"I knew in my gut he wasn't dangerous," I answered. "It was his legs. Kid legs, sticking out from those shorts. Like Son's, when he's fallen asleep on the couch watching TV."

Hubby sighed, exasperated. "He's not going to call."

"Probably not. If he doesn't, I'll call campus security. Or the registrar."

"If he gave you his real name."

Now I sighed. "Yeah."

"Why didn't you call me? You could have gotten hurt."

I gave him a Look: *Don't be silly. What could you have done?* Actually, it hadn't occurred to me. "Nah."

He shrugged and let it go, trusting my track record of sound judgment and solid saves. I leaned across the corner of the dinner table and kissed him. He put his arms around me and squeezed.

Justifying Myself to My Office Manager Monday Morning

"I can't believe you didn't call the police!" Kathy's tone mixed incredulity with admiration. Her look said: *This better be good.*

"Fastest diagnostic reflexes in the East, ma'am," I drawled, holstering my invisible Colt .45.

She smiled.

"So," I said, "has the kid called?"

"Yup. Fell all over himself apologizing."

Actual proof I had read him right? Life was good. "When will Handy Randy come by to assess the damage?"

"This afternoon."

"Great. What about Danny Boy?"

"Calling back later today. Says he'll bring the cash right over."

"Beautiful. Let me talk to him when he shows up."

"Where's a college kid going to get that kind of money?"

"Maybe he's a pampered prince," I said. Kathy, raised on a hardscrabble dairy farm, made a rude noise.

"Maybe he'll actually bring it. You never know. Stranger things have happened," I said.

One for the Gut

The way Danny Boy stared, I could tell he had expected a Gorgon: tall, roaring, eyes shooting flames, head wreathed with writhing snakes. Instead, he got me: short, ordinary brown eyes, salt-and-pepper hair well cut. He had dressed up for the occasion: khakis, blue button-down shirt, brown corduroy sports jacket.

I led him into The Office, offered him a seat on The Couch. He looked away from The Door, now repaired and locked, peace lily blocking it.

"Any memory return of Saturday night's events?" I asked.

He shook his head: *No.*

I shook mine: *Too bad.* "Black outs are a diagnostic feature of alcoholism. You realize you have a drinking problem?"

He nodded, not making eye contact.

"You know why I didn't call the cops?"

He shook his head.

"You need treatment, not punishment, though most people would disagree with me."

He just looked at me, hangdog. I looked back. Should I say anything else maternal or shrinky? *Nah.*

"Well. I expected you to let me down. Instead, you've shown up and paid for the damage. Thank you." I stood up.

He rose with me. I extended my right hand.

215

He pumped it. "No, no. Thank *you*. Thank you for not calling the cops. I'm so, so sorry."

I smiled, "Don't you think it's significant you broke into a psychiatrist's office?"

He stared: *What now?*

I couldn't help myself, I had to help him: "Take it as a message from the universe: Time to stop drinking. AA: 90 meetings in 90 days. Do it."

He nodded.

I watched him walk down the sidewalk in the direction of the college, pleased I had trusted my gut. *A nice boy. Maybe he'll stop drinking. You never know. Stranger things have happened.*

Health Care Catch-22
February

"So, I've probably got cancer," Jeb announced as he preceded me into the office and took a seat on the couch, unzipping his jacket, though not taking it off. He sat very upright, hands on widespread knees, feet in construction boots firmly planted. Poodle Oodle trailed in after us, jumped up on the couch beside him, settled her head on his thigh and looked at him with love. Jeb was one of her favorite patients. He scratched her head gently, then ran his hand down her back. She nestled in and closed her eyes. It was our monthly session. We'd been working together maybe a year.

He was a wiry, edgy man pushing sixty, single, extremely intelligent, opinionated, and caustic. He insisted he hated people, especially women in positions of authority.

"I'm a female authority," I'd said early on. "What about me?"

"You're exceeding expectations. But don't get too comfortable."

He was very close with his one long-time friend Dwayne (and Dwayne's wife) and devoted to his dogs (two) and cats (three). I liked him.

He hadn't worked as an excavation contractor for eight years, not since a drunk stranger had randomly and viciously attacked him at his favorite dive bar.

"You didn't know the guy?" I'd asked, incredulous.

217

"Nope," he'd said. "And nobody was talking." He'd shrugged. "Just one of those things."

He'd suffered a severe head injury, requiring neurosurgery and weeks in hospital to "recover." As is typical in our rural area, he was not referred to neurology or psychiatry for follow up. Obvious changes in impulse control, cognition, memory, and emotional regulation had gone unaddressed until he came to me. He should have been on medical disability, but wasn't. He eked out a marginal living: factory work, one rental property, some trading on the stock market. He was uninsured, paying for his sessions out of pocket. I took that for the compliment it was.

I stared at him for a few beats. "You've got cancer," I said in a tone that demanded *More, please.*

He shrugged. "Squamous cell cancer of my gum. My teeth are falling out. Dentist sent me to an oral surgeon, who took one look and told me not to wait getting it biopsied."

"So when are you going?"

"I'm not. I can't. I don't have insurance."

There was a silence while I considered which of the many things I could say would be the most helpful. "You could pay for the biopsy out of pocket."

Another silence. Outside, a city snowplow slowly ground by, clearing the street of the snow that had been gently falling for the last twenty-four hours.

"Sure I could," Jeb said, with a sarcastic edge. I raised my eyebrows. *And?*

"But then I'll have a diagnosis," he explained, with the patience required for dealing with the very stupid.

"Which means a pre-existing condition. Then I can't buy private insurance because they won't insure me with a pre-existing condition. My COBRA from the last job ran out months ago. I make too much money to qualify for Medicaid. I can't pay for treatment out of pocket. The bills will bankrupt me. I'll lose my house. I don't want to be sick *and* destitute."

There was no denying that his logic was impeccable. "What about President Obama's legislation making it illegal for insurances to refuse coverage for pre-existing conditions?"

"The House just repealed it. But even if the Senate passes it next year, it won't start till 2010. I'll be dead by then." He was chillingly matter-of-fact.

"Besides," he continued, "I have my doubts about treatment. If the cancer spreads from the gum to the bone, they'll want to start chopping. I don't want to be horribly disfigured. Or say it spreads through my body. Then I'd need chemo and I'll be really sick from that. For what, to gain a couple of more years?" He paused and shook his head.

"I'm not married. I don't have parents or children or other family. I have my dogs and my cats, but Dwayne will help me place them. I've accomplished everything I'm going to. I'm at the end of my cycle."

"So…. You're going to do nothing?"

"What choice do I have?"

I could think of one, and I bet he had too. "Are you thinking of killing yourself?"

"Yes." Given his personality, his certainty there was no God or afterlife, and the health insurance double bind he was in, it would seem a rational option. I nodded and his face relaxed when he saw I understood. Still, understanding didn't mean I agreed.

"Have you researched how much the biopsy and immediate treatment would cost you out of pocket?"

"When I was in the hospital getting steel plates put in my head, it cost $16,000 a day!"

"Come on, we're not talking a neurosurgical emergency here. Squamous cell cancers are usually slow growing. Still, the sooner you get it out, the better. If it hasn't spread, you could have many pleasurable years of loving pets and hating people ahead of you."

He rolled his eyes and shifted his weight, which lifted one side of his jacket, releasing a warm smoky scent. Like many people, he heated with wood. Little holes, probably from flying cinders, pocked his brown wool sweater. Poodle Oodle scratched his blue-jeaned leg with one paw.

He looked down at her and smiled. She pawed his leg again. "You want something?" She pawed him again. "Oh, all right," he said in mock exasperation. He stroked her back and she instantly rolled over, giving him her belly. He visibly softened. We took a few moments to enjoy Poodle Oodle dispensing love and happiness.

"Both the biopsy and treatment will probably be done outpatient. It may well be affordable," I said eventually. "The hospital will definitely let you set up a payment plan. Interest-free."

He smiled. "You think?"

"What the heck. You can always die later."

I'll Try Anything Once
July

It was our first (and only, but I didn't know that yet) session. Jimmy, twenty, sat before me in the upholstered chair by the window and told me this story.

"I was sixteen and I had this friend. I knew he used and his father used and they partied together. His father offered me a Vicodin.[21] I'll try anything once. One dose, I was a slave."

I'd imagined addiction might start this way, but to actually hear an addict describe it was a first.

"It's been hell. For my parents, too. I've been through inpatient rehab twice. Now I'm doing outpatient. The shrink there prescribes the Suboxone." He paused. "You know about Suboxone?"

"Yes. It's the new methadone. It's supposed to stop the withdrawal and the cravings so you can kick the habit."

He nodded. "It's stopped the withdrawal. Thank God I don't have to score from creepy people anymore." He closed his eyes and shuddered. He opened them, "But it hasn't stopped the thinking. It's all I think about."

He looked at me sadly, obviously well cared for in his pressed jeans, ironed polo shirt, clean sneakers, and good haircut. I had no doubt his parents were working

---

[21] A prescription opiate.

overtime to pay for his rehab and losing their minds with worry. Meanwhile, what was he doing to help himself?

"Are you living at home?"

"Yeah."

"Going to school?" He shook his head no. "I can't concentrate. If I had an endless supply, I could do anything," he said wistfully.

Ah well, I thought, *if wishes were horses, beggars would ride*. I considered saying it and decided against. For him to get the irony, he'd have to know what he wanted was a fantasy. Did he? Or was he serious? Better check.

"Really? When you're high, you're focused and productive?"

He met my gaze then broke it, sheepish. "Nah. I lie around feeling good until I don't."

"Do you have a job?" He shook his head no. "Going to meetings and counseling sessions makes it hard. Employers don't like you to leave and come back." The classic addict-in-recovery double bind. "My parents say my recovery has to be the priority."

"What do you say?"

"Sure. But what can I do between meetings?"

I studied him. "Think about using?" I asked, raising my eyebrows.

He startled: *Busted*. "How did you know?"

"You told me."

"Oh, right." He sighed and nodded glumly, "Yeah, it's always there." That he admitted it was good. That he exuded resignation was bad. How long would it take for the relentless craving to wear him down?

Sixteen. The dope dragon had sunk its claws into him so young, so unformed, so without direction. Did he have anything to return to? Kicking required energy and determination.

"Do you have any interests?"

He just looked at me. "Like what?"

My heart sank. *Like anything.*

"Play an instrument?" Another no.

"Any sports?" No.

"Do you like to fix things?" No.

"Cook?" No.

"Read?" No.

"Run? Go to the gym?" No and no. An empty life. I felt sadder by the minute.

"How do you pass the time?"

"Oh, I don't know. Watch TV. Play some video games. Browse the net. I avoid people. Everyone I know uses and even when I meet someone new, it turns out they use." Another addict-in-recovery experience: everywhere they went, drugs and temptation found them.

"Your parents work?" Another nod.

"Do you have chores? Help around the house?"

"Not really," he looked down, not meeting my eyes. He knew.

"Jimmy, have your parents gone into debt over your rehabs?" He nodded, with an expression that said he felt bad about it. *But not bad enough.*

"Have you considered paying their devotion back? You could do a lot for them. Cook dinner. Make them bag lunches for work."

He looked at me.

I continued, "Do the laundry. Clean the bathroom. Mop the kitchen floor."

I paused again. He kept looking at me. "You're able-bodied and young. Your parents are worn-out and old. It'd be a win-win if you pulled your weight."

We looked at each other. He drooped back in the upholstered chair next to the window, one arm in his lap, the other on the armrest. Mid-day sun shone through the shade, lighting it up.

The window next to me was open from the bottom. Through the screen floated the humid perfume of greenery and flowering spirea, the low hum of bees, the twittering of birds, and in the far distance, the sound of a lawn mower. It was a gorgeous day out there.

"I don't know how to do most of those things," he said sadly. I studied him, slim but soft, his clean-shaven face pale, as if he never went outside.

"Learn," I said kindly. "Listen, it's not good for you to mooch off your parents at your age. You're not a kid to let them carry you like that." He nodded.

"You're bored, too. You know the expression 'Idle hands are the Devil's workshop'?" He nodded.

"What does it mean?"

"If I don't keep busy, I'll get into trouble?"

"Yup. What trouble are you likely to get into?"

"Using. Relapsing."

"Yup."

"But how do I learn all that stuff?"

I just looked at him and shook my head. "You didn't have any trouble figuring out how to get the next hit. Come on." He gave me that sheepish smile again: *Busted*. None of his tricks were working on me. *His poor parents.*

"Here's a fact you can use to help yourself: Your mind can only do one thing at a time. There's no such thing as multi-tasking. What that is, is doing one thing at a time really fast." He was paying attention.

"So. You can think about using. Or, you can take your mom's grocery list, drive to the store, and shop." He looked alert.

"You can lounge around, counting the seconds till your next dose. Or, you can go to the gym and work out. Or, snake that slow drain in the bathroom sink, mow the lawn, clean your room. You get the idea. Have your parents give you a honey-do list."

He looked blank. The silence lengthened until I broke it, "What?"

He shook his head, "I don't know. It seems like a lot."

Sadness took me again. These were such undemanding, low-level tasks. "Jimmy, your job is to grow yourself into a competent adult with skills and a life. Being a junkie isn't a life. It's being shackled and whipped by craving and withdrawal, 24/7. Go for something bigger."

"Like what?" There it was again, the lack of interest and motivation, the shrinking from the struggle that defines living. Was that the consequence of the addiction? Or did he start with a passive temperament that the addiction eroded into existential emptiness, like strip mining destroys habitats?

"That's your task to figure out. And it's urgent. You won't kick otherwise. It'll save your life to find something you want more than using."

Giving me a look heavy with resignation, he turned away toward the window and said in a voice so low I shifted forward in my seat to hear him, "My dad used in Nam. He came back strung out, but he kicked, no problem." He looked in my eyes.

Wow. Here was the family secret. "Did you know that before you took that first Vicodin?"

He shook his head no. "He told me after I couldn't hide any longer. He hadn't even told Mom…. He kicked cold turkey. Why him and not me?"

I sighed and shook my head. "I don't know. There are so many variables, I can only speculate." He stared: *Give.*

"Well, he was an adult when he started; his brain was done growing. That helped. He had more wiring, more experience, and more resilience than you did at sixteen. The brain goes through a huge growth spurt that begins in adolescence and completes in your mid-twenties. Because your teen brain was actively building itself, it was much more vulnerable to addiction than your father's adult brain. Worse, your brain stopped growing as soon as you started using. Now that you're clean, it'll pick up where it left off, *IF* you give it a challenge and make it work."

"Really?"

"Really." I nodded. "Another thing your dad had was something to come back to, something to fight for. Loving your mom, being married and feeling a responsibility to her, those were good motivators that helped him stop using, too."

"I'm not friends with that guy anymore, the one whose dad got me started. He's still using."

"Good move," I said, nodding. He broke eye contact, despondent.

"I'm sure your dad had to fight hard to kick." I said. "And you do, too. It's great that you've let go of bad influences, but you have to add positive motivators. Get busy learning new stuff. That'll grow your brain. Work your program. Get serious."

"All right."

"I want you to sign a consent so I can send a copy of my evaluation to your rehab shrink. I think a little medicine to dial down the craving might help. There are a few options. I'll include them in the write-up. Let him know I'd be happy to talk to him anytime."

"Why can't you do it?"

"Too many cooks in the kitchen."

I never saw him again. I don't know why he consulted me or what he was looking for. I hope I gave it to him.

"He wanted you to prescribe a higher dose of Suboxone than what he's getting at rehab," Hubby said cynically at dinner, after I told him the story (withholding the kid's name of course). Possibly. Probably.

Afterthoughts.

Jimmy haunts me. Along with the questions that can't be answered. I think about Jimmy's friend's father, an addict himself and possibly a sociopath, too. How could he have offered Jimmy that Vicodin? There is something so utterly lost to love and decency that he corrupted his own son and his son's friend into ruining their lives.

It seems more depraved that he offered opiate instead of alcohol. But is it? I know many otherwise respectable people who allow their kids and their kids' friends to get drunk, regularly, in their homes with alcohol they supply. They know drinking is "habit-forming" (i.e. addicting) and toxic to teen brain development. Yet they argue, "They're going to do it anyway. This way they're safe."

Are kids going to do it anyway? Not necessarily. That's a matter of their home and social life. Are they safe? From a drunk driving accident, maybe. But not from addiction.

I imagine Jimmy's father racked with guilt and regret: *If only I hadn't kept it secret. If only I had told. Then Jimmy would have known and he wouldn't have taken that pill and none of this would have happened....* Maybe. Maybe not. After all, Jimmy is his own person with his own agenda.

Nevertheless, it's true that secrets always carry a price tag. And it's also true that knowledge is power. As parents, we owe our kids the stories of our falling and overcoming—to warn and to inform—so kids have the option to say no to dangerous temptations offered by dangerous adults.

That protects parents, too. It's easy to fall into the trap of rationalizing something that's prevalent (such as teen drinking) as "normal" until the consequences catch up with us. Once a child has fallen into the abyss of addiction— don't kid yourself, alcoholism is addiction— it's the social norm to blame the victims. As if any parent would choose addiction for their child. As if anyone would choose that for themselves.

Addiction is a brain disorder, a neurological design flaw that is kindled by exposure. And it's not just drugs. You can get strung out on *anything pleasure-giving*— beer, video games and porn; donuts, wine, and shopping; soap operas and gambling— if your brain is wired for it.

Once your brain has derailed, so has your mind. You are no longer yourself and no longer in a healthy state of self-control. All mental resources— intelligence, personality, problem-solving skills, willpower— are hijacked by the addiction for its own purposes in the same way a cancer hijacks nutrients from the body to grow itself. At the outer limit of severity, both processes, if left unchecked, end in death.

Addictions are grotesquely profitable and the purveyors are predatory, investing heavily in the making and harvesting of addicts. We *all*, but especially teenagers, think: That will never happen to me. I'll try anything once.

Don't. As Don Henley eloquently sang, once it's out, "…you can't get the genie back in the bottle."

Flying Plus Family Equals Stress

"…everything about air travel is so revolting, from the food to the security to the crowding to the simple fact of being thirty thousand feet in the sky…." *from Watch Your Back,* Donald Westlake

LaGuardia Airport, Queens, NY, 8:30 p.m.
August

I'd worked a full day, flown the first leg from Burlington, Vermont, and was waiting to board my connection to Atlanta. It was a crush at my gate and at every adjacent gate. The ventilation system strained from too many bodies inside and too much heat outside. With every breath, I smelled sweat, coffee, and designer perfume. The din of crowd noise, ringing cell phones, soft rock, and multiple boarding announcements over the public address system pounded me in waves.

The gate agent picked up a mike. His lips moved. *I couldn't hear him.* Panic swept through me. I couldn't get enough air. And this was the easy part of this trip. On the return—my heart pounded, my skin prickled with current—I'd have Bro with me. When I'd made the reservations, I'd thought, *Of course I can handle flying him up and back. I'm a board certified psychiatrist.*

What's up with Bro?

Bro—fifty-five, a chain-smoker and schizophrenic—lived in Atlanta, as did Mom, Little Sis and her family, while I live in upstate New York with mine. Air travel had changed a little since Bro last flew, oh… thirty-five years ago. No way could he fly alone. What with the paranoia and the voices in his head (ongoing, despite meds), Bro stressed with crowds, noise, and changes in plan. (He was OK with smells. His nose was shot.). He needed a lot of quiet time, as in most of his waking hours, most days. And that was when he was smoking, which he wouldn't be, from airport to shining airport.

My thoughts raced as fast as my heart. I wasn't worried he'd get violent but *what if* he parked himself in the smoking lounge, refused to budge, and we missed our flight? Caterpillars skittered in my innards. I slammed shut the mental door on that and all the other what-ifs lining up behind it. I'd deal with whatever came up, when it came up. Maybe nothing would come up. Just in case, I had fifty bucks worth of nicotine gum stashed in my carry-on bag. Mom's only comment on the hours-long period between smokes had been shockingly hands-off: "Good luck with that."

What's up with Mom?

Why the sudden lack of opinion? Bro was Mom's *raison d'être*, her cover, and her sickness. WMOM ("All Mom, All the Time") usually played classical symphonies such as "You May Be a Psychiatrist, But What Do You Know about Schizophrenia" and "Don't Bother Me with Reality, I'm the Mother."

Every year for fifteen years I'd invited Bro to come visit, and Mom had always said, *in front of him*, "Bah! You have no time for him." Obviously, Bro's feelings were her top priority. My feelings too, of course. *Oh*—It came to me. It wasn't that *he* needed a vacation. ("Poor thing. He has nothing.") *She* needed a vacation. ("I'm making plans to visit friends in Nashville.") Still all Mom, all the time. Now that Bro visiting me worked for her, I had plenty of time. Great. That worked for me.

Bro is a sweetie. He and I were close growing up. When he lost his mind at nineteen, I lost—we all lost—the adult he would have become: a warm and witty English professor, married with three children (now his delusion). Still, the essential Bro abided. In disagreement with Mom, I was of the opinion—But, what do I know?—that Bro was psychiatrically stable, modest in his needs, and (relatively) easy to be with.

Mom insisted he needed one-on-one attention. Yet he consistently got agitated when she pressed him to converse. She insisted he got up at eight in the morning, took his meds, and laid down for "a rest" around noon. I was sure that's what he told her, but I suspected he slept in. She insisted his psychiatrist was inadequate: "Bah! He only spends a few minutes. He never returns my calls." Bro liked him, took his meds as prescribed, and hadn't required hospital admission since his late twenties, a gold medal win all by itself.

Bro had lived in his own apartment for decades and, giving credit where it was due, Mom's helicoptering was why. Still, when she insisted he didn't clean his stovetop, drop off his recyclables, or change his bedding because of the illness, Little Sis and I rolled our eyes. Our husbands were the same and they're not psychotic.

I figured, leave Bro alone (beyond tactfully making sure he took his meds). Let him hang around the homestead without demanding conversation. Let him smoke on the back deck without the third degree. Add a daily run for a decaf mocha latte (extra large, iced) and a short afternoon excursion for novelty and I was sure Bro would have happy memories of his time with me and mine.

The problem was the travel before and after.

Two seconds later.... The gate agent's lips were still moving without sound....

The crowd surged behind me, shoving me hard into the woman in front of me and crashing me out of my thoughts. "Excuse me!" I said when she turned her head and scowled. "Sorry! Were you able to hear?"

"Weather. Flight's delayed."

I HATE FLYING. But no choice: Atlanta is 1200 miles away, too far to drive in one day, or even two.

Two days later, the return trip home with Bro.

Little Sis dropped Bro and me at the Atlanta airport two hours early. We'd checked on-line for flight delays: all clear to LaGuardia. The connection from there to Burlington was on time, too. Bro donned his sunglasses, smoked an unfiltered cigarette till it burned his fingers, then followed me through security. We walked, we escalatored, we trained, we arrived at our terminal. We strolled to the gate, the one at the end (of course) and passed a smoking lounge. *O! Happy day!*

At the gate—we were so early the agent hadn't arrived yet— Bro gave me his carry-on and u-turned for a smoke. Just as I opened my novel, the red lights on the information board flickered: the departure time for our flight to LaGuardia was now delayed three hours. *We would arrive after our connection to Burlington had left.* I ran to the first gate with an agent, who sent me to another, where I stood tensely in line, keeping an eye out for Bro. We were rerouted to a flight that was boarding *now, at another terminal.*

I rushed to the smoking lounge—a gray-scape of smoke fug, cinder-burned plastic seats, ash-covered side tables, and butt-littered linoleum. Bro looked up from his enjoyment. He dropped his lit cigarette to the floor, stepped on it and walked to me, a large, iced decaf mocha latte in hand, no lid.

I explained and bolted ahead. I looked over my shoulder and stopped. Bro was a small dot, enlarging v-e-r-y slowly. I doubled back and urged him on. We power walked, we escalatored, we boarded the inter-terminal train. He grabbed the floor-to-ceiling pole and caught his breath.

The train jolted forward. Bro, six feet tall and stinking of stale smoke, stumbled into the tiny Asian woman standing beside him. The hand holding the uncovered coffee container tipped with him. A coffee tidal wave sloshed up the inside wall of the cup, over the lip—and just missed her.

He found his balance and righted the cup. She looked disgusted. Sweat ran down his temples. I wanted to kill him. He always tossed the lid.

"The coffee has to go," I said as we exited, looking around for a waste bin. Not a one to be seen for miles. (Later, Little Sis informed me this was an airport security, anti-terrorist strategy. No lie.) Bro just stood there, reluctant to part with his daily brew. Those babies cost upwards of five bucks, and he'd only drunk half of it. I felt for him.

"Put it down! Now!"

"Where?"

"Anywhere! We gotta go!" S-l-o-w-l-y, he set it on the floor against the wall. I jack-rabbited toward the gate. He kept up. We arrived, sweaty and panting, to an announcement inviting priority and gold-club members to board.

We found seats in the waiting area opposite each other. I breathed and enjoyed a few moments of stillness, despite the bedlam. I pulled out my cell phone, took a picture of Bro, and texted it to Little Sis: "Chillaxin'!"

The gate agent announced boarding would resume shortly. My belly clenched with fear-of-missing-the-connection tension. The agent announced the flight was delayed. I texted Little Sis. Bro sat placidly, lips moving in silent conversation with his internal companions. The agent announced the flight was cancelled. I texted Little Sis.

All flights on *all* airlines to LaGuardia, Kennedy, and Newark were cancelled due to weather. All flights going out tomorrow were *stand-by only*. I looked at Bro in his Ray Bans, talking to himself. We couldn't fly stand-by.

I beat two people to the gate agent, who did her best for half an hour, but finally gave up. Bro and I joined the l-o-o-n-n-n-n-ng queue at Bad Air ticketing. We did time for over three hours in three different lines. Bro left me only once to smoke.

The first available flight to Burlington through LaGuardia was *two days ahead*. On either side of us, customers raged in frustration. Bro stood by. *Idea!* Could she get us to Albany? True, the drive home would take two and a half hours. But driving, we'd be on the move. In control—well, the illusion of it anyway. She looked: there were two confirmed seats available the next day. A *direct* flight. No layover. The relief was orgasmic. I texted Little Sis to pick us up.

The next day.

The flight to Albany went down like a fruit smoothie on a hot summer day. So smoothly that upon arrival, I commandeered the gate agent to reroute our return flight to Atlanta from Albany instead of from Burlington. No layover in LaGuardia. Less time in the airport. Less time in the air. Less stress. The money (extortionist penalty fees plus the difference in the cost of the tickets) plus the drive time were well worth it.

Bro smoked and I drank coffee sitting at peace on a bench outside while we waited for Hubby (*My hero!*) to pick us up. It was a beautiful North Country summer day: clear, sunny, deep blue sky, no bugs.

A week later.

Just as I anticipated, Bro's visit was a walk in the park and a piece of cake after. Driving south to the Albany airport through the evergreen mountains and slate-glass lakes of the Adirondack Park, we listened to "classic" rock (aka golden oldies), a nice soundtrack for a stroll through our teens. Before entering the airport, Bro donned his sunglasses and smoked an unfiltered cigarette till it burned his fingers. We shuffled through security, bought coffees, and waited companionably at the gate. We boarded.

Overhead, the pilot's voice smarmed it was an honor to serve us (*Honor? It's a business transaction*), thanked us for choosing Bad Air (*Choice? It was the only option,*) and apologized for the delay taking off. (*My belly clenched.*) Something had broken in the cockpit. The mechanic had been called. As soon as the repair is made, we'll be taking off. Your safety is our first priority.

I reminded myself safety was good. I breathed, shallowly, to take in as little of Eau de Bro as possible. We sat on the tarmac for two hours. I read. Bro, in his shades, leaned his head back against the seat and chatted with his inside friends. By the time we landed in Atlanta, he hadn't smoked for six hours. (I offered nicotine gum, but he refused it.)

Waiting to deplane tasked him to the limit. The humid, dead ash reek coming off him tasked *me* to the limit. But as soon as we walked off the plane into the airport — a smoking lounge! *O! Happy Day!* I breathed deeply, visited the facilities, and texted Little Sis we'd arrived.

Bro emerged from the scorched-earth lounge rejuvenated, fresh as a nicotine-dependent daisy, with an all's-right-with-the-world expression. He was fine, no crazier and no more stressed at the end of this nightmare round trip than at the beginning. I, on the other hand, was only-one-more-thing away from a calming injection and escort by two nice men in white coats. And that was my professional assessment.

A week later.

Bad Air e-mailed me requesting feedback on my travel experience. I obliged, with enough arctic air to cause frostbite on contact. They asked for it.

Then I got a surprise call from Bro. "Only eleven months till next August," he quipped. He'd enjoyed himself! Flying hadn't bothered him. Whew.

"He says you gave him a wonderful time," Mom huffed. Ha.

That made two out of three family wins. How to make it three for three next year.... Road trip?

Stop It!

October

I walked into the waiting room with Poodle Oodle and knew at a glance that Elaine—hunched on the edge of the wooden chair, hands clenched between knees, head down—was having a bad day. She yanked her head up, eyes wide. She struggled to her feet, lost her balance from the pain of bearing weight, and steadied herself with a hand on the wall. She wailed, "I'm sorry! I'm so stupid and clumsy!"

Fortunately, we were alone. I shot her a concerned look and shook my head: *No worries.* Something had happened. It didn't take much to set her off into a frenzy of verbal self-whipping.

We walked slowly, Elaine limping, to my clinical office with its full bookcase, the top covered with an expanding collection of historical glass bottles of all shapes, colors and sizes. They'd been given to me over the years by patients who had dug them up on their properties. People loved to treasure hunt for late 1700s and War of 1812 artifacts. Being a dog lover, Elaine adored the green bottle shaped like a Labrador sitting at attention.

Elaine not only suffered crippling pain from multiple herniated discs in her neck and lower back, but also had arthritis, degenerative disc disease, and asthma. The awful state of her back was due to a combination of bad genetics and horrifying physical abuse in childhood. She was in her early forties.

During her elementary school years, her mother locked her in closets, starved her, beat her till bones broke, kept her home from school to do house and farm work, and then beat her some more for "not doing it good enough." In her middle and high school years, she was used sexually by various men in the family, including her father and two brothers. Her father also passed her around to his friends, once to pay off a gambling debt.

Had any public authority ever intervened on her behalf? No. Domestic violence and physical and sexual abuse are endemic in our rural community. Social service agencies are understaffed, underfunded, and overwhelmed. Physical injuries are explained away as farming accidents to emergency rooms, pediatricians, and school nurses.

Elaine suffered from severe PTSD: flashbacks, nightmares, panic attacks, and depression. She was disabled and impoverished, her Social Security disability check barely enough to live on. She avoided leaving her rental one-bedroom apartment. She'd lived alone since escaping the family in her early twenties, after the miscarriage that continued to haunt her. She'd hemorrhaged, required admission, and told the hospital social worker enough about her home life to be discharged to a safe house. She had never gone back.

"Have you ever considered pressing charges against your father and brothers for molesting you?" I'd asked her fairly early in the treatment. She'd looked askance at me.

"Who would I report it to?"

"The chief of police of your town?" I'd said.

"That would be my uncle, my father's brother. He molested me too, and his daughters. My cousins. They're just as messed as I am," she'd said, tearing up.

PTSD results when a person survives an experience of inescapable terror. Elaine had been subjected to countless inescapable terrors since childhood at the hands of her parents (and family), the worst-case scenario for treatment and recovery. The destructive consequences to a child's developing brain and psyche cannot be overstated.

EMDR (Eye Movement Desensitization and Reprocessing) therapy is a treatment that uses eye movements to activate the brain in a way that helps people heal from trauma *without talking about it*. Trying to talk about trauma usually triggers flashbacks, re-traumatizing the patient. Despite the fact that EMDR doesn't address the betrayal and abandonment issues of severe childhood abuse, Elaine had found a past course somewhat helpful.

The medications I prescribed helped some too, but disabling symptoms persisted. Nightmares disrupted her nights and flashbacks her days, though less frequently. She startled daily, multiple times a day. Her mood remained depressed and anxious.

Then there were all the counterproductive ways she coped with the people who triggered symptoms. We were making some progress with those.

She'd never married and had no friends. She tolerated the company of a couple women from her church. ("I don't trust anybody.") Two years ago, when her sixteen-year-old dog Boxter passed away, she was inconsolable for months. "Dogs are beautiful. They always love you. They don't betray you. How am I going to live without him?" she'd wept.

With time, she had come around to the idea that it wouldn't be disloyal to his memory to let another dog into her life and she adopted an abandoned puppy from the local ASPCA. "I call her Toast because without me, that's what she'd be." *And vice versa*, I thought to myself. Elaine's spirits had lightened a bit since. Between the PTSD symptoms and the pain, it was hard for her to make her appointments with me. Yet she rarely missed one.

"My back is killing me," she said as we entered the office. "Driving kills me, walking kills me. I can't do anything!" she moaned. "I hate my life! Look how skinny I am! How ugly!" She swept aside her unzipped coat, pulled up her sweater and shoved her protruding ribs at me. "See?!" Poodle Oodle, who ordinarily ran right up to Elaine, stood quietly beside my left foot, head cocked, brown eyes alert.

I closed the door. She dropped her sweater, swiped her eyes with a forearm, and gave me an *Admit-it-you-find-me-repulsive* glare. Certainly, skeletal thinness is not pretty. But I wasn't accepting any invitations to that party. The anguish in her voice broke my heart. No one should hate themselves that much. Except her vile parents, who wouldn't, of course.

Elaine was a lovely person, warm and caring, eager to learn and desperate to feel better. She worked hard at it. Fury—at her family for warping her into this dreadful shape—blazed through me. Then despair: evil people are a fact and so is the hell they make for the rest of us. Finally:

You can't do anything about that. Get to work. Focus. I took in a breath and released it slowly.

Elaine lowered herself to sit on the couch with a grimace, but pulled up immediately. "I can't. Do you mind if I sit on the floor? It hurts less."

"Of course not. Do what you need to do to take care of yourself," I said, seating myself while keeping an eye on her. Poodle Oodle sat on the floor beside my chair, also watching.

She paused in mid-lower—one hand on the sofa and one knee on the ground—to throw me a brilliant, guileless, girlish smile that told me I'd hit it, said the right thing, met a need she didn't know she had.

"Thank you!" She groaned as she sat her butt down on the rug, scooched her back against the couch, and stretched her legs carefully, shifting in search of the least painful spot. She had kept her coat on. I leaned forward and pushed the ottoman toward the bookcase to give her more room. Poodle Oodle padded over to her and snuggled next to her thigh. Elaine leaned down to stroke her head, "Sweet girl."

A few peaceful moments passed before she looked up. I smiled before speaking, "Bad pain day?"

"Yeah," she frowned. "These rainy fall days are murder. But the winter cold is worse. The ice. I'm so afraid of falling." Her eyes filled. "I'm so sick of not being able to do anything." She paused. "Having no life," she muttered. "Being so stupid and useless!"

This was too much. "Hold on. Did something happen?"

"Nothing! I'm home all the time. Nothing happens! I don't see anyone or do anything. I'm a lazy cripple!" Tears spilled.

I knew what this was: someone had been mean to her.

"Did you get any phone calls today?"

She stopped crying abruptly. It was interesting how mercurial she was. One minute she was weeping; the next beaming; then suddenly, pensive.

Now she lit up. "Yes!" Just as quickly, she darkened and looked down. "How did you know?" she whispered.[22]

I hastened to reassure her. "I didn't know!" I smiled. "You forget. I've seen you like this before, usually after you get a call from family. You say awful things to yourself after. It's a pattern." I smiled again, turning up the warmth. She relaxed, slumping back against the couch, stroking Poodle Oodle from head to tail along her back. Poodle licked her hand. She smiled.

"Who was it this time?"

Her hand on the pooch stilled. Her face contorted and her eyes flashed. "My mother! I hate her! Whenever I

---

[22] I've gotten this kind of reaction since my teens. What seems uncanny actually comes from being a close observer of people and patterns of behavior, the ability to imagine myself in a person's place, some logical extrapolation, and years of honing these skills for a living. Patients aren't the only ones who get spooked. In an earlier time, I might have been burned for a witch.

talk to her, I'm a wreck after." She rubbed the free hand across her eyes, and shook her head hard.

"I shouldn't hate anybody! I'm bad. I know I'm going straight to hell when I die!"

Elaine was deeply religious, both a boon and a bane. Her faith had kept her alive; otherwise she might have killed herself long ago. But it was a torment, too. She was convinced she should turn the other cheek, and when she couldn't (being of sound mind), judged herself cruelly. As cruelly as she'd been treated.

If she could accept her hate for what it was—the natural and logical consequence of how she'd been abused—she could begin the work of accepting that her mother would never love her. Not because she was unlovable, but because her mother was incapable. Letting go of her mother would open up space in her heart for someone who *could* love her.

That's incredibly hard work to do. We know from monkey research that monkey children mistreated by their mothers cling to those mothers when adult. They won't let go. They don't move on to finding a mate and building their own family. The abuse stunts or stops their ability to mature.

My therapeutic goal for Elaine was to help her fill in the developmental holes and heal the psychic wounds enough "to have a life." I knew that's what she wanted, but could we do it? That was a many years' project and it was still early days in the treatment.

I didn't try to reassure her she wasn't going to hell. She'd reject that for the platitude that it was. Besides, how could I possibly know? If hell existed, I didn't have any say about who went there.

The moment I'd taken to think had given her time to settle down. She was calm, waiting for me to respond.

"Have you considered not taking the call?"

"I can't *not* talk to her! She's my mother!" she said, scandalized. I ignored the urge to explain why my suggestion was reasonable. Better for her to draw that conclusion herself.

"Why did she call?"

"I don't know! It's not like I have any money to give her."

Nice lady, Elaine's mother. "What does she want that you *can* give her? Is she lonely?"

"No!" She paused. "I think... she's bored." Another pause. "She likes to get me upset!" She jerked with the insight and gasped from the resulting jolt of pain. Poodle Oodle raised her head, ears up, eyes on Elaine.

"She asks me what I've been doing, and no matter what it is, I'm stupid and useless!" Her face crumpled. I handed her a few tissues. The pooch cushioned her chin on Elaine's thigh.

"What do *you* get when you talk to her?"

"What do I get?" She blew her nose and tilted her head. "What do you mean?"

"What's in it for you? Besides hating yourself, of course." She lifted one side of her mouth ruefully at that, and dropped the used wad of tissues into the small wastebasket beside the couch.

There was a long silence as she went deep inside, hands folded in her lap. In the street, a car whooshed by. A couple blocks away, a dog barked. Faintly, from far away, a police siren wailed. Outside the office door, the white noise machine droned. When she resurfaced, she looked.... Puzzled? Astonished? Hopeful?

"I... I don't know," she said. "What *is* in it for me?" She looked at me for The Answer.

I shook my head. "Only you know. Take a wild guess. Be bold."

Another long silence. She took a deep breath. "Nothing?"

Wow. Most people, even if they can, refuse to see what isn't there. Elaine was smart. And open.

"I can't stand her! Do you know what she said? She said I should be dead! She said she should have aborted me!" She broke down sobbing. Poodle Oodle ran from her side, vaulted into my seat, and wedged herself facing front between my leg and the chair arm. I ran a hand down her back, while I pulled tissues from my box with the other, and handed them to Elaine.

"And then...." She clenched her fists, punched down on her thighs and yelped. "And, and, the miscarriage!" She covered her face, wretched. "But, but... God hates me too! He punished me when He took the baby." Her body shook. "I must be really worthless...."

The words poured out in a flood, one memory triggering the next, wave after wave of misery, harsh judgments rushing after, in a rapidly escalating cascade. Her neck muscles stood taut like ropes, her torso heaved, a deep red flush suffused her neck, ears, and face. She gasped, increasingly short of breath. She was heading for an asthma attack or a panic attack or both—

249

"STOP IT!" I barked, and shifted forward in the chair, my weight over my feet, ready to rise.

Abruptly she stopped, panting, the sudden quiet pounding with all the words dammed back. Her tears dried up. The flush receded, leaving her neck and face blotchy pale. She stared at me.

"Good," I said carefully. "Well done." I leaned forward and handed her the wrinkled tissue I'd been clutching.

"Thank you," she said and blew her nose. I handed her another. She wiped her eyes and took a moment to breathe, then gave me a tentative smile.

"You were working yourself up." I said.

She thought about it and nodded.

"You might want to try not doing that."

She thought some more. "How?"

My turn to think. "You know how bad it made you feel to hear your mother say you shouldn't have been born?"

She nodded, her red-rimmed eyes glistening. I hurried before the floodgates opened again. "Then she said 'abortion' and that triggered a memory of your miscarriage, and more bad feeling and so on. It kept building. It was turning into a tidal wave." I paused. *Was she with me?*

She nodded: *Go on.*

"If you'd kept going, you might have had a panic attack or an asthma attack—" I stopped. "Do you have your inhaler on you?"

She shook her head no. Images flashed by my inner eye: Elaine passed out, blue-lipped from lack of oxygen. Punching 911 on the phone. The ambulance rushing to the hospital, red lights flashing. I'd definitely done the right thing though when I did it, I'd acted without conscious thought, directed by that knowledgeable, wordless self that jerks my hand away from a hot burner before I even know I've touched it.

"When I shouted at you to stop, you did. Instantly. Good job." I steepled my hands to my chest, bent forward from the waist, bowed my head— *Namaste*— and straightened, dropping my hands to my lap. Beside me, head on crossed front paws, Poodle Oodle watched Elaine, too.

The silence was deafening. She stared at me, unmoving, for so long it became uncomfortable. Then her face split into a radiant, charming grin. "Really?" Poodle lifted her head and ears.

"Yes. You can work yourself up. But you can stop, too. At will. That's what we both learned today."

Her grin broadened.

"You can do it again. Whenever you want."

She looked even more astonished. "How?"

"The key is *to notice* when you're sliding under—" I interrupted myself. "What shall we call it? That wave of bad memories and bad feelings?"

Silence. "A tantrum?" Elaine giggled. Her sense of humor was back! Sunshine, after heavy rain. I grinned, delighted. Poodle jumped down, ambled over to Elaine and sat down beside her.

"Tantrum is such a judging word. How about we call it a surge?

She nodded.

"As soon as you notice that surge of self hate—"

"But I *always* hate myself!"

251

"Well... not always at the same level, right? Sometimes it lightens up and you can feel your loving self, yes?" I paused to give her a chance to explore that.

She nodded, a bit hesitantly. Poodle Oodle pawed her thigh. Elaine smiled, and stroked her head.

"Your loving self comes here to work with me." I raised my eyebrows and smiled: *Right?*

"Ohhhh.... I see. Yeah, yeah," she said, her hand stroking Poodle's back.

"When your loving self *notices* a surge of self hate, let her ask: What happened? Was someone just mean to me?"

I paused. *Did she get that?*

She nodded.

"You want to find the pattern of cause and effect. The cause is what triggers you. The effect is the surge. You see?"

Her hand went still: *YES.* She raised her eyebrows: *Then what?*

"As soon as you notice, you stop. You say to yourself: I'm not going there. I'm putting my mind on something else. I'm distracting myself."

She nodded.

"Like say, your laundry hamper is full of dirty clothes. You say to yourself, I'm putting a load in."

I studied her closely. She looked back, alert.

"Your mind can only do one thing at a time. You either melt down or you put the garbage can at the bottom of your driveway for pick up." I paused. She nodded.

"You either sink into a horrible memory or you take the puppy for a walk." I paused.

"A walk? Toast runs!" She grinned, and looked down at Poodle Oodle. "Toast is so good!" She looked up at me. "If I didn't have to take her out, I'd just stay on the couch. It hurts to walk her, but it's a good hurt."

"See? You're smiling! Walking Toast puts your attention on her and gets it off you. Whenever you get upset, walk Toast."

"I can do that?" she asked with wonder. Was she asking for permission or if it could be done? Either way: yes.

"You can do it. I can do it. Anyone can do it. Distracting yourself from your upset is a technique. You use it to calm down. To soothe yourself." I smiled.

"Wow," she said.

"Elaine, you've just never asked yourself to, is all. It's a skill. It gets easier with practice."

She gave me a beatific, loopy grin.

"I'll try it! I'll try anything!" We both watched Poodle Oodle stretch in downward facing dog, then the other way, and finish with a total body wiggle.

I smiled at Elaine and stood up. She was a joy to work with.

It didn't matter that she wouldn't hang on to it. She'd forget. But each time I reminded her, she'd be thrilled, grateful, and she would redouble her efforts. *"If that isn't nice, I don't know what is."*[23]

Using the couch for support, Elaine levered herself up off the floor. "Whew," she said, giving herself a little shake to balance herself. She smiled at me.

---

[23] Kurt Vonnegut, *A Man Without a Country*

I smiled back, amazed at how good she looked. The tipping point of the session flashed briefly through my body, an electric charge that raised all the little hairs and made my heart race. It could have— so easily and catastrophically— tipped the other way. I saw her fighting for air, face red and neck veins bulging. I saw her face after, paper white, as she shook her head no.

"Elaine, one more thing," I heard myself say, the words emerging from that wordless knowing that, in this case, made forethought redundant. "Carry your inhaler in your purse, so you always have it with you."

Failure: Can't Live with It, Can't Succeed without It

December

Son, eighteen and finishing his first semester at the local college, abruptly pulled over to the curb and said, "You drive."

We were one block away from the test area where he'd just failed the driver's license test for the second time. Silently, we changed sides. Silently, I pulled out, rolling through a drift of dead leaves and snow, eyes forward to give him privacy.

Low snuffles. Small rustles. I snuck a glance. His eyes were squeezed shut. Tears tracked down his cheeks. His expression shifted like black cloud cover moving in for a storm. His lips twitched.

Tentatively, I patted his arm. His eyes snapped open, his hand slapped mine away, his eyes shuttered closed. Barely controlled rage steamed off him.

When you really, *really* want something, and you have worked really, *really* hard for it, and you fail— Well, we've all been there. It's the end of the world. Nothing makes sense. The betrayal is bottomless. The first time is especially brutal. You have no experience to put it in perspective.

For me, it happened when I repeated my first year of med school. When I learned I had to repeat, I thought nothing could be more terrible. Yet, there I was, attending classes for eight hours a day during the week; followed by another eight of study in the evening; and twelve to sixteen on both Saturday and Sunday. I was barely passing. Again. It was shocking. Shattering. Maybe… I hadn't been *unfairly* held back. Maybe… it was far worse than that.

Meanwhile, Hubby lounged around for two weeks of the month, watching TV, going to the gym, and sleeping in. Two weeks prior to the test period, he put in his earplugs and hunkered down at his desk. The night before the test, he didn't sleep, cramming to the last minute. After the first day's tests, he'd sleep for four hours, then pull another all-nighter for the second day's round. Then two weeks off. His grades were excellent. It was maddening.

"Cramming is the way to go," he kept telling me. Did I listen? No. Did I pull all-nighters? I refused. Did I take his test question predictions seriously? "That level of detail? Give me a break!" He would shake his head. *"Insanity: Doing the same thing over and over again, expecting a different result."*[24]

I was positive I'd do well on the pulmonary physiology exam. I didn't. I blew up in a way I'd always wanted to and never let myself. I threw textbooks at the wall. I knocked all the other books off their shelves. I ripped the linens off the bed and wept with rage. I kicked the couch leg and howled with pain, hopping around holding my foot. Hubby trailed behind me, the voice of reason, "D, it'll be all right."

---

[24] Albert Einstein

I yearned—no, *craved* to break dishes— *Crash!* And throw fruit— *Splat!* But even when enraged, that sensible and pestiferous voice inside my head doesn't shut up: *The clean up. The expense. Don't do it.* I tossed all the clothes out of the drawers. I was done. I threw myself on the stripped bed and blubbered, "I'll have to drop out."

Hubby sat down next me and patted my back. "That's ridiculous."

I rolled over, tears running into my ears, and glared at him. "I can't do it! I'm not smart enough!"

"Cut it out. You've got to change how you're studying, is all. I know how to play the test game. Let me help you. You'll be fine."

For the first time, I considered it. I slowed my breathing. Certainly what I was doing wasn't working. Stupidity was out of my control. If the problem was technique, though, I could change *that*. I took a deep breath, sat up and mopped my face with the hem of my tee shirt. "Okay. I can always drop out later." I got up from the bed and started the cleanup.

When I told this tale to Kathy, our office manager, she'd stared at me. "To think you would have given up your career!" I know. Crazy. But frustration can feel intolerable and force you to take action. When that happens, what matters is what you say just *before*. I said I was a failure. Hubby said I had a problem to solve. I went with his interpretation. It felt better and, after I stopped bawling, that sensible and annoying voice agreed: *Dropping out would have cost too much. Not worth it.*

I decided to share the incident with Son, as a life lesson. Later. I pulled up to the college entrance. He shot me a bleak look, got out of the car, slammed the door shut, and trudged off to class. I watched his bent head, slumped shoulders, and bowed back move away from me. He took one hand from his parka pocket to yank open the door of the building and vanished into his life.

When the blackbird flew out of sight,
It marked the edge
Of one of many circles.[25]

That night, at dinner, Hubby and I listened and made sympathetic noises. "I didn't go to my first class. I was too upset. But I checked in with the professor and he was OK with it."

"Very responsible of you," I said. "I'm glad you took care of yourself." He sat before his empty plate, staring off into space. I served him some salad, spaghetti, sauce, and three meatballs.

"I went to my second class, but I stayed away from people after that. One wrong word, one wrong look, I'd have hurt somebody."

Hubby nodded, "Good job." He twirled spaghetti on his fork, speared a chunk of meatball, and popped the mass in his mouth.

Son looked at me, eyes blazing: "When you drove me to school after the test, all I could think about was killing that fucking instructor—" he grabbed and shook the air, "breaking his neck, stomping him into the ground...."

---

[25] from "Thirteen Ways of Looking at a Blackbird" by Wallace Stevens

I snapped my head at Hubby, alarmed. He shrugged, his expression tolerant: *The kid is just venting.* True. In the clinch, he had controlled himself. Still, I didn't like the f-bomb and the graphic imagery.

I told my pulmonary physiology test story. Son's eyes re-ignited with rage. "Yes! You work and work and they take it all away from you! It's so unfair! I deserved to pass!" His hands clenched into fists.

Okay, not the point I wanted him to get.

"I just want to kill him," Son growled, staring down at his untouched meal.

"Sure, that would relieve your feelings," I said. "I felt the same way: they were out to get me with trick questions. It felt excellent ripping up the apartment. But when the rage passed, what did I have? A big mess to clean up. And I still didn't know what I'd done wrong."

Son looked up and stared at me.

"You're assuming you drove competently and your instructor was out to fail you. But maybe you didn't, and your instructor was simply being objective."

Son stared at me.

"Would killing the instructor help you pass? No. And what about the consequences? Prison time for murder one? Over a failed driver's exam? Come on."

Son stared at me.

"Dad got me to see that test-taking is a game. A game I didn't understand. That's a technique problem. I *could* do something about that. And I *did* do something about it. If I hadn't, I wouldn't be a doctor today." I raised my eyebrows: *How about THAT?"*

Son stared at me. What was he thinking? Was I getting through?

"Maybe the same thing is going on with you and the driver's test. Maybe there's something you need to learn that you haven't identified yet."

Son kept staring at me, expressionless, and now I got annoyed. When was he going to speak?

Hubby said, "Working hard is good, but it's not enough. You have to work smart, too."

"But I have been!!" he burst out.

Hubby said, "How about a couple of driving lessons? With a pro. To fine tune your skills and anticipate what they'll test?"

Son's eyes flamed again. "I should have fucking passed."

Tuesday, Bill Shot Himself

Tuesday to Saturday.
Late March

When Bill missed his appointment that Tuesday, I was too pressed to take in what an anomaly that was. The next day, Wednesday, the mailman delivered Bill's good-bye note, so carefully written in blue ink: *"My lifelong nightmare is over. I've enjoyed working with you. I'm sorry."* I broke down. Even in his final moments, he'd thought of *me*. *He* was sorry. Sorrow took me and I cried again.

At the end of the workday I called his wife, who was tearful but composed.

"You aren't surprised, are you?"

"No," she said.

"He seemed fine last month when he came in. And he'd been fine, for over a year."

"I know. Nothing was different when I left for work. His cousin told me he called yesterday morning to wish him a happy birthday. Then he walked a couple miles to the back of the property and shot himself behind the tool shed."

"I'm so very sorry," I said, my throat tight.

"Thank you."

No matter how many times I reviewed the course of treatment, I circled around to: there was nothing I could have done. He had made up his mind. With each pass, grief overwhelmed me.

I kept the newspaper with his obituary and reviewed it Saturday morning at 10:15 for the funeral specifics. Just below the fold, I found the address and read: memorial service at 11:00. *What? I thought calling hours were between noon and 3:00.* The church was twenty miles away. *Church? I thought it was a funeral home.* If I left immediately, I would barely make it. I pulled into the church parking lot as cars were exiting. Inside the church, I asked for the widow and got blank looks. I had arrived late to the wrong funeral.

I thought I was "fine." But clearly, I wasn't. Back in the car, I looked at the paper and there it was *above* the fold: funeral home, noon to 3:00. It was twenty miles back to town and another fifteen beyond.

Bill and I had worked together over ten years. His last ten years…. Driving, again I reviewed the course of treatment, again drew the same conclusion, again felt the overwhelming tragedy of it.

At the funeral home, I signed the guest book and took a laminated Mass card with his photo. A younger, slimmer Bill, the same eyes. The lyrics on the back (from a song he'd written) read as if he were speaking. My nose started to run; my eyes burned; my throat swelled. I pulled myself together in the receiving line, studying the various photos mounted on corkboards propped on two small easels. There were several of Bill with his wife, including a wedding photo of them, happy, cutting the cake. Bill as a boy. As a young man, long hair, Hawaiian shirt, guitar. With assorted family. With his dog. Beside a new truck. As people chatted and hugged, I heard: "…very sensitive…." "I'll miss him." "…was a good man." Yes, he was.

When I introduced myself to the widow, she took my hands in hers and said softly, "Thank you for coming." Our eyes welled simultaneously. We stood there, holding hands and eyes, the silence too full for words. She squeezed my hands, leaned in a little, and asked in a voice so low only I could hear, "Did he leave you a note?" I nodded.

"You?" I asked, equally softly.

She nodded, "He respected you." Our eyes welled again.

"I'm sorry I couldn't do more," I whispered, my throat painful. She closed her eyes briefly and shook her head, dismissing that. We spoke a little more, her eyes so deeply sad, her demeanor so deeply dignified.

Turning, she released my hands and introduced me to the woman on her left, Bill's mother, who took my hands in hers and talked so long without a break, I smiled inside. I had just gotten a taste of Bill's issues with his mother. I nodded and murmured soothingly until she had said everything she needed to say. When she released my hands, I offered my condolences again and slipped away.

I wept in the car in the parking lot. How had Bill lived with so much psychic pain? The magnitude of it. The trap of it. The never-ending-ness of it. Remarkably, his suffering hadn't made him bitter. He was loving, and beloved. What an act of courage it must have been to carry on day after day.

I thought about my med school and residency years, how sorry I had felt for myself and the darkness of my favorite joke of the time: *First, A Little Momba*. My suffering had been voluntary and time-limited. It was nothing. *First, A Little Momba* was Bill's lifelong nightmare.

Rest in peace, Bill.

Is it possible to grieve and be happy at the same time?

April.

When Bill took his life, my heart broke. Yet it beat on. And though I demanded the world stop, if only for a moment, it didn't. In the morning, starting around 6:00, the birds sang madly, joyously. The crocuses sprang from the dark, damp earth beside the back door, their yellow and purple heads and slim green arms reaching up, up, up to the sun in the blue bowl of the sky.

I ate my usual breakfast of fruit, plain yogurt, and granola. I kissed and hugged Hubby before he left for work. I kissed and hugged Son when he dropped by to raid the refrigerator and do his laundry. I went to work and did good work. I took a dance class after and felt happy. I slept.

Bill had returned to wherever we are born from. As the empty space within defines a pitcher, his absence revealed the undeniable throb of life. Even as my mind resisted, my body flowed with the deep wellspring of it: Life goes on. And on. Relentlessly. Vigorously. Not our individual lives, of course. But the stream of life, the comings and goings, without end.

Perhaps it *was* possible to grieve and be happy at the same time. Provided I didn't think too much about it.

"*...Let the body's doings speak openly now,*

264

without your saying a word,
as a student's walking behind a teacher
says, 'This one knows more clearly
than I the way.'"[26]

---

[26] Rumi, from *On Resurrection Day*, <u>The Essential Rumi</u>, translation Coleman Barks.

EARLY ADVANCED PRACTICE

The difference between stupidity and genius is that genius has its limits. Albert Einstein

Mayday, Mayday

May 1

Sunlight lanced through the windshield into my eyes, triggering a migraine. Poodle Oodle stood on her hind legs in the passenger seat, paws on the door handle, nose pressed against the lowered window, enjoying the ride. We were on our way to the vet for her weekly allergy shot. My right jaw ached, the pain radiating deep into my ear. Involuntarily, I pulled on the lobe, as if that would help. A grinding tiredness took me. Thank God I didn't have any patient care responsibilities for the next four days unless someone paged.

At the end of February, I had bitten into a piece of rye bread and broken my right rear lower molar.[27] The first week of March, my dentist applied the temporary crown and made the imprint for the permanent one. That's when the headaches and jaw pain started but I was busy, took migraine medication, and ignored it.

The first week of April, he put in the permanent crown, and though I'd expected the pain to go away, it didn't. The second week of April, the pain radiated into my right ear and down under my chin. He took an x-ray looking for an infection, didn't find one, but prescribed a

---

[27] Yes, on a piece of bread.

seven-day course of ampicillin[28] anyway, which didn't help much.

The third week of April, a golf-ball sized lymph node popped up under the right side of my chin. He took a CT scan of my jaw and, again, couldn't see a source of infection. Given my symptoms, he prescribed a second course of antibiotic, ten days of penicillin, [29] which I'd finished yesterday. I massaged the golf ball gently: still there but smaller, and still very tender. The right side of my face throbbed, from jaw to ear to temple. The headache filled my head with a painful, high-pressure fog.

At the T-intersection, I squinted into the glare and looked left before turning. A navy minivan trundled over the bridge and crossed in front of me. A familiar-looking, chunky young woman sat in the passenger seat, hunched over, probably focused on her cellphone. That hair…. That frown…. Was that Jordyn? Wasn't I supposed to see her this week?

In early April, the session with her father had gone badly. Remembering it, I groaned involuntarily. *That blasted blurt!* But I'd turned it around. *Hadn't I?* Last week's session with Jordyn had gone okay. *Hadn't it?*

Jordyn lived across the lake an hour away with her divorced, gay father, a family practice doc. He had brought her to see me three years earlier, at the end of her freshman year at an out-of-state college. Though she had spent that

---

[28] A commonly used antibiotic for gum, ear, respiratory, and urinary tract infections
[29] Ditto.

spring semester in bed unable to function due to an untreated clinical depression, during their weekly phone call, she'd lied and said she was fine. The transcript filled with Bs gave her away. Jordyn was a math and physics major, and her IQ was in the gazillion range. She'd never before made a grade below an A, so the Bs shocked and scared him. What worried *me* was the lying.

Treating the depression took over a year after which she transferred to the local college and resumed her studies as a sophomore. But instead of that being the end of active treatment, it was only the start. Severe obsessive-compulsive disorder (OCD) emerged and, lastly, attention deficit disorder (ADD). In the fall of her junior year, symptoms finally stabilized with medicine. Now, in her senior year, enmeshed family dynamics had become the primary treatment issue.

Dad excused away his genius daughter's dependence and eccentricity. She didn't clean her room, do her laundry, or prepare food for herself. She had no interest in driving and had never held a job. She had no friends and had never dated. Even with symptoms controlled, her eye contact was poor and she spoke only when spoken to.

She did, however, have goals: "I'd like to drive. I'd like to date." These were achievable. She also wanted to work for the military. To that end, she was taking advanced math and physics electives at the graduate level, online, through McGill University in Montreal. Addressing the gap between present reality and the skills needed to achieve that goal was a long-term project, with an uncertain outcome.

Jordyn Makes Her Move

Flashback 1, this past January, before I broke my molar.

After almost a year of doing well on a long-acting stimulant for her ADD, she demanded I change her back to short-acting. "I just like it better." That was Jordyn's story and, no matter that I'd explained— three times— why it wasn't a good idea, she stuck to it, like a burr to a wool sock.

We looked at each other. She leaned forward in her seat, hands clenched on the arm rests, with the alert look of someone prepared to keep going indefinitely. This was the first time she had been this engaged. I, on the other hand, was drained. Why? Because she was dominating me— or trying to, anyway. Diagnosis: Power Struggle. Treatment: The Talk.

Outside, a city snowplow rumbled by. A dog barked down the street. The sound machine on the floor outside the office door white-noised. I gathered myself.

"Listen to me, Jordyn. I'm not repeating myself again. Bottom line, your functioning has only gotten better on the long-acting." *And there's less risk of abuse with it.* Her press for short-acting was setting off alarm bells.

"Furthermore," I said, studying her expression closely, "your only argument to change back to short-acting is that you like it better. You can't tell me why. That's not clinically persuasive. I'm not restarting it."

Her eyes flashed, exactly like our med school cat's eyes had when prowling the apartment looking for, and not finding, the bird she had brought in.[30]

Oh boy. She opened her mouth, but I raised my hand in the universal "stop" gesture. "So, now you have a choice to make." She closed her mouth.

"You can do what I recommend and treatment continues. Or you don't, and treatment ends."

She glared, leaned forward, and raised her voice: "You can't make me take long-acting!"

I looked her in the eye and waited a beat. "Of course not. That's my point."

She shook her head, as if to straighten up what was jumbled in there.

"Jordyn, I'm not family and I'm not a friend. Our relationship is professional. You've consulted me for my expert opinion about your problem and how to help you with it. We *are* in agreement that I know more about these meds than you, yes?"

She nodded, grudgingly.

"Good. Until today, we've been of like mind. Now, we're in conflict. Like I said, if you want to stay in treatment, I'm keeping you on long-acting. If you don't want to take it, we're done." Again, her eyes flared. Could she be abusing? Was an addiction emerging? *Please, no.*

A long pause, then a sullen "Okay."

Time to throw her a bone. How could I affirm her sincerely? "You know Jordyn, this is the first time we've butted heads. I'm impressed by your tenacity."

---

[30] Hubby had caught and released the bird outside.

She smiled. That was a first, too. "Really?"

"Really." I nodded. "You were totally on task and showed great energy. I'd say your depression has definitely lifted. Give the long-acting a chance."

I Blurt

Flashback 2, late April, after the first, but before the second antibiotic course.

Jordyn's treatment had proceeded without incident until I walked into the waiting room and saw her father— *Oh no.* My jaw throbbed. My right ear ached. My eyelids hung heavy. Jordyn herself sat as still and blank as a statue in the armless chair, hands clasped on her lap, feet close together. She was wearing an oversized gray sweatshirt, matching sweatpants with PINK emblazoned in college font on one thick thigh, and dirty sneakers.

He jumped up. "May I join you?" Mindful of HIPAA privacy regulations, I glanced at Jordyn, now twenty-two years old. It was her call.

"Jordyn?" She shrugged. In my clinical office, she took the upholstered chair opposite mine. Dad took the couch end closest to her, farthest from me. He sat upright with modest man-spread and clasped his hands in his lap.

It was late afternoon and the light filtering in through the shades of the two south-facing windows had dimmed. I walked through the space between them to turn on the floor lamp in the corner, the light making the diplomas on the wall pop, and me flinch. The leaves of the potted peace lily beside the lamp's base gleamed. I looked away and saw that he was watching me; she wasn't.

I smiled at him, "Excuse me," and with a few steps took my seat. "Much better. Now we can see each other."

Dad clasped and unclasped his hands, staring at me. He was slim and proper in his khakis, button-down shirt, tie, and v-neck wool sweater, thick hair brushed neatly from a side part. *What was wrong?* Jordyn sat stiffly with forearms on the armrests, staring into the middle distance.

"How is everything?" I asked.

He darted a glance at Jordyn, who didn't look at him, and said, "Her medicine isn't working!"

"It isn't?" I looked at Jordyn in surprise. She didn't respond.

"You have to change her back to the short-acting! Her grades have dropped!"

They had? She hadn't told me that either. I said to him, "I agreed to change her to long-acting—when was it? About a year and a half ago?— after you made a compelling argument for it. It was clinically sensible. If long-acting works, it's always a better choice."

He nodded and looked down, wringing his hands. "I know."

"Jordyn, you agreed to the switch, too." She nodded.

"Well," he said, agitated, "I wish I hadn't. Jordyn says you refused to discuss changing her back." He looked at his hands wringing themselves, and clamped one down on the other.

Refused to discuss? My eyebrows jumped to my hairline and my eyes shot to Jordyn. "Tell your dad about our January session."

She looked at me without expression.

Come on! "We spent forty-five minutes beating it to death."

I turned to her father. "I was really impressed. She advocated passionately for herself." I turned back to her. "Remember?"

"No."

The kid had a steel-trap memory! I stared at her, plump and ramrod straight in the chair. She'd lied to her father when she was depressed her freshman year. *Now, as a senior, she was lying again. Why?*

The band tightened around my head. The pressure increased behind my eyes. The ache through the right side of my face—jaw, mouth, and ear— bloomed. I had to confront her, but I couldn't do it now. I just didn't have the energy to do it therapeutically. Another opportunity would present itself. People always repeat their coping strategies. Liars keep lying.

I summarized that January session for Dad and turned to Jordyn, "Just how much have your grades dropped?"

She returned from wherever she'd drifted. "My GPA is down from a 4.0 to a 3.8." She glanced at her father.

"See!" he said to me, jerking forward a little and involuntarily twitching his hands apart.

"That's not much of a drop," I said to the room at large. "How do you explain it, Jordyn?"

"I—"

"It's terrible!" Dad interrupted her. "Her GPA is always a 4.0. You have to put her back on the short-acting! I'm sorry, I don't mean to tell you how to do your job but..."

I gave him a penetrating Look: *Oh, but YOU DO.* He looked away and reclasped his hands, tight.

"Jordyn, you were going to speak?" I said.

He looked at her, his hands coming apart again. He leaned forward, anchoring a hand on each knee, "Excuse me, I'm sorry to interrupt—"

She shrugged.

He turned his head to look at me, his gaze focused like a laser, and said: "You. Need. To. Put. Her. Back."

I stared back: *No. YOU need.*

His eyes blazed: *DO IT. DO IT. DO IT.* I boiled over, just like a simmering pot does when the burner is jacked up from medium to high heat.

"Look," I said through clenched teeth. "I've gone over why I think it's a bad idea. With Jordyn in January. With you now. There are other psychiatrists who might see it your way. Or," I hissed, "prescribe it yourself." I leaned forward, glare dialed up to maximum voltage, "I'm. Not. Doing. It." I bared my teeth. He jerked back on the couch.

He thought he could run me! I'd agreed to his one suggestion, and now he presumed he was in charge. Well, he wasn't the first to make that mistake and he wouldn't be the last. I leaned back and slowed my breathing. My cheeks burned. My head had swollen tight and I was yanking my right ear lobe. I dropped my hand and took in his stare, which ferried the fury of a privileged medical man and father unused to be being crossed. He went right for the metaphoric jugular.

"I will not prescribe for my daughter," he said flatly, staring at me with distaste. "That would be wrong. I'm shocked you suggest it."

I deflated with a sigh. He was right. It was appropriate to set limits, but *not with an uncontrolled blurt. God. What was wrong with me?* My head pounded like a punishment. I'd offended him and lost his respect, too. Now I had to clean *that* up, adding to the work already at hand. I breathed deeply, in and out, in and out. He was just taking care of his daughter. He was entitled to be demanding. *I* was the one out of line.

I looked into his condemning eyes, "Yes, it *would* be wrong. I'm very sorry I said it." I meant it. There was a long pause. His eyes softened. I took a relieved breath.

"Let's back up. I guess I'm not understanding why you're so worried about Jordyn's GPA," I said to him. "It might have dropped two tenths, but 3.8 is still excellent."

'It's mid-terms!" He practically ground his teeth. "Science careers at the Pentagon are very competitive!" *The Pentagon?* Her GPA was the least of her problems with regard to those shark-infested waters. *Not going there.*

"Jordyn, has your ability to focus and concentrate worsened?" She shook her head no. "Are you sleeping?" She nodded yes. "Eating?" Another nod. "Are you more distractible?"

She hesitated, smiled a tiny private smile, and drifted off. I waited, but she was done.

"Jordyn?" She came back. I smiled, "Where'd you go? You were smiling."

She glanced at her father. "Well… I have a boyfriend."

My jaw dropped. "You do? Since when?"

"About six weeks."

"How'd you meet?"

"At the Dairy Queen. He works the window."

"Hold on! You're driving?"

She nodded. "I got my license two months ago." *OMG.*

"Congrats! That's wonderful." My irritation had evaporated. I was thrilled for her.

"She's been getting up at five in the morning to drive him to work," Dad added.

"You? Miss Get-up-at-the-crack-of-noon?"

She smiled that little smile. Was that a blush?

"Motivation," I said. "Makes all the difference, doesn't it?" I smiled at Dad, who smiled back— *Oh nice!*— and turned back to Jordyn.

"How much time are you spending with him?"

"I drive him to work and pick him up after I'm done with classes Monday, Wednesday, Friday. We text every day. We go out once over the weekend. He lives at home, too."

"So, let me ask you. Is the time you're giving him time you previously used to study?"

She went still. His mouth rounded, "Oh!"

She nodded. "I guess it is."

"So…. You're spending less time studying, more time socializing, and your GPA has dropped from a 4.0 to a 3.8." Nods from both.

"Guess what? That's not a medical problem. It's a time management problem. You'll get the hang of it with practice."

"I never thought of that!" Dad smiled.

Mess cleaned up. My authority re-established. Parent happy. Patient fine. Good work, right? I was exhausted.

They left and I lay down on the couch with my eyes closed for an M & M conference[31] with myself. *What the hell! You lost your temper. IN SESSION.*

That was so utterly unlike me. In fact, it had never happened before.[32] Panic shot through my belly and my hands clenched, hot through my blouse. *Not that he didn't need to be put in his place. He did, but Oh. My. God.* A groan escaped me.

If only I could un-say: Prescribe for her yourself. If only I hadn't shown him my teeth, wolfish. Yes, he'd invaded my space. Yes, I had to protect my territory, but still— Wait. Wait a minute. *Jordyn. She'd witnessed it.*

I imagined myself in her chair, watching me spar with her father. If *I* found it hard to push back against him, how much harder would it be for *her*? Much, much harder. It came to me. *That's why she lies.*

Perhaps being so unpolished and harsh had cost me his respect—I groaned involuntarily again—but *maybe it had been therapeutic for Jordyn* to observe me shut him down. The next step in the treatment presented itself. At twenty-two, she needed to separate from him, become independent, become her own woman. I'd tell them both at the next session.

---

[31] A medical heart to heart (see glossary).
[32] Well, with Mom and Hubby, yes. As a professional, no.

Flashback 3, April, last week's session, half way through the ten-day course of penicillin.

But Jordyn came alone and was her usual withdrawn self.

"Your dad has your best interests at heart, and he also has firm ideas about what you need. Ideas you may not agree with." She nodded.

"I had a hard time pushing back against him. I bet you do, too." She nodded.

"Call me yourself from now on. When you have a question about your medicine, when you need to change an appointment, whatever. And from now on, let's meet, just us, without him."

She'd shrugged.

Back to May Day, at the vet's. The tech took Poodle Oodle back for her allergy shot and I called the office.

"Hi, it's me," I said when Kathy picked up. "Was I supposed to see Jordyn this week? Did she cancel?"

"Let me see," she said. I listened to the *tap tap tap* of her fingers on the keyboard as she searched the scheduling program. I knew the answer before she spoke.

"Yes, you were supposed to see her yesterday but she left a voice mail cancelling. Didn't say why. Didn't ask for a call back either." *She's dropped out.* "It's mid-terms," Kathy said. "Maybe she had a scheduling conflict?"

"Maybe…. Give her a call. Ask her if she'd like to reschedule." I knew she wouldn't.

The vet's office was in a strip mall anchored by a grocery store. I pulled out of the parking slot to the exit, Poodle Oodle curled on the passenger seat like a fuzzy gray comma. When I squinted against the sun, pain knifed through my right ear and jaw. The headache pulsed electrically, blue cold-hot. Heavy-duty medicine, a big glass of water, and a lie down in the dark sang like sirens from the house. But first, I had to drive there.

Up ahead to my left, on the sidewalk in front of the grocery store, chatting with a short, stooped old man, stood a tall, heavyset woman. *Dana?* My stomach dropped. *God.* Keeping my eyes straight ahead, I whizzed past, praying she didn't recognize me, or the car. She was the type that would. A wave of nausea washed the back of my throat. Heat rolled through me and I broke out in a sweat.

Whipped by a loose end...

Flashback to Dana's treatment, two years ago, December, when darkness fell by 4:30. I had been so glad to hear from Dana's oldest son, the "nice" one. At the end of that summer, after several weeks of emergency appointments and many calls to my pager to cope with breakthrough panic, Dana missed an appointment and disappeared. I left voice mails. I called the emergency room and the morgue. I checked the obituaries. Nothing. Months had gone by between that missed appointment and this call from her son.

"Thank you so much for getting in touch," I'd said, pressing the phone to my ear with one hand and twisting the cord with the other. "I've been so worried!"

"We had to put our mother in rehab. To get her off the medicine you got her hooked on," he snapped.

My jaw gave. Sitting at my administrative desk, my eyes wandered. Over the computer monitor in front of me and the charts stacked next to the phone. Out the window, across the shadowed lawn littered with leaves and the yellow triangle of streetlight thrown across both lanes of the road. From the next room, I could hear the muted rise and fall of Kathy's voice checking out Hubby's patient. Poodle Oodle, in her bed under the desk, put her head on my foot.

I swallowed, "Excuse me?"

"I said. She's. Been. In. Rehab. She's an Addict. Thanks to you," he spat in my ear. Again, I was speechless.

For fifteen years, I had prescribed Dana a benzodiazepine. The symptoms of Dana's panic and post-traumatic stress disorders had responded fairly well, with intermittent flares, to a combined medication regimen of the benzodiazepine and an antidepressant. Simultaneously, psychotherapy had helped her process her traumatic childhood, her enmeshed relationships with her two adult sons, and her abusive marriage to their father whom she'd divorced before she came in for treatment.

My mind raced. Benzodiazepine is chemically similar to alcohol and carries the same risk of abuse. But she had never "lost" a script after filling it, had never run out of meds early, had never manifested the tells which alert a clinician that addiction is encroaching.

The accusation was vicious and unfair, and there was nothing I could say that wouldn't sound defensive. So I didn't try.

"I'm glad Dana is OK."

"She's not OK! I've had concerns for years you've been overmedicating my mother," the son hissed in my ear. "I wish I had spoken up sooner!"

"Yes, I wish you had, too," I said, glad to lob that one back over the net. "That would have been helpful."

"You should have—" he started, but I interrupted.

"Please ask Dana to call me to set up an appointment. I really want to see her."

"Appointment! She's not making an appointment. She's never coming back!"

I let a couple beats go by. "Thank you for letting me know." I listened to his breathing and accepted it. "Goodbye." I hung up.

I bowed my head and pressed my hands to my eyes— everything went black, tinged with red. I had missed something. Dana, an addict. Unbelievable. Part of me *didn't* believe it. A decade and a half, over. Just like that.

Home at last. Same day, May Day.

Pulling into my driveway, I turned off the ignition and sat. Jordyn had dropped out because of me. *That stupid blurt.* Dana, an addict, *because of me.* I dropped my forehead to the steering wheel, sick to my stomach. Poodle Oodle pawed my thigh to open the car door. I couldn't pick my head up. Tears burned under my eyelids.

How easy it was to miss something critical. To slip, despite the best intentions, rigorous self-examination, and deep thinking. *Maybe it's time for me to stop practicing. I'm never going to get it right. Maybe I'm not up to carrying the responsibility any more.*

I let Poodle Oodle out into our fenced back yard and called the office. "Yes," Kathy said. "I spoke to her father. He said Jordyn's seeking treatment elsewhere. That the two of you had discussed it at her last session."

I sucked in air. *She'd lied!* My face was killing me. The weight of the migraine was crushing my head. I had to lie down.

Reality Check

"I need to run something by you," I said that night to Hubby. We sat catty-corner to each other at the kitchen table, eating a dinner cobbled together from leftover chili and sautéed veggies. Well, he was eating. I couldn't. Thank God Son was doing his college thing and hadn't come for dinner. I had Hubby to myself.

He looked at me with kind eyes. "What's up?"

I respected Hubby. He'd be honest with me. I pushed the plate and my shame away. I told him about Jordyn and Dana (without their last names, of course). "Maybe I should retire. Do something else."

He goggled, as if I'd turned a violent shade of green—which, actually, was just how ghastly I felt. He shook his head. My hands resting on the table trembled. He took the one closest to him and squeezed it, smiling. "Are you kidding? Couple of weasels! You're well out of it."

"What?" Relief washed through my queasiness. "Really?"

"Come on." He squeezed my hand again. "Notice how they both used a third party to dump you. That's not psych illness. That's who they are. They get other people to do their dirty work. 'Character is destiny.'"

Yeah. That's right. "Good old Freud," I said. The original anger stirred a touch, the despondency receded a bit, and a hot nausea welled up. "But—" I glanced at him, then looked away. I could hardly say it.

"What if… what if…," I gulped down a spurt of thin saliva, "what if… my prescribing unleashed addictions in both of them?" My gorge rose with the horror of it. I swallowed down hard.

"Come on," Hubby said again. "Dana gave no clinical signs of addiction. Why are you taking her son's word for it? You don't actually know what happened. Dana didn't call you." *Yes. That's right.*

"What about Jordyn?"

Hubby shrugged. "You did everything you could. You refused to switch her back to short-acting. She sicced her father on you. That failed. Then you banned him from the treatment. She got it: her tactics weren't going to work. But notice how she left. *He* told you she wasn't coming back. She didn't tell you herself."

"Right. Right."

"God help her father," Hubby said. "A high IQ plus lying means trouble."

"But the blurt!"

"Yeah, well. That *was* unfortunate. So what? We can always do things better. Even if you'd been perfect, I bet nothing would have changed. She knows how to play him."

"But Dana," I moaned. "Fifteen years!"

He looked off into space for a minute. "Look, for all you know, working with you…. Maybe she wasn't taking as much of her sons' crap. Maybe that got her in trouble with them." He grinned at me and laughed. "You're such an instigator!" *I love Hubby.*

"Or maybe she used her son to get rid of you for some other reason." He paused, thinking.

"How much do patients actually tell us anyway?" He looked at me. "They dole out info on a need-to-know basis. Good old need-to-know."

Yeah, that's right. We're always working blindfolded and ear-muffed. "True," I nodded and gasped from the resulting wave of pain.

"I know I shouldn't feel sick over it, but I do." My head was too heavy to hold up. It was a relief to let my forehead rest on the hard coolness of the table, to let my eyelids drop.

"Sweetie!" Hubby shook my shoulder gently. "Look at me."

I lifted my head up, the skin under my chin and neck pulling painfully. My eyes closed involuntarily against the light from the rice paper chandelier hanging over the table. "Check out the golf ball," I said and tilted my chin up a little more so he could see it.

He looked askance, then palpated it gently.

"Ow!"

He pulled his fingertips away. He laid the back of his hand on my forehead. "You're burning up!"

Dental Disaster

I lay in bed for two weeks, septic. Bacteria under that new crown had drilled through my jaw in the one spot hidden from x-rays and CTs. That explained the golf ball; the headaches, jaw and ear pain; my poor self-control and depressive self-doubt.

I knew I was sick, but not *how sick*. It didn't occur to me that my mind was affected because my brain—the organ—was impaired. Therefore, my mind—its function—was, too.

Stress, no matter the cause, siphons off energy. On the most basic level, that translates into exhaustion—physical and mental. We default to a less controlled, more emotional place. As energy was deployed to battle the infection, there was less available to finesse my feelings and behavior and to put things in perspective.

The space between life and death is porous, and the flow of energy traveling back and forth a negotiation between forces outside of awareness. It's shocking to consider how easily, without antibiotics, my energy might have flowed out into the void. It's terrifying to acknowledge that it's possible to lose contact with the part of your brain that knows what's going on *and not know you've lost it.*

It's folly to assume your mind and your ability to reason is constant. It's not. You can't always count on your perceptions, feelings, thoughts, and conclusions, especially when ill. It's not a personal failing but a limitation of the body, specifically the brain. There is no escape.

When I was twenty-six, I married Hubby and started medical school. Of the two decisions, Hubby has proven more consequential to the quality of my life. I find this ironic. There is no formal training for choosing a life partner.

He accepts my tendency, especially when stressed, to take responsibility for outcomes beyond my control, the dark underbelly of conscientiousness. He also accepts my tendency to keep going physically when I shouldn't. He reminds me that all I can do is my best and that sometimes it's best if I stop. I believe him because I trust him.

Thank God I shared my shame and pain with him. When he felt my forehead, I came to. He'd exposed the fever *and* the false operating premise that had driven me to keep working. It wasn't incompetence making me sick; I was too sick to work competently.

Work is compelling, as in fascinating and meaningful, but it also compels, as in coerces. Those of us who carry responsibility for others—mothers and fathers, doctors and nurses, teachers, you know who you are—sacrifice our health, and more, for others. And what good is that? There is a limit. When necessary, we must go to ground, to the ground of being, to heal when ill and recharge when drained, in order to rise once more from the ashes to resume our work. But we can't do that alone.

We *all* need one person who loves us and whom we truly trust to be our back-up brain when ours browns out. That's a comfort and the only security, such as it is, in this unpredictable life.

Despite His Best Efforts, Hedley Gets Cheryl to the Dance on Time
Mid-October

It was a gorgeous Saturday afternoon, about five-thirty. The Twinkle Toes were driving to a seven o'clock ballroom dance class in a town across the lake. The first half hour of the ride traveled rural routes; the second half hour, interstate, with exits ten to fifteen minutes apart.

Who were the Twinkle Toes? Terence and Cheryl. Hedley and Donna. Hubby and me. We were all seasoned professionals in our respective fields and, with our twenty-ninth anniversary behind us, Hubby and I were the newly-weds of the bunch. Cheryl and Terence actually practiced between lessons. I wanted to, but Hubby made it clear that attending class asked enough. Hedley insisted weekly he couldn't dance on an injured left foot. Donna just smiled.

Hedley was driving Donna's van, with Cheryl riding shotgun. I sat in the middle row with Terence. Donna and Hubby were in the way back. The ferry ride across the lake was glorious—snow-capped mountain vistas, ducks bobbing on the slate blue water, golden sun and super fresh air—the sort of thing travel agents gush about. Driving through country aflame with fall foliage, we passed a gas station. Donna called from the way back to Hedley, "You'd better fill up."

Hedley glanced at the dash, "It'll be OK," and drove on. Donna raised an eyebrow.

Just past the halfway point of the journey, Hedley interrupted animated conversation to announce, "I'm losing power," and pumped the accelerator. Slowing inexorably, the van crested the hill, then coasted down. Hedley bumped it to a halt on the side of the highway. There was a respectful moment of silence.

Donna: "We're out of gas. I told you to get gas."

Hubby: "Get out of town! We're out of gas?" in a tone that sang, *O Frabjous day! Callooh! Callay! No dance today!*

Cheryl looked at her wristwatch. "Hedley. Are we out of gas?"

"I guess so. The needle isn't all the way on empty though. Maybe it's something else."

Donna: "That gauge isn't accurate. I drive this car all the time. That's why I told you to get gas. We're out of gas."

Hubby: "We have to find a gas station, bring back some gas." With that Hedley hopped out of the car. Hubby followed to slow progress. His cowboy boots weren't made for walking. Hedley bounded like a mountain goat through waist-high grass up an incline topped by a guardrail, beyond which lay the yellow brick road to carbon-based fuel. Hubby slogged behind. They disappeared from view.

Donna: "Maybe we should call AAA."

Spirited discussion erupted: How long should we wait for the guys before calling? Where were we anyway? Assuming AAA could locate us, how long would it take them to reach us? How far away was the nearest gas station? (We had phones, none of them smart.) It didn't look good for getting to class on time.

"I'll call Hubby. Maybe they've already lucked out." The call went directly to voice mail. I sighed. "He left his phone at home. Of course."

Donna: "Hedley didn't bring his either."

Me: "Great. The two people in the group without phones are out who knows where, for who knows how long."

Cheryl: "Maybe we should have made a plan." Wild female laughter.

"We have to get to class by seven," Cheryl took charge. "Time to call AAA."

Terence: "What about Hubby and Hedley?"

Cheryl: "They're on their own. We're getting to class on time." More wild laughter.

Donna pulled out her AAA card, dialed, and handed the phone to Terence. "Here. You have the best sense of direction. You talk to them." He tried, but the operator spurned him: no password. Just as Donna was delivering her mother's maiden name, Cheryl called out, "I see Hedley! I think he's got something red in his hand!"

We gave Hedley and the red gas can a hero's welcome. Hubby gimped up behind him. Hedley emptied the can into the tank, turned the key in the ignition, and the engine turned over. Cries of joy.

Hedley did the mountain goat thing up the hill to return the gas can to the ever-ready homeowner who'd loaned it. Ten minutes later, we were on the road. Cheryl consulted her watch: six-thirty. Tight, but now looking good.

Hedley took flack and gave it right back, all very funny. Still, tension ran high. There was only a drop of fuel in the tank and still a ways to go. Smiling a Cheshire cat smile, he whizzed by the next exit: "There's enough gas in the tank, including the fumes, to get us to class."

Shocked silence. Followed by outraged screams.

Donna: "Hed! We need gas! One gallon isn't enough to get us there!"

Me: "Hedley! This is a joke, right?"

Cheryl: "Hedley! If we run out of gas, we'll miss class!"

Hedley: "But that's why I'm not stopping, Cheryl. It takes too long to get gas. I want to get you there on time."

More female shrieks all around. "Get gas! Get gas!"

"All right, all right. If you want me to," he groused. "But the needle isn't on empty any more."

Donna: "Hed! I told you! That gauge is broken!"

"I just don't want to be late," Hedley muttered, finally pulling off into a gas station. He pumped gas into the tank, got back in the car, started it up and — Where was Terence? The exterior men's room door opened, answering the question. Terence ambled back to the van to a soprano chorus of *"Come on! Come on!"*

"You did that for the drama," Hedley said as Terence climbed in. They smiled Cheshire cat smiles at each other.

We were the first to arrive at the dance studio, getting there even before the instructors. We cracked up. During the break, Hedley pointed out that he (and Hubby) had risked "life and limb knocking on the doors of strangers to beg" for the gas that got us to class on time. "I don't feel sufficiently appreciated." Cheryl and I drenched him with buckets of gratitude even as Donna drily observed that if he'd listened to her in the first place such a risk wouldn't have been necessary.

The Blue Danube started up and a stream of dancing couples flowed onto the dance floor. Hedley waltzed Donna out into the moving space, Terence and Cheryl followed, *one-two-three, one-two-three*, then Hubby and me, all three men smiling Cheshire cat smiles.

Couples fly-fishing lessons, anyone?

Pierre and Judy IV, Cassandra Syndrome Strikes Again
February

Three years had passed since Judy kicked Pierre out. In December, he'd finally moved from the motel into a rental apartment. With his retirement check, he covered his rent, utilities, phone, and medical co-pays, as well as the monthly amount he gave Judy to replenish the savings he'd burnt through. He was taking his meds and insisted he was sober. I knew he wasn't. My office manager saw him at a sports bar one night in January when she was out with friends.

"I hate to say it," she'd told me, "but he was plastered."

"Did he see you?"

"I don't think so. He was at the bar when we got there. We walked through to the bistro and I sat with my back to him. He was still there when we left. He was talking to a woman who wasn't interested." *Oh, Pierre. We have to talk.* Maybe an opportunity would present itself today.

He was often tearful in session, as he was now. "Why won't Judy let the Ina thing go? I have." His tone was less peevish and more bewildered, which told me he was slowly coming to terms with the new reality.

He'd felt crowded being married; now he had plenty of space. He'd misread Ina and pursued her against her will; she'd had him arrested. He hadn't wanted the work of considering Judy's feelings; now she didn't consider his. He'd ejected her from the center of his world; he was no longer the center of hers. Or of anyone else's.

"Are you two talking?"

"Yeah. She still looks out for me with the paperwork. But she won't let me see her." He shifted in the seat and made that *tsk* noise, a sound of dissatisfied puzzlement. "She says she likes thinking of herself first. Says she likes doing what she wants, when she wants to." He *tsk*ed again.

"She's taken up tap dancing again. She's been performing with her teacher and a few girls." He paused. "Around the area. At fundraisers." His forehead corrugated. "Says she likes it, makes her feel good." He *tsk*ed and shook his head, hard, as if to get water out of his ear.

Poodle Oodle, lying next to him on the couch, lifted her head up and sneezed. "Bless!" he said absently. She settled her head back on her front paws and looked across the room at me.

For a few moments he was pensive, staring inside. When he looked up, I suffered a moment of hope he'd had a productive insight. His face split with a grin. "I saw this hot girl at Starbucks today who looks just like Ina! Only she was with some guy."

The Drill
March

"Your painting is great. I hate my painting! It sucks! Yours is so good— I'm going to slash it with a knife!" An incredibly loud, incredibly penetrating, nasal soprano drilled itself into my ears from behind, stopping me at the door on my way out. That voice, combined with a jackhammer delivery, had made me jump many a time. The Drill did it on purpose.

The hubbub of fifteen people putting on coats, talking, shuffling canvases off table easels, and scraping chairs died down to a ringing silence. Twisting towards the room—paint encrusted brushes in one hand, container with paint-thick water in the other—I looked over my shoulder at her. She stared at me from behind her painting on the table, hand on one hip, daring me to respond. My painting stood all alone on its easel a couple spots down.

I was sick of her. She'd harassed me with her envy for a couple years. The classes happened irregularly, but still, even one class ruined by this nonsense was one too many. They were held at our local art center on Wednesday evenings and led by a local artist and author, my friend Amy. Monet and Merlot, Van Gogh and Vino, Picasso and Pinot Grigio, no experience necessary, materials and vino included, two hours of enjoyment. Unlike the Paint and Sips held at a local bar, these were real art classes. Amy was an excellent teacher, with a deceptively simple method.

Tonight we had copied Van Gogh's "Starry Night." First we'd penciled in the basic shapes. Then we painted over the lines in black or blue paint that Amy squeezed out in small dollops onto our paper plate palettes. Roughing out of the core shapes *just as I saw them*, not as I "thought" they should look, caused my know-it-all mind to start screaming—*That's wrong! Wrong!*

After that, Amy doled out one or two other colors, instructing us to paint in the areas containing only those shades. This also caused a desperate shouting in my head: *You're messing it up! You need yellow! You don't have yellow!* All around me, everyone else was having the same anxiety attack, out loud.

Again, painting individual colors in this way forced me *to see what was actually there*, not what I "thought" was there. Amy gave us colors in a specific sequence, usually from dark to light—"Do what Bob Ross says, 'Go to the light!'"—with the lightest color at the end, for highlights.

In addition to these constraints, I imposed a deadline on myself: I had to finish by the end of class. This made the voice in my head even more frantic: *You can't leave it like that! Fix it! You need more time! You'll never finish!* But I knew if I slowed down to correct anything, I definitely wouldn't finish. And if I didn't finish in class, I knew I wouldn't go back to it at home.

The day we copied a Frida Kahlo still life with fruit and parrot convinced me my Inner Bully knew nothing, *nothing,* about painting. I made up my mind to stop listening to her. (Though of course I continued stressing.

Screaming is hard to ignore and change is slow.) With only ten minutes left, I had a *third* of the painting still to finish. (I had spent way too much time on the parrot.) I swept my eyes over the whole, focused on what was left to do, dismissed the embellishments and painted in the essentials with the broadest of strokes. I "finished" only because time ran out. *Horrible! The worst!*

Amy said it was one of my best, especially the part I brushed in last. So strange. What was that about? I was hooked. I became a regular, along with The Drill and a few others. A big part of Amy's job was soothing and reassuring everyone that their painting was coming along just fine. With time, I became more comfortable with the discomfort. When the susurration of people's self-criticism would start, I'd paint without pause (unless I missed the rinse water and put my brush in my drink). I had a lot to do if I wanted to meet the deadline.

"Stand up and walk around," Amy would say. "See what other people are doing. Get ideas. Steal from each other!" That's how The Drill started in on me. She'd stand behind me as I soldiered on and power her metallic screws through— *brzzt brzzt brzzt*, "Hers is so good! Mine sucks! I hate mine!" At first, I'd just give her a *Cut it out!* look over my shoulder. After a few classes of the same, I turned around with a frown and said, "Don't be like that. This is supposed to be fun." Didn't work.

Amy would call the time to end the class and instruct us to turn our paintings on their table easels to face the front of the room. Tonight was no different. We'd strolled through the "exhibit," murmuring in appreciation of others' work and shaking heads in dissatisfaction at our own.

We're all so critical, I thought. *So competitive. What does it matter how it turns out? Not one of us is any "good." The point is to learn something. Discover something new. Maybe, even...* enjoy *it.* I learned from reading Lynda Barry[33] that making art is another way of thinking, a way that speaks with images instead of words. Making art isn't about producing a *thing* that others judge as good or bad. It's about having an *experience.*

"You've all copied the same painting, but look, they're all so different and so amazing!" Amy said. "Now line up, holding yours. I'm going to take a photo!" she said in her schoolteacher voice and everybody laughed. Being short, The Drill and I knelt in the front row. Amy, also short, stood on a chair to get us all in and shouted, "Say Vincent!"

So now, class photo taken, just as everyone readied to go, I got it — The Drill, in her way, *was* bullying me. She wouldn't — couldn't let me be. Ignoring her hadn't made her slink away as I'd hoped, instead it had made her snarl and snap. I turned to face her, went completely still and looked her in the eye. The room was silent, everyone holding their breath. She had frozen too, everything about her on high alert.

I narrowed my eyes to slits. *Slash my painting? No way, José.* A sepia movie scene superimposed itself: high noon in front of the town saloon; sheriff and bad guy face

---

[33] See the Recommended Reading list in the Appendices.

off, hands hovering over holstered pistols; soundtrack, *The Good, the Bad and the Ugly*.

The silence deepened around us. I let it stretch as I considered my options. Her expression and body shifted subtly from pugnacious to uneasy, as if she were a repeat-offender kid standing before the principal waiting for the inevitable. Just like that, I knew she'd been that kid. Was still that kid. It was comical. I knew what to do.

Keeping a straight face, I said in a soft voice, so low she had to strain to hear me, "Excuse me?"

She didn't move. She didn't breathe.

"Did you say... you're going *to slash* my painting with a *knife*?"

The Drill was a tiny woman, four-foot-something in high wedges, busty and curvaceous with a hand-span waist, huge brown eyes, and bravado for days. She didn't walk, she sashayed. Now, she forced a grin and nodded, both hands on her bodacious hips, sticking her chest out and chin up.

"That's what I thought," I said even more softly, dropping my voice into an even lower register, channeling Clint Eastwood's squinty-eyed coiled menace. Expressionless, keeping my eyes glued to hers, I growled, "That... would... be... a... very... bad... idea."

She didn't move, but I felt her shrink back nonetheless. Then she rallied with a toss of big hair.

"Oh yeah? What'll you do to me? Have me arrested? You a cop?"

I gave her an evil grin and shook my head —*you have no idea*—looking slowly around the room for maximum drama. A crowd of wide eyes stared back. I let my eyes land gently back on hers.

"Nooo. Something worse." I paused. "Much.... Much worse."

She laughed, nervously. "What?"

I shook my head. "Cut my painting and you'll find out." I broke eye contact and turned to Amy with a smile. "Thanks for another great class." I looked around. "See you all next month."

The group exhaled as one, then separated into individuals talking, gathering up stuff, and putting on coats. Jenna, a retired elementary school teacher, paused on her way out the door and put her hand on my arm. She tipped her head with an eye roll in The Drill's direction, "Boy, I'm glad she doesn't like *my* paintings."

I laughed, with an eye roll of my own. "Yeah, I'm a martyr to my art."

Smiling, we walked out together. In the bathroom, I washed out the brushes and water container. The Nasty, the Nice, and a Victory, all in the last five minutes. Back in the classroom, I put on my coat, scarf, gloves, and hat in a daze.

"I cannot believe how well I handled myself," I said to Amy as I walked her to her car, carrying one of her heavy bags in one hand, my painting in the other, and watching my step. It was dark and the sidewalk to the parking lot was hazardous with patches of icy snow. "I said and did exactly the right thing, at the right time. How often does that happen?"

We burst out laughing and said together, "Never!"

"Usually, it comes to me later," I said, giddy, "when I'm trying to get to sleep!"

"Me too," Amy grinned, popping open her hatchback. "I felt bad just standing there. What you did was perfect." I lifted the bag—plastic cups packed with brushes, water containers, paper towels, and bottles of acrylic paint—into the cargo area. "Thanks." She paused, and shook her head. "The glass of wine she drank in class wasn't her first." We hugged and parted.

The Drill was laughably respectful at the next class. Just to keep her off balance, I interrupted myself to get up, walk around, and look at everyone's work in progress. I found something in hers to sincerely compliment, but when she started whining—"I hate it! It sucks!" I jammed that with a Look and gave her my back. Then she missed a class.

At the one after that, she approached me after the group photo. I raised my eyebrows. She looked sheepish. Taking a moment to work up the courage, she asked, in her carrying voice, "What… uh, is it that you uh,…, do?" Everyone stopped talking to listen. Some of our classmates knew, but others didn't. I let the silence lengthen. *What the heck.* I smiled a dangerous smile.

"I'm a psychiatrist."

"What! A shrink?"

"Yes." I gave her The Eye. "Watch yourself. I can read minds."

She giggled. And that was that. Hostilities over. She had her charms, much like my cat from med school, and I enjoyed her the same way: alert for that playful raking of my bare ankles from under the bed skirt.

Monkey Trap

July

Monkey trap: a cage containing a banana with a hole large enough for the monkey's hand to fit in, but not large enough for fist plus banana to come out.

"I need more money for supplies," said my patient Guy.

Already? I was running late and didn't have time for this. It was hazy hot, almost noon, and a patient was waiting. I'd just rolled into the only shady slot in the office parking lot, the one next to the tall spruce tree centered in the postage stamp patch of lawn. Two high hedges fronted the street, one on each side of driveway, blocking the parking lot from view.

The open car windows let in humid air heavy with the scent of mown grass. Guy leaned down bringing his face, shiny and flushed through his unshaved cheeks, level with mine. A cloud of aromas rolled in: sweat and earth, metal, lumber and solvent. The brim of his reversed baseball cap was dark and wet, as was the neckline of his tattered tee shirt.

Poodle Oodle jumped in my lap from the passenger seat and stuck her face out the window to say hi. Guy ran his fingers through the curly gray hair on top of her head, then gently stroked under her chin. "How's the little beastie today?"

305

Before they got into it—Poodle was starting to sink on her haunches to better enjoy herself—I grasped her middle with my right hand and opened the door with my left, saying, "Excuse me." Guy stepped back. I swung my legs out and placed the pooch on the asphalt, looping the leash around my wrist.

"Let me get my bags," I said, shutting the driver door while opening the passenger side. I gave him my back and let myself scowl.

I admired Guy. (This showed positive counter-transference.) I was desperate. (This showed rationalization.) I'd hired him to put a new roof on the building. (This showed I was an idiot.) It was an obvious conflict of interest. It was egregiously unprofessional. I knew better. And yet, here I was.

The Backstory

When Hubby and I bought the property eight years before, the roof had been replaced in sections, which made sense, given the various additions.[34] We decided to redo the entire roof in one go, to save on labor and unexpected future repairs. In the last four years, three contractors had committed to the job and then bailed at the last minute. Hubby had been in charge, which caused innumerable arguments between us. I wanted it done. He dragged his feet. It made me crazy. Finally, to save the marriage, he handed the project over to me.

---

[34] The original building dated to 1830, with subsequent add-ons over time.

A fourth business was on the job in May when Guy had said, as I walked him to the check-out window after our session, "I don't know if it's my place to tell you this, but the contractor who's working on your roof doesn't know what he's doing." I went outside with him and he pointed out the various ways the work in progress was structurally unsound. My stomach sank. *Not again.*

"You know I do roofs?" Guy said. "I'd be happy to give you an estimate."

There was another problem. Thuggish youth had infested the parking lot after dark. A carful would pull in at night and park for hours, music and smoke pouring from the open windows. The trash they left behind was telling: cigarette butts, torn rolling papers, beer cans, fast food bags, and used condoms. We had two one-bedroom apartments rented on the second floor of the building and Son, in his second year of college, lived in the studio. His windows overlooked the parking lot.

"They always hide behind the taller hedge."

"Is it the same car every night?"

"I can't tell. It's dark and so is the car. It's not every night. It creeps me out that I can't see they're there until I've pulled in."

In June, around the solstice, a neighbor walking her dog after sunset (around 9:30-10 p.m.) called to let me know the parking lot was crowded with guys in hoodies, milling and mingling, smoking, drinking from cans and bottles, raucous as a murder of crows.[35]

"The word is out: your lot is the spot," the cop said from behind his bulletproof window at the police station. "We'll drive by and shine our lights in. Don't worry, they'll move along. They want a dark place out of the way." I raised my eyebrows. He nodded. "To make it really uncomfortable, put up a light that stays on all night. That'll definitely do it."

And so it was that I stuck my hand in the monkey trap by hiring Guy to install lights in opposing corners of the lot. Then I grasped the banana by giving him the roof job, which he was doing competently but with minimum speed and maximum drama. Now a month in, I was twisting this way and that, looking for a way out without letting Guy go, which I couldn't bring myself to do. I needed the roof off my to-do list, off my mind. *Gotta get it done. Gotta make it work.*

Guy was forty-two, a former emergency medical transport worker now in business for himself as a contractor and in treatment for ADD. He came from a large, extended family of local dairy farmers, who'd worked the land for generations. Physical abuse, alcoholism, and addiction dominated both sides of his family. In contrast to most farmers in our economically strapped area, his father and uncles were wealthy because they dealt drugs as part of an organized crime distribution chain between Montreal and New York. I'd been astonished.

"Oh, yeah," he'd said. "They're flat-out criminals. I stay far, far away."

---

[35] What do you call a gathering of young males up to no good? A vandal?

"Wow."

"Don't kid yourself. There's lots of struggling farmers around here making ends meet with a little dealing on the side. Pot mostly. Don't get me started about the cops and border patrol."

He was the sole survivor, i.e., only functional person: intelligent, never drug-addicted, gainfully employed, with a solid friendship circle, and married seven years to the love of his life, a school teacher in her early thirties. Of course they had their problems, but what couple didn't? He had grit. I respected the life he had built for himself against all odds.

Back in the parking lot...

"I just gave you money to buy shingles last week, Guy. What now?" I said, my voice calm and my face smooth as I pulled my bags out of the car and turned to face him.

"I put a deposit down and they should be here next week. But I need to buy flashing, lumber to replace what's rotten, paint...." His voice washed over me. Heat shimmered up from the asphalt. Poodle Oodle had wandered onto the grass and was sniffing the base of the spruce with close attention. Time was passing, and too quickly.

"I have to get inside," I said. "Write me an estimate and I'll give you a check on my three o'clock break. Also, give me the receipts for what you've already bought."

He looked down, hangdog. "I left them home. I'll bring them to our session tomorrow." I bit back my exasperation. How many times had I asked for those receipts? He always had some excuse for not delivering them. The ADD meds had helped his concentration—he was able to read now—but he remained disorganized. Managing paperwork competently, even while taking medication, is a challenge for most people with ADD.[36] I sighed.

"Okay." I turned toward the stoop to the kitchen door, our staff entrance. Poodle Oodle trotted up, ready.

"How are the lights working?" he asked, clinging. I looked across the lot at the ten-foot pole in the far corner with a wide illumination light mounted on top and then up at the building roofline, where there was another.

"Great. The lot is bright all night. Our friends seem to have moved on."

"See? I do a good job!" he grinned.

I gave him a small nod, no smile. "Gotta run. See you tomorrow." He touched his sweaty forehead in salute.

Murphy's Law Strikes Again

"My wife's left me," he sobbed the next day, bent over on the couch with elbows on knees, head in hands, his thin back shaking. "She says I'm never around and she doesn't love me anymore." He sat up breathing heavily, and with obvious effort, pulled himself together. He grabbed a tissue from the box on the end table, blew his nose and hurled the tight ball into the wastebasket beside the couch.

"I'm working so hard! For her! For us! To make our life better!" he said.

---

[36] At least in my practice.

"I know," I nodded.

A session from a few months back flashed by me with new meaning. Now I saw that Melanie, the wife, had been drifting for a while, but Guy couldn't see it. He'd been furious. "Mel got her Master Teacher certificate and she didn't call me first! She called her bestie Laura. Not only that. She spent the day with her, not me! I found out about it days later."

I'd asked then if he was worried he was losing her. "No way! We're forever!"

I studied him thoughtfully as he sat hunched over, head down, forearms on knees, hands dangling. The afternoon light through the shaded south-facing windows cast a glow on the knobby back of his neck and glossy dark hair. The air conditioner hummed in the window next to me as it cooled the room.

"Have you shared your hopes and dreams? Given her an idea of when the long hours might end?"

"No," he moaned. "I'm a horrible communicator."

Melanie had my sympathy. Deadlines never met. Expenses always underestimated. Constant scrambling and lame excuses. Guy was in trouble, and worse luck, so was I.

I had fallen—*Woe is me!*—for Guy's sales pitch. He had oversold himself. He was no pro, just a talented amateur acting as if. I needed those receipts to account for the money. I didn't think he was scamming me. More likely, he was making the expensive mistakes of a person figuring it out as he went along, while stashing receipts in a pocket here, a glove compartment there. *Dammit.* I sighed to myself. No way could I bring up those receipts today. First, he was my patient. Second, I was his client.

"Guy, don't work any more today. I don't want you hurting yourself because you're too upset to pay proper attention." *Ugh*. I had meant it clinically, but could I sound any more self-serving? No matter what I did, the hand holding the banana caught at the edge of the hole. It hurt.

He looked at me like I'd sprouted a second head. "I can't do that! I need the money! Especially now that Mel's left."

"I meant just this afternoon, after you leave here."

He shook his head. "I'll feel worse at home. Mel's moved out!" He started to break down, but caught himself. He grabbed a tissue from the box and blew his nose, a good honk, and swiped his eyes with the wad. He lifted his cap off the couch by the visor, snagged it over the back of his head and tugged the visor down, shadowing his eyes. He muttered, "What am I going to do?"

The summer wore on.

We spent his sessions processing the breakup, tracking symptoms, and tweaking meds. He doggedly proceeded with the roof, one glitch at a time. I refused to discuss business during sessions. That happened outside in the parking lot, where I became increasingly exasperated. "Give me the receipts, Guy."

He'd shake his head, stubborn. "I have to organize them."

"I'm tired of waiting. I'll organize them."

"It's not your job. It's my job. I'll have them for you Monday." Since it *was* his job *and* I didn't want to do it, I'd say okay and then once again he wouldn't deliver.

Finally at the end of August, my patience ran out. "Hand them over. No more excuses."

"I'm embarrassed. They're a mess. I don't want you to see how bad it is."

"Being embarrassed won't kill you. But *I* might. Stop tempting me." I gave him The Eye.

He laughed. "Okay, okay."

It took me two eight-hour days over Labor Day weekend to organize the pieces of paper spread to the edges of the dining room table. Hubby ate standing at the kitchen counter while I refused to make eye contact. He strolled by me with pitying looks and knowing shakes of his head. The receipts added up. All the money I'd given Guy was accounted for. It's always gratifying to tell my inner Doubter (and Hubby): *Told ya.*

Let go or be dragged.

Now it was September. Guy, like many people with ADD, was accident-prone and didn't know how to take care of his body. Overuse and inattention injuries plagued him: excruciating bursitis in both elbows, banged up knees and ankles, severe back spasms. The pain kept him up at night, which worsened his chronic sleep problems.

"Guy, you can't keep working sixteen-hour days, seven days a week." He juggled several jobs simultaneously, another thing that made me grind my teeth. *Get my roof done!*

He wanted to keep working for the money and the hell with his elbows and back. As his doctor, I wanted him to give them a rest. As his frustrated client, I wanted him get the roof on. His needs and my needs were in direct conflict. I squashed the agonized groan that wanted out.

"We have bills to pay!" He and Mel were attempting to reconcile. It was increasingly obvious from what he told me in session that Mel had both a drinking and a spending problem, a big improvement on the crack, meth, and heroin he'd grown up around… but still. Enabling is enabling, and Guy was enabling Mel by overworking. I recommended Al-Anon. "I don't have time! I can't break up my workday for that!"

Then he delivered a body blow. "You of all people can't tell me not to work!" He grimaced as he massaged both elbows simultaneously, arms crossed over his chest.

Horror overtook me: I was a significant source of his income. I helped him by employing him, but he hurt me by not delivering. In attempting to deliver, he was hurting himself. I was his doctor and doing him harm, a breach of the Hippocratic Oath. Perhaps not technically, since it wasn't the treatment that was harming him… but still. I was out of integrity.

The roof wasn't finished. The maples blazed orange-red and the birches shivered yellow. It was too late to find someone else this season. The stress of Guy's imperiled marriage made him more psychiatrically unstable, more preoccupied, and more likely to have an accident. I imagined finding Guy sprawled on his back on the office lawn, limbs at unnatural angles, ladder beside him. *I'll never get over it. I have to take him off the job. Now.*

Relief made me sag back in my seat. I'd let go of the banana! My hand was out of the cage. *Free! Free at last!* Light-headed, I looked at him. The pores on his straight nose and the individual hairs on his unshaved cheeks jumped out at me. The colors in the room pulsed brighter and richer, the edges cut cleaner and sharper. I blinked a couple times and sat up.

"You have two choices, Guy." He looked alert.

"Stop working on the roof until your primary care doc gives you the okay or you're fired."

He gaped at me. After the obligatory rant, he chose option one, which meant we were done. He wasn't getting medical clearance any time soon.

What the hell took me so long?

Your average third grader could see what I needed to do. Well, I was obsessed, i.e., unreasonable. My judgment was impaired; I rejected reality; I wouldn't budge. Think: *Stubborn as a box of rocks.* Or *Love is blind.* Granted, wanting a new roof can't compete with lust, but you get the point.

Newbies make this kind of mistake from inexperience, while I, the seasoned practitioner, made it from wishful thinking. When you have two competing duties, staying in integrity requires a solution that meets the needs of both. I'm very good at that. I'd proceeded with Guy hoping against hope a solution would come to me that would save us both, but alas, no. Some conflicts are irreconcilable. Fortunately, I came to before there was a reckoning.

The late Dick Francis noted in his crime novel *Ten Pound Penalty*, "It's the people with obsessions who do the real harm in the world." Well, we harm ourselves with obsessions, too. In fact, we're first in line.

Epilogue

If you define pleasure as cessation of pain,[37] it was a pleasure once again to work with Guy. With my needs back where they belonged, dealing with just his felt like a vacation.

The leaves fell, the snow blew, and Guy tried in vain to seduce me into giving him back the job. I always said, "I've hired someone else to finish it," and would proceed to have him examine why he persisted. He always pouted. When the geese flying high in the spring sky trumpeted their return, the pattern had repeated enough that we both found it amusing, though it didn't stop Guy from trying a new angle. It was a challenge.

"Then let me repair the wrap-around porch," he bargained.

I shook my head. "You get an A+ for persistence, but no."

"I need the money. I'll give you a great deal!"

Again, I shook my head. "No deal. For you or me. It'll always cost too much."

"What do you mean?" he asked, put out. He tugged his black fleece beanie down to his eyebrows and leaned back, resting a gentle hand on Poodle Oodle, who sat between him and his hard-used jacket in the upholstered chair before me.

"It's not the money, Guy," I said. "It's the conflict of interest. It's impossible. When I'm your client, *you're* supposed to take care of *me*. But I can't ignore your needs

---

[37] Thank you, Plato.

to let you do that because as your doctor, *I'm* taking care of *you,* and that always comes first."

"I can handle it!"

"Well, I can't." I smiled and raised my eyebrows, tilting my head a bit. He raised an eyebrow back.

I said, "Which do you want first, the good news or the bad news?"

Silence. "Uh…. The bad news, I guess."

"You're not working for me ever again."

"Aww…. No, come on," he whined. I shook my head with a rueful smile and waited him out.

"So…. What's the good news?"

I grinned. "You're not working for me ever again."

"Ha, ha."

"We're keeping our relationship simple.[38] I'm the doctor. You're the patient. It's the only way."

He exhaled loudly and stared into inner space. He shifted his weight, inhaled and stretched hugely, then collapsed, his plaid flannel shirt rumpled over his skinny hips. Poodle jumped off his chair to trot over beside mine and sat down at attention facing him.

Guy ran his eyes over my face, sizing me up. I smiled wider. *How many sessions would it take for him to let go of the banana?*

"But enough fooling around, Guy. Ready to do some work?"

He gave me a rascally grin. "What did you have in mind, Doc?"

---

[38] Ha. Too late for that.

"For starters, how's it going with Mel? Is she working her rehab?"

Breaking Gender-Specific Rules of Social Conduct Proves Effective in Stopping Inter-family Bullying, Study Reveals

By D. Essem

April, *DweebMD, Internet Medical News.* Yet another landmark study published in the esteemed science journal *Family Hell* confirms that "to make a marital omelet, sometimes a wife has to break some in-law eggs," according to I.M. Trapt, MD, primary researcher and wife. She reports that this study is the first to examine whether violating female norms of conduct in an extended family setting stops higher status females from bullying lower status females.

Power dynamics in most families mirror the cultural gender bias, Dr. Trapt says. "The men do whatever they want. The women do everything else, such as the physical work of maintaining family life, greasing the gears of interpersonal relations, and waging internecine war between themselves, which the men ignore until it becomes intrusive or entertaining."

Dr. Trapt informally observed for over a year the interpersonal dynamics at in-law family gatherings hosted by her husband's sister or mother. She noted that her sister-in-law, Wanda Bee, regularly ambushed her with nasty asides, in the way mosquitos dive-bomb one specific person in a crowd. Her husband advised her to ignore his sister, which she did.

"Silly me," said Dr. Trapt. "Ignoring people is a strategy only men are allowed." Instead of reducing the asides, her sister-in-law took offense and complained to Dr. Trapt's mother-in-law, Queen Bee, who initiated a campaign demanding Dr. Trapt apologize for hurting Wanda's feelings.

"What about *my* feelings?" Dr. Trapt said. "I asked my father-in-law to talk to Queenie, but he just shrugged and turned me down. When he said, 'I have to live with her,' I had an *aha!* moment: Queenie and Wanda were assuming *I* had to live with *them.* But if that was true, so was the inverse: *they* had to live with *me.* That's when the idea for the study came to me."

Study Highlights:

- The goal of the study was to assess which of two techniques was more effective in making Dr. Trapt's female in-laws leave her alone.
- (1) Knight in Shining Armor (KISA) method: This utilized a third party, her husband, to rescue her. Dr. Trapt employed the following strategies: screaming; sobbing; guilting ("You love them more than you love me!"); shaming ("How could you let me suffer like this?"); getting disgusted ("Grow up!"); punching below the belt ("Who are you married to? Me or your mother?"); and threatening divorce ("I don't stand in line.").
- (2) Ripples in Pond (RIP) method: This required Dr. Trapt to rescue herself. She went on strike as a working member of the female pack. The strategy was two-fold. First, she didn't enter the female social zone, the kitchen. She did no cooking, serving, or cleaning up. Second, for the duration of each event, she hung out with the men in the male social zone, the den.

The KISA method failed so utterly (Disgusted Wife Interval 100%) that Dr. Trapt abandoned it after three months to initiate the RIP method.

- The RIP method proved spectacularly effective in stopping female bullying (Confidence Interval 150%).
    - However, it also caused massive system disruption. The men were highly entertained and the women seismically appalled. (Social Hazard Risk 100%).
    - In the immediate aftermath, Dr. Trapt was loved by the men (i.e., they encouraged her to join them in the den) and rejected by the women (i.e., they acted as if she wasn't there), both favorable outcomes.
    - At four weeks, Dr. Trapt remained the darling of the men and the pariah of the women.
    - At twelve weeks, Dr. Trapt's mother-in-law formally terminated her campaign to make Dr. Trapt apologize to her sister-in-law.
    - At six months, not only had her sister-in-law stopped bullying her completely, but Dr. Trapt's pack status had gone up with both genders.
    - At one year, Dr. Trapt decided to keep her husband.

Clinical Implications:

Dr. Trapt was unimpressed by the failure of the KISA method. "Duh. Of course my husband wouldn't rescue me. The men in his family don't tangle in women's affairs. They want to live, damn them. Of course my husband sees that his mother and sister are a problem. *My* problem, not his."

However, Dr. Trapt was "so blown away" by the magnitude of the success of the RIP method, she consulted (via Ouija board) Salvadore Minuchin, MD (1921-2017), world-renowned family therapist, for help with data analysis. "The evolving nature of the results really confused me," she admitted.

Family systems theory states that if one person in the system changes, everyone else is forced to adjust against their will. "That's why Queenie and Wanda stopped talking to me, to make me behave. But they miscalculated. I left high school a long, long time ago," Dr. Trapt said, rolling her eyes. "Totally worked for me."

Dr. Trapt speculates that when Queen Bee realized that she, Dr. Trapt, could (and would) maintain her position indefinitely, Queen Bee saw the downside. "She couldn't let me keep hanging with the men. It undermined her authority and elevated mine. Besides, she needed me in the kitchen."

But why would the men encourage her to join them? That's what Dr. Minuchin helped her understand, she reports. Like her, the men just wanted family peace, "but Dr. M said they weren't getting any. Their wives may not have been talking *to* me," she said, "but *about* me? Non-stop. Made the guys crazy." Being too lazy to do anything about it themselves, Dr. Trapt said, "the guys let me have at it. Watching how I handled myself had more entertainment value than TV mud wrestling."

She reports one of the iconic moments of the war occurred during Thanksgiving. "There I was, sitting in the center of the couch in the den, father-in-law on one side, husband on the other with his arm draped over my shoulder, brother-in-law in the wing chair. We were watching the game, laughing, eating pretzels, and carrying on. Queenie came in and asked me, extremely politely, if I'd like to come help in the kitchen. I said, 'No thanks, I'm good.' She was speechless with shock. She had to choose: make a scene or go away. She went away. All three men chuckled. It was great!"

As for the boon of finding her status in the pack hierarchy elevated above her sister-in-law's? "That's all about the patriarchy," Dr. Trapt said. "A man's status always trumps a woman's. When Queenie backed down to me, her son's wife, she was choosing her son over her daughter. That demoted Wanda, who was *not* happy. But for a change, I was."

As for feeling her husband should have stood up for her, Dr. Trapt was philosophical. "It would have been romantic, but I'm no damsel in distress. Besides, it was doomed to fail. Dr. M said that even if her husband had jumped on the horse, lance in hand, armor spit-shined—which he wouldn't, being a slob—the women would have concluded I was pathetic and escalated their bullying behind his back. I don't need a hero," she said.

"What I need is a good man who's devoted to me," she went on. "He believes, without doubt, that we'll be together forever. So really, why should he put himself out if I'm not going anywhere? He figures if I get mad, I'll get over it," she said. "It's incredibly annoying, because he's right."

There are two take-home points from the study, Dr. Trapt says. One, a shrink's database has uses beyond patient care. "Be flexible," she advises her colleagues. "Use what you know to help yourself." Two, it takes backbone for women to stand up to systemic oppression. Women are encouraged to sacrifice themselves for the larger group and vilified (especially by other women) for putting themselves first. Meanwhile, men are allowed to be relentlessly selfish. "It's so unfair. But that's the way it is. Ladies, we have to push back against those of us that keep the double standard going. But also, in general, to increase fairness and stop the madness."

Limitations of the study included a sample size so small as to be non-existent, lack of control group, unbelievable social media, iffy professional consultation, and unbridled subjectivity. Dr. Trapt shrugged, "No animals were injured in the course of this study, only deserving humans."

Random Act of Shrinkage

August

Eugene, our freelance contractor, pulled into the driveway as I walked out of the garage, squinting into the sun as the door rumbled up. Nothing said summer like the swelling saw of cicadas, ninety-degree heat, and 80% humidity. The scents of hot asphalt and mown grass hovered in the still air. Crows cawed from the top of my neighbor's skyscraper spruce.

Eugene entered our lives after the monkey trap fiasco and finished roofing the office building. He did excellent work, was reliable, smart, and affordable. My life had gotten better with him in it. Projects pending for years were dropping off my to-do list, one by one.

However, it wasn't possible to just say hello to Eugene and move on. Any and all contacts ended only when I set the limit. Today was no different. He stepped out of his truck and boomed, "Hello Doc!" That was Eugene: loud, vigorous, and cheerful. Mid-forties, holey tee missing its sleeves, cut-off jeans, contractor boots, scraggly goatee, bright blue eyes—

"Eugene!" I gasped. "What's happened to you?" I waved my hand in the general direction of his face. The left side drooped grotesquely, from almost-shut eye to slack cheek to practically vertical left side of mouth.

"What? This?" He pointed to that side of his face. "It's nothing."

My jaw dropped. I stared, speechless.

"I got bit by a tick when I was walking the back property." Eugene and his long-time significant other Alice homesteaded on a big spread in the mountains west of town. "With Tulip." He tilted his head toward the truck, where his yellow lab sat in the passenger seat surveying the yard, her head stuck out the open window, mouth open in a smile and tongue flopped out. Lyme Disease was prevalent here. Anyone going out in the woods to hike, paddle, or whatever checked for deer ticks after.

"You found the tick?"

"Yeah," he shrugged. "Got the sucker off."

His blasé demeanor was starting to get to me. There's macho and then there's macho. "Eugene, you look like you've had a stroke!"

I can talk like that to Eugene. Tact blows by him. "The left side of your face looks like it melted!"

"I know," he shrugged. "It's OK."

"It's not OK!" Now I was alarmed. Eugene's IQ was sharp, but sometimes his judgment was dull. A few years ago (before I knew him), he'd almost died from a ruptured volvulus.[39] He'd had plenty of warning pain, but he'd ignored it (and Alice's screaming) by drinking. "I'm an idiot," he'd said, by way of explanation.

With that in mind, I asked, "Have you been to a doctor...? Or the ER?"

"Now you sound like Alice," he said. "I'm not going. Don't need to."

---

[39] A loop of intestine twisted around itself, causing a blockage.

"You do too need to!" I said, more alarmed. "You need an antibiotic. You've got a Bell's palsy. The bacteria are in your facial nerve, the seventh cranial nerve. Cranial, Eugene." I paused, grabbed my skull with both hands and popped my eyes cartoonishly for emphasis. "Cranium. Your *brain*."

He remained impassive. "I saw my doc," he said, without expression. Now I was totally alarmed. Eugene was always animated. Happy, pissed off, preoccupied, whatever it is, you knew what he was feeling. Normally when I gave him unwanted advice (what can I say?), he'd push back, persuasively, loudly, and with enjoyment.

"What'd he say?"

"Just to watch."

"Just watch!" I said, incredulous. "Did he see your face like it is now?"

"No," he shrugged again. "But I had the target lesion."

Now I was irritated. "Eugene, it's evolving. You have to go back to see him. Or go to the ER."

"Nah. They're not going to do anything for me."

"Since when are you a doctor? Come on. They're going to give you an antibiotic. Trust me."

"I'll be fine. Don't you worry," he said, in a tone that patted me on my little head. "Let me get started before it gets any hotter."

Utterly exasperated, I gave up, got in my car, cranked up the air and drove to work, now late. I could imagine Alice shouting at him, hands planted on her hips: "You moron!"

Eugene weighed on my mind all that day and overnight, disrupting my sleep. The next day, our interaction kept playing back like a video loop and I kept hearing the phrase *la belle indifference, la belle indifference,* like an earworm. *La belle indifference* is a technical term dating back to the psychoanalytic literature of Freud's time. It describes a patient's bizarrely unconcerned response to symptoms that should cause severe anxiety.

Not only was Eugene's indifference unsettling, reason and logic had bounced right off him. Being closed to reason is a symptom of many conditions: psychosis, intoxication, dissociation, sleep deprivation, stroke. Anything, really, that compromises brain function, like say… *infection.* Eugene's brain was full of Lyme bacteria! It wasn't working right. The indifference was a *symptom,* as was his impaired judgment. *Eureka!*

Alice picked up the phone. I explained my hypothesis. "Eugene!" she shouted away from my ear and deep into their house. "Dr. D wants to talk to you!"

"Jesus, Mary, and Joseph," she said, returning to me, her tone both fervent and disgusted. "Maybe he'll listen to you. I'm worried sick."

How to get the idea across to him, that was the question. I knew I was right, but of course he was thinking *he* was right, and that's always the rub.

"Hey, Doc, what's up?"

I presented it to him as a matter of brain science because anything to do with science fascinated him. "You should be upset about the left side of your face, but you're not. That part of your brain's been knocked out by the Lyme's. Your indifference is a symptom."

"Really?" he said, thoughtfully. "You think the bug is making me not care?"

"Yup," I said, relieved he'd caught on. "I know it's weird. It's one of those concepts that's hard to wrap your head around."

I consult to the doctors at a local nursing home to help them medically manage dementia patients whose deteriorating brains cause them to misbehave, often dangerously, both to themselves and others. It took years for these docs— all of them smart—to accept that when a person has dementia, changes in that person's behavior, emotion, thinking, personality, self-control, etc., aren't *choices* but *symptoms* of brain breakdown. We understand this intuitively when someone is drunk. Beyond that, the idea that it's possible to permanently lose your mind is too scary to consider and the mind (also a brain function) shuts down. We just don't want to go there.

I could tell Eugene got it but just to keep up appearances, he put me through a few more no-ways, what-ifs, and are-you-sures.

Then, "I'll go to the ER tomorrow."

"Go *now*, Eugene!"

"Okay, okay, take it easy."

Alice drove him there and— *Be still my heart!*— he took the antibiotic as prescribed. A couple weeks later, *la belle indifference* and the Bell's palsy vanished, no harm done. Fortunately.

ADVANCED PRACTICE

There is no end to what a living world will demand of you.
Octavia Butler

Sociopaths Do Plague Us, *A Tragicomedy of Private Practice*

In which our heroine, aka She Who Must Be Obeyed, *will be…*

Perplexed by
>Kathy, Office Manager

Disgusted by
>Mora, Assistant Office Manager
>The Evil Empire (EE), a health insurance
>A City Police Detective

Freely obeyed by
>Cherie, Office Staff
>Lucy, Office Staff

Aided by
>Janine, Freelance Billing
>Mary, Business Consultant

Backed and loved by
>Hubby, aka the Cash Cow, Spouse and Business Partner

Soothed by

Poodle Oodle, aka Zen Sage Trapped In A Poodle Body

I. Let The Games Begin

~In which our Protagonists sustain two body blows: one acutely painful, the other as yet unfelt~

Late October, 11:30 a.m.

"I don't know how to say this, so I'll just say it," said Kathy, our long-time office manager, taking a deep breath. She, Hubby, and I sat at the office kitchen table, having our Tuesday administrative meeting. She looked down and twisted a pen between her fingers, hands over her ruled yellow pad to-do list. "I'm retiring at the end of December."

I sucked in air. My life was over. I looked across the table at Hubby, who stared back at me. I had "run" the office for ten years before we hired Kathy. Hubby, while an outstanding clinician, was administratively impaired and denied it. He'd promise to do his paperwork and then wouldn't, which infuriated me and lost us a painful amount of money. Finally, I got sick of enabling him: "Either we hire an office manager or get a divorce, your choice."

Kathy was one of the 10 % that got 90 % of the work done, and she'd started young. While she had no prior experience managing a medical office when we hired her, we took the risk because she'd run her small diner restaurant in the black for ten years before she got tired of it and sold it at a profit.

"Budgeting to the penny wasn't a problem. It was employees that wore me out," she'd said to me in passing, long after we hired her. "When I got ripped off by one of the girls who'd been with me the longest, I was done."

Hubby took care of patients fifty hours a week and I managed everything else— the practice, the house, Son, the pooch— in addition to the twenty-five hours a week I saw patients. Kathy had brought us back from the brink of insolvency, freed me to spend time with Son through his late elementary, middle, and high school years, and do a little recreational sleeping.

I put my head in my hands, elbows on the kitchen table, and projected myself into a dystopian future without her. We'd have to close the practice to stay married. Hubby would have to get a job at the prison or the county mental health clinic, which he'd buck. There would be fights. *So what*? I sulked. *I've done my time. I've lost sleep, half my hair, and most of Son's childhood. It's his turn.*

"It'll be all right," Kathy broke in. I dropped my hands and sat up, chilled in my light sweater. I got up and turned on the wall heater. "Mora will be OK," she reassured us as I sat back down.

Mora was Kathy's right hand and had been with us about a year. She was twenty-three, married with one child and finishing up her college degree in accounting, one course a semester. Last July, Kathy had delegated significant financial responsibilities to her: payroll, patient collections, and the forwarding of claims information to our freelance billing agent Janine. These were Mora's strengths. Our third employee, Cherie, hired in August, could have been a therapist, she was that good with patients.

Why would we need three employees for one and a half doctors? You would not believe how much administrative work health insurance companies generate, and that excluded billing.

"I recommend you put up a timecard machine," Kathy said. "Mora's always pushing for more hours. She knows I watch when she comes in and leaves, but you'll be in session."

"Are you saying she'll take advantage?" Hubby asked.

Kathy paused, reluctant to go that far. The pause had answered the question. Hubby and I looked at each other. *Not good.*

"Let's start that while you're still here," I said. "I thought we were already doing that. What happened?"

She looked sheepish. "She talked me out of it. I told you."

Did she? I couldn't remember. If she had, it would have been on the fly, in between other things. Would I have challenged her decision if she'd presented it formally at our weekly meeting? Maybe. Probably not.

"Have Mora and Cherie start clocking in and out as of today." She nodded. "And write up descriptions of everything you, Mora, and Cherie do. No more hedging, Kathy. How long do you think that will take?"

I'd been after her forever to create a procedure manual detailing the specifics of their jobs, something she always resisted with assurances she'd get to it, and then didn't. Without it, I wouldn't be able to formally assess Mora's performance, especially dealing with health insurance companies who stonewalled paying claims for services rendered. It wouldn't take much for the practice to become insolvent and fall into chaos.

"Don't worry. There's not that much to it. It's easy."

"No, it's not easy. It's one more thing I have to do on top of taking care of sick patients. Get started. I'm not convinced Mora's got what it takes."

"We need to hire someone else to do basic filing and clerical work, don't you think?" Hubby said. "That would free Cherie to learn what Mora does now, which would free Mora to take on your responsibilities."

"Sure, if you want to spend the extra money," Kathy said.

"Good idea," I said. Sometimes Kathy nickel-and-dimed things too much. This wasn't a time to be cheap. And that's how Lucy joined the team.

Second week of December, Tuesday, 11:30 a.m.

Hubby, Kathy, Mora, and I sat around the kitchen table at the last administrative meeting of the year— and Kathy's last ever—before we closed for our annual two-week holiday break. Cherie was covering the front desk and Lucy was due in around two. I saw through the kitchen windows that it was snowing, big fat flakes falling slowly.

"How's everything going with the transition?" I asked Kathy, who sat at the head of the table.

She smiled, casting her eyes at Mora, who sat at the other end. "Good. Mora's been doing my job so well for the past couple weeks, I feel like I'm underfoot." She shook her head. "Time for me to go."

I turned to Mora, "Do you feel ready?"

"As ready as I'll ever be," she said, without inflection.

"You start as provisional office manager next week, with a three-month trial period," I said. She nodded.

"We'll meet once a month to evaluate how you're doing. We're counting on you to help us keep the practice financially healthy. It's a big job and a big responsibility." She nodded.

"You understand the hours will vary?" She nodded. "And that thirty hours a week will be the average?" She nodded again.

"Good. Starting next week, as a token of our faith in you, we're giving you a two-dollar-an-hour raise."

She nodded, again without any change of expression. Two dollars an hour more was a big raise by local standards. Kathy hadn't known to tell her. At the least, Mora should have been surprised. A pang of unease shot through me. I glanced at Hubby, sitting across me on the long side of the table. He was looking at Mora without love.

"Do you know what to do while we're on vacation?" he asked her.

"Cherie and I will come in alternate days for a couple hours to pick up voice mail, take patient calls, and take your daily phone call in. The vacation message is up."

We carried our pagers even while on vacation—we had no coverage outside of each other—but having staff at the office during the workweek, even for a few hours, stopped pages for prescription renewals and other non-emergency matters. Calling in was a way to deal with these things, on our terms. A few days in a row without the anxiety-provoking intrusion of a page was always a vacation. If, God forbid, a patient required admission, having Mora or Cherie in-house would be a huge help.

"If something's urgent, don't wait for us to call you. Go ahead and call," I said. She nodded.

"Let's see the procedure manual you wrote up," I said to Kathy. She handed over a green three-ring binder with colorful dividers labeled Payroll, Claims, Job Duties, etc. I sipped coffee and read through it. Pretty thin. I had called Janine that morning, who confirmed that Mora was filing claims on time and following up reliably. *It would have to do*, I sighed to myself.

"Well, Kathy, this is it, huh? I'm going to miss you." I studied her with envy. She wasn't even fifty! Hubby and I were both staring down the big 6-0. He would never retire, which meant I couldn't either. Even if I didn't see patients, I'd still have the office. She smiled her sweet smile, her eyes crinkling.

"Thank you for everything," Hubby said. "Here's to roasting you at the party Friday." He grinned and lifted his coffee mug, miming a toast. We had started the office tradition of taking our team and their beloveds out for the holidays the first year Kathy was with us.

She grinned back. "Be nice now."

"Don't look so damn happy," I smiled. "You must be crazy to think babysitting three grandkids under the age of four will be fun." I waggled my eyebrows and said with mock hope, "Maybe you should rethink that. Working for us would be *way* easier." She laughed.

"Cherie confirmed her boyfriend can come to the party," Mora said in a monotone.

"Oh good!" I said.

"My husband and I aren't going to make it," Mora said blandly, without looking at anyone. "My mother-in-law needs emergency surgery."

"Oh no!" we all said together. "Let us know if there's anything we can do to help." She nodded.

I glanced at the wall clock. Time to see patients. I started to rise. "Is there anything else?"

"Yes," Mora said. She slid a stack of vendor checks toward me. I scrawled my signature on the line on the bottom right of each check, then slid the stack back to her. "There you go. Thank you." She nodded, squared up the checks, picked up pad and pen, and left the kitchen first. Hubby and I looked at each other.

Outside, the wind picked up, sending gusts of snow whirling and shrub branches ticking against the windows.

II: Double Whammy

~In which our Protagonists remind themselves that revenge is a dish best served cold~

Mid-January

"Do you really want to close the practice?" Hubby asked me over a Friday night dinner at his favorite steak restaurant.

"Yes!" I said. "I'd love for you to take a job, bring home a paycheck, and support me in the style I've never become accustomed to."

"Ha." He cut up steak.

"But it would be stupid. We're flush. We've cleared our business debt and finally, finally, we're bringing in a little extra."[40]

"Moooo!" quipped Hubby. "Call me Cash Cow."

"Don't make me nag you about your paperwork."

"Your command is like an order, O She Who Must Be Obeyed!"

---

[40] Thank you, President Obama. In 2013, he passed legislation mandating health insurance companies reimburse psychiatrists at the same rate as physicians in other fields, i.e., 80 % of the allowable (see Glossary). Prior, psychiatrists were reimbursed at 50 % of the allowable. That 30 % had made a huge difference to the practice's financial health.

I stuck my tongue out at him. He blew me a kiss, forked up a piece of steak with mashed potato, and chewed thoughtfully. I followed suit, but with a flaky piece of haddock smothered in onions and tomatoes. Being with Hubby over a tasty meal was a treat.

"I don't like Mora," he said.

My stomach sank. I sighed, "I don't either. But I can't do everything!" I looked into his hazel eyes.

"You can't?" He smiled.

"Ha ha." I sighed. "Well, Kathy says she's good."

"Maybe with bookkeeping. Not with people. My patients have complained."

"Mine, too." I sighed again. Longing to close the practice washed over me. I wished I were Kathy and could just walk away. But even if we decided to close the practice tonight, it would take months and months to actually do it. And where would our patients go? There was no one to refer them to. No exit.

"I've told her to stay in back and put Cherie and Lucy up front," I said, "but she doesn't."

"Why not?"

"She says she has to cover when they're not there. The thing is, though, she under-schedules them. She takes more hours for herself than she should. More, more, more. That's Mora. And she's our most expensive employee. She's not thinking about the needs of the practice."

"I'll tell you, she's not nice to patients, and she's not nice to Cherie," Hubby said, shaking his head. He put his fork down. "I like Cherie. I don't want her leaving because of Mora."

"I'm with you," I sighed again. "But we can't demote Mora to promote Cherie. She'll leave, and Cherie's not fully trained to take over."

End of January

Mora had started as provisional office manager with the two-week holiday break and as soon as we'd reopened, the trouble began. While reliably clocking in and out was not a problem for Cherie and Lucy, Mora often "forgot," usually times when Hubby and I were in session, such as when she took lunch and when she left for the day. She would handwrite those times in on the time card.

I had spoken to her about it, stressed it was important that she use the clock, and that when she forgot, I expected her to bring me the timecard so I could sign off on it. She "forgot" to do this, too. The weeks, always too full, got away from me.

"How did your doctor's appointment go? Everything OK?" I overheard Cherie ask Mora on the last Thursday of January while they sat at the front desk behind the check-in window. I was in the back room at my administrative desk doing chart work.

"Fine. It was my yearly."

I rose from my desk and walked to the kitchen where the time clock was mounted by the exit. Mora hadn't clocked out when she left for her appointment, nor had she clocked back in. Friday morning, I checked her card to see if she'd been honest and handwritten in those times. She hadn't. She was taking advantage. At the Tuesday administrative meeting, Hubby and I put her on notice.

"You're an hourly worker, Mora. You're not entitled to leave the office without clocking out," Hubby said.

"Kathy did," she said.

"Kathy was salaried," I said. "You're not. You're setting a bad example for Cherie and Lucy. This is not office manager behavior. You're still on probation. Consider yourself warned."

Later that day, as I poured myself a cup of coffee in the kitchen, she approached me, eyes down, plucking at her fingers, prettily remorseful and dewy in her soft pink sweater, "I'll do better. I'll make it a priority to clock in and out." She looked up from under her lashes, her expression as good as saying, *Pat me on the head and say, 'There, there, dear.'*

"You do that," I said coldly. "And," I added, "don't cut payroll tomorrow until I've signed off on the timecards." I stalked away, itchy and uncomfortable.

The next day she cut the checks without having me sign off. I stood at her desk, glowering. "Sorry," she said indifferently and broke eye contact.

First week of February, Tuesday administrative meeting, 11:30 a.m.

"I have two things," Mora said. "First, our biggest insurer, the Evil Empire (EE), cut our reimbursement rate by 50% as of January first."

Hubby and I locked eyes: *Disaster.* Our rural practice survived with insurance reimbursements only, without the fee-for-service [41] cushion that urban practices enjoy. EE

---

[41] When patients pay with cash.

insured all the state employees—the prison, the public school teachers, and the college—about 45 % of our patient base.

Every three years, EE subcontracted mental health benefits to the lowest bidder.[42] We would be notified who the new carrier was the last week of December, and by mid-February would finally receive contracts and fee proposals to review. Meanwhile, we continued providing service in good faith.

"That's illegal," Hubby said.

"Get the EE contact name from Janine," I said.

"I've already got it and I've already e-mailed."

The discussion was prolonged. When I looked at the clock, we had run over and patients were waiting.

"To be continued." I was in mid-rise when Mora said, "One more thing."

I paused, "Yes?"

"When you don't see patients and close the office, us girls can't work either. I think you should give us vacation pay for those times. I need a forty-hour week. Cherie and Lucy need more hours, too." I sat down, my knees jelly.

Hubby and I again locked eyes: *Disaster.*

I took a breath, and said flatly, "The practice income is down by half and you want us to increase expenses." She just looked at me. I stared back, with the same lack of expression, actively disliking her.

At my three o'clock break, I sat down at my administrative desk to address the mile-high stack of patient charts, all needing prescriptions renewed, phone

---

[42]Another, different, insurance company.

calls returned, or disability paperwork filled out. Mora, sitting at the next desk over, turned to me and picked up where she left off, "You know, we're not giving Cherie and Lucy enough hours. If you paid us more vacation time, we might not lose them."

A hush closed down around me. *Was that a threat?* I scanned her bland brown eyes, peaches-and-cream cheeks, and ingénue lips, her face unreadable. *Did she actually think I couldn't do without her? That she could bend me to her will? Against my best interests?* What had been runny around the edges pulled together inside me and hardened.

"Another way to handle that risk would be to give them more hours and yourself less," I paused to let that sink in. "That would also save the practice money. You're much more expensive than they are."

She dropped her eyes, but not before I caught the flash of fury. A chill ran through me.

First week of March

I hired Mary, our business consultant, to run a forensic audit on our books and payroll. A partial audit revealed that, *since the previous July,* Mora had several times paid herself at higher rates of pay than her actual rate, paid herself for overtime she hadn't worked (and we didn't even offer overtime), and paid herself for more hours than she'd actually worked.

"You're fired," I said at the next administrative meeting, heart racing and stomach churning. Hubby sat across me at the table, silent with fury, his eyes trained on her.

"Excuse me?" she said, completely still and without expression.

"You're fired," Hubby said. She cut her eyes at him and back to me.

"Can I ask why?"

I told her. She didn't deny it. Instead, she teared up, "I told you I needed forty hours a week."

"We told you the job was thirty hours. We gave you a two-dollar-an-hour raise. Get your stuff and get out."

Tears rolling down her cheeks, she rose abruptly. My body jumped up, but I forced myself down. She left the kitchen, and Hubby got up. "I'll keep an eye on her."

A few moments later, she stalked through the kitchen wearing her coat and carrying her purse along with another bag, eyes dry and feral. She smacked the door open, letting in a gust of early spring birdsong, chilly air, and the scent of wet earth. The door slammed shut behind her. I watched through the bare shrub branches outside the kitchen window as she got in her car parked across the street. She put her phone to an ear, face blank. She spoke, nodded, put down the phone, fired up the car, and drove off.

"You OK?" Hubby came up behind me and put his arms around my waist. I pressed against him. He felt good.

"It's only noon and I'm exhausted." I felt him nod. He squeezed harder.

"Me, too. I couldn't stand her. Let's tell Cherie she's our new office manager."

III: The Plot Sickens
~In which our beleaguered Heroine overrides shame to do the right thing~

Mid-March

Mary finished the audit and found three unauthorized petty cash checks, each for $600, which Mora cashed the last two weeks of December when the office was closed. There was no record of the cash or what it was used for. Maybe we spent $600 total over the course of a year for the occasional pizza, a few rolls of stamps, and a holiday gratuity for the postman. But $1800 two weeks immediately *after* the holidays? No way. Although I had apparently signed the checks, Mora had endorsed two with her own signature *(Oh. My. God.)* and Cherie had endorsed the third *(What?)*.

"You have to go to the police and press charges," Mary said, sitting at my desk with Quickbooks opened on the desktop and flipping through the audit, a thick stack of Excel spreadsheets. It was eight o'clock in the evening and all I wanted was for this day to end. Sitting at the next desk over, I moaned, my head in my hands to get away from the bright overhead lights.

"This happens all the time," Mary's voice came from far way. "You don't have eyes in the back of your head. You caught her really fast, only two months." She paused. I moaned some more.

Her voice washed over me, "I audited a lawyer whose office manager drained him of close to a hundred thousand dollars over twenty years. He thought of her as family. Invited her to his daughter's wedding, her school events, her son's christening."

I looked up, not soothed, eyes burning. "I know there are worse situations! The cops will still treat me like I'm an idiot. Which I am."

"Well, you're not. Why shouldn't you trust your office manager? Come on."

This is what rape victims feel like, I thought, hands limp in my lap, staring into space. They haven't done anything wrong. But they're ashamed anyway, and if they're lucky and don't get blamed by others, they still blame themselves.

"I feel violated."

"That's why you have to press charges. She'll do it to somebody else. You have to start the paper trail."

I groaned and put my head in my hands again. "Oh God." Now I had a responsibility to others, something I couldn't say no to. *Why, oh why, did I care?* I didn't want to care. But I did. I couldn't help it.

"I'll go with you," Mary said.

"You will?" I lifted my head. "Really?"

"Yes. I'll bring my analysis and the copies of the cashed checks. I can't believe she endorsed them." I called Hubby to let him know, and we went to the police station. I got home around ten-thirty and tossed and turned all night.

The next day, I pulled Cherie into the kitchen to ask her about the check she endorsed, leaving Lucy at the front desk. We sat catty-corner at the table.

"She made me sign it. I told her I didn't want to, but she said she was office manager and I had to do what she said. I'm so sorry." Cherie's eyes filled and she wrung her hands.

"No, don't worry. *I'm* sorry. We should never have made her office manager. She bullied me too, always pressing and pushing. I can't believe how insubordinate she was and how long I put up with it."

"If you don't mind me saying, I figured you'd fire her for *that*. But stealing? How does she sleep at night?"

"I know, right? Cherie, she cut those checks right before we went on vacation and hid them in that last stack of vendor payments. She waited to have me sign the checks at the end of the meeting, knowing I wouldn't look them over because I was in a hurry to get to patients. She'd thought ahead. She cashed them while we were away and kept the money. She's stone cold." I shuddered.

We took a moment of silence for our lost innocence. Then I sighed, "The cops were surprisingly sympathetic."

"Well, that's different," she said tartly. The local police had a reputation for corruption, not compassion. "Get a load of this. Mora applied for unemployment. Papers came in the mail this morning." Cherie handed me the form and a pen. I shook my head. The girl's gall had no limits. *Has the employee done anything that would make her ineligible for unemployment insurance?* On the line provided, I wrote: *Yes. She is a thief. We have pressed charges against her for embezzling. Police case number ICU2L8.*

I signed it and gave it to Cherie while again shaking my head. "Make a copy and put it in her personnel file before you mail it. When's my next patient?"

"I meant to tell you, you're free for the next hour. She cancelled."

"Perfect." I threw on my raincoat, changed my shoes for wellies and drove through the sleety downpour to the employment agency that had sent us Mora. I updated the manager, a harried woman in her late thirties dressed for business in skirt suit, white blouse with ascot, and pumps. She was horrified and defensive.

"How could either of us have known?" I reassured her. "She's too young to have a criminal record. Though we're working on getting that changed," I added darkly.

"We'd be happy to run a criminal check on your other two staff, free of charge, to make it up to you."

I shook my head, "Not necessary. Watch out for Mora, though. She's money-hungry and likely to come back to you now we've fired her."

"It's funny you should say that. She has and she didn't say why her employment with you ended. Always a bad sign."

IV: War

~In which our Protagonists, like the Spartans who burned their ships on enemy Athens' shore before battle, commit to victory as the only course of action~

Early April, Tuesday, 11:30 a.m.

Cherie, office manager in training, reported that the Evil Empire (EE) continued to reimburse at 50% of last year's rates while ignoring our outreach.

"What! No response at all?" said Hubby.

She shook her head. "I keep leaving messages and sending emails to the Liaison, but he doesn't get back to me."

"They're in violation of our contractual right to negotiate fees. That's illegal!" Hubby said, outraged.

"Yup. And after four and a half months, they're not worrying we'll do anything about it," I said.

"Bastards!"

"I confirmed with Janine that about half our patients are insured by EE," Cherie said.

"Oh. My. God," I said. "We can't afford to disenroll."

"Regardless," Hubby said. "We're done."

My jaw dropped, my eyebrows shot up, and my eyes popped. Hubby tended to resist all actions that might rock the financial boat. Astonishingly, for once we were in the same place at the same time and in agreement about what to do. "You're willing to disenroll?" I paused. "Really?"

Hubby nodded. "You can't work with thugs." Hubby is the best.

"Patients will freak out if they can't use their insurance to pay us," Cherie said.

"We'll harness that energy," I said.

Mid-April. We declare war.

To: EE

From: Us

Apply last year's reimbursement rates to this year's claims, retroactive to January 1, by close-of-business May 30. Or else.

Sincerely yours.

We mailed the letter, return receipt requested, and e-mailed it, also, to the EE Liaison, with a c.c. to the Employer Contact. Our administrative office, aka The War Room, exploded with ringing phones, tapping keyboards, zipping faxes, and whirring copies. Cherie and Lucy proved stellar soldiers in battle while Poodle Oodle maintained a zone of Zen calm from her bed under my desk.

I wrote patients a letter apprising them of the situation and how it would affect them if we disenrolled. I recommended they advocate against this with EE, their Employer, their union, and our local elected official. In addition to providing the contact names, phone numbers, and email addresses, I also included a template complaint letter for their use, should they want to write (*hint hint*). Lucy deployed the mass mailing: stuffing envelopes, then addressing, stamping, and delivering them to the post office.

I also wrote the union and our local elected official to inform them we had given EE notice, attaching a copy of the ultimatum. Meanwhile, Hubby reviewed prior contracts and initiated a chain of phone calls with the legal departments of EE and the Employer (the State of New York).

End of April, Tuesday administrative meeting, 11:30 a.m.

"The EE Liaison is playing games," Cherie said from the head of the table in the kitchen. "He says he hasn't received any of our e-mails. None have bounced back, so that's a crock."

"Why am I not surprised," I said.

"He says he didn't receive our certified letter in the mail, but the green return receipt came back, signed. So I know they have it. I scanned it and emailed it to him. He didn't acknowledge receiving it, but it didn't bounce back."

"Unbelievable," Hubby said in disgust, our eyes meeting across the table. Fresh air, bird chirps, and light streamed in through the two open windows above the sink: *Spring!*

"We're flooded with panicked calls from patients," Cherie said.

"Don't worry," Hubby said, leaning back in his chair, one hand on the table. "EE is caught between us and the Employer. The Employer is mandated to provide mental health services to their employees. EE is mandated to pay for them. Between them and us, EE is getting squeezed big time. Classic war strategy." He nodded, a satisfied general.

Cherie and I studied him, our eyebrows raised: *Go on.*

"Pincer movement," he said. "It's a maneuver where the good guys simultaneously attack both sides of the enemy formation, surrounding it." He leaned forward over the open pizza box on the table and took a moment to inhale the heady aroma of fresh baked pizza. He pulled out a slice by the crust and folded it in half.

"We're providing service in a physician-shortage area," he said to me. "They can't let us disenroll." He bit off the point of the slice and chewed.

I wasn't so sure. If the Liaison wasn't playing hardball but instead was foreshadowing EE's decision to let us go, what would happen to the practice's finances, and ours? I couldn't let myself go there. It would ruin my appetite.

"Tell patients to call everybody on the list we gave them," I said to Cherie. "Urge them to customize the template complaint letter and mail it. Tell them creating a paper trail applies serious pressure." Looking dubious, she nodded and took a bite of her slice.

I considered her doubt. Would patients go to the trouble? No…. They wouldn't. Too much work. It wasn't their problem our fees had been cut, *as long as we stayed open.*

"Tell patients," I said to Cherie, "if EE doesn't raise our rates back to last year's level, they'll put us out of business. We'll have to close the practice. What good would that do?"

354

She nodded a big *Yes!*, her mouth full of pizza. She swallowed. "*That's* good. A few people might actually write or make calls."

I looked at Hubby. "It's not like we're even asking for a cost of living increase."

"Maybe we should have," Hubby said, ripping a bite off his slice.

V: Yet Another Gift Wrapped In Black Paper

~In which our Protagonists, thrice betrayed, limp off into the sunset, arms around each others' waists~

May

After the April games, EE went silent. Then a patient brought in EE's response to her letter of complaint. It stated that she would not be able to submit our charges for out-of-network[43] benefits because there were other psychiatrists in the area accepting EE. ("Please see the attached list.") In other words, she was welcome to pay us cash or seek treatment from another shrink that accepted EE.

However, the list was a "ghost" list. One psychiatrist on it had worked temporarily for the hospital's inpatient service years ago, a second was dead, a third had moved away, the fourth didn't exist, and the fifth had retired. Lucy mass mailed my update informing patients that the list lied and so did EE.

Meanwhile...

"No!" Hubby sucked in air on the other end of the line when I called. He was home having finished his day while I was at the office, working late. The sky was still

---

[43] We were "in-network," unless we disenrolled, at which point we'd be "out-of- network." Some insurances will pay a small portion of an out-of-network clinician's fee, after the insured meets the small print criteria.

light though the sun had set. Birds twittered in the leafy bushes on the other side of the window that fronted my administrative desk. I twisted the phone cord between my fingers.

"Yup. I tore the office apart looking for last year's petty cash records. They're gone. Vanished. The detective needs them to validate that those three $600 checks are a break from the usual pattern and to confirm the cash is missing."

"Did you call Kathy?"

"Yup. She swears all the records were there when she left. And they are, except for the months we need."

"Mora destroyed them. Probably while we were off for the holidays."

"Yup."

"She's going to get away with it."

"No!" I cried.

"Yes," he said.

A week later

I had just washed up the dinner dishes when my cell phone rang on the counter: Mary, our business consultant. Hubby and Son had disappeared into the basement to watch TV. "Hi there," I said, drying my hands on the dishtowel and walking to the living room. I turned on the table lamp and sat down on the couch. "What's going on, Miz Mary?"

"Well," she said, "the detective called me in to the station today and reviewed my audit with Kathy there." She paused. I was unpleasantly surprised. Why hadn't he informed me?

"Really? How'd it go?"

"Kathy shook like a leaf and could hardly speak, she was so scared."

"What! Why?" I sat up and pressed the phone more firmly to my ear.

"I don't know, but it was weird. The thing is, the time sheets are a mess. Too many days with hours whited out and written over. Without punched timecards, it's impossible to prove Mora doctored her hours. Kathy wouldn't confirm or deny any of the changes."

"No!" I had expected Kathy to have our back.

"She said she couldn't remember. Really, she was pathetic, wringing her hands and keeping her head down."

My belly clenched and my hand clutched the phone. "What about the petty cash checks?"

"She wouldn't say the amounts or the time of year were out of the ordinary. She just shrugged and said that was a decision you would have made."

"Come on! There's no precedent!"

"She just kept whispering she couldn't believe Mora would do that."

I found myself on my feet, pacing the living room. "What did she say about the different rates of pay?"

"Maybe Mora made a mistake."

I stopped dead.

"More than once? Come on!"

May 23rd, 2:30 p.m.

The EE Liaison called and spoke with Hubby. "We'll raise your rates back to what you were paid last year, effective immediately."

358

"Retroactive to January 1?"

"Uh…. No."

"Goodbye."

Disenrollment Day, May 30th

10:00 a.m. Hubby and I crossed paths in the office kitchen and talked a few minutes. "Well," I said, "we haven't heard anything since May 23rd. I guess they're going to let us disenroll." We both sighed in disgust.

I pulled a mug from the cupboard, raised my eyebrows, and pointed: *You want?* He shook no. I poured coffee from the pot on the counter, sipped, and made a face. Burnt, from sitting too long on the warmer. Ordinarily, I take my coffee light with milk. Today, I preferred it black, like my mood.

"If they do, they'll have stolen half the money they owe us for services rendered since January first," Hubby said, his eyes blazing.

"They know we can't afford to sue them for it," I said, draining the bitter cup.

"Bastards!"

"It's not right," I said, "ripping us off like that. Along with patients who pay premiums. Patients shouldn't have to pay cash for services that are supposed to be covered."

"We have to make sure Cherie reassures people we'll work with them around payment."

I nodded, washed the cup in the sink, and set it bottom up in the dish drain. I shook my head. "What I don't get," I said, throwing down the dishtowel, "is how EE can break the law with such impunity."

"Maybe we *should* look into suing," he said. "We can't be the only ones they're robbing."

3:23 p.m. We all happened to be in The War Room when the call came in. Cherie, grinning, waved the phone receiver on its long cord over her head. "They backed down! We're getting our rates retroactive to January One! Woo hoo!" She dropped it into the cradle and jumped out of her seat, waving her arms above her head. "YES!"

The theme from the movie *Rocky* swelled in my head. I hummed the melody and we danced around each other, punching the air, "Yeah! Getting stronger! Ta da da dahhh *dahhh*!"

Hubby watched us from his administrative desk and grinned from ear to ear. "Damn! We're good!"

Lucy, always reserved, grinned too, standing by the eight-foot-high chart cabinets, a patient file in her hands.

"Those bastards!" Hubby said, making eye contact with me across the room. "We gave them till 5:00. They caved at 3:30. They were playing chicken!"

"Checks will be here in two weeks," Cherie said.

"I can clear the overdraft!" I danced some more. "We won!" I planted my feet wide and threw my arms up in victory.

Mid-June

"Look at these," Cherie said to me, walking over to my administrative desk where I was paying bills. I took the checks from her hand. *Tens of thousands of dollars.* We stared at each other, shocked.

She said, "That's a salary!" It was horrifying. EE *would* have put us out of business.

"Cherie, you and Lucy are a fantastic team. We couldn't have gotten this money back without you. Big bonuses for you both."

Cherie turned red and pressed a hand to her mouth, her eyes filling. "Thank you!"

"You earned it," I said, my eyes filling, too. "The two of you made all that extra work look easy."

"It was stressful, but Lucy is great," she beamed. "Super organized."

"Cherie, what do you think? Do we need a third person? Or can you and Lucy handle the work load together?"

"Funny you should bring that up. Being back to normal these past two weeks, we've been fine. We talked about it. I was going to suggest it."

"Awesome!"

"We've started beefing up the procedure manual, too."

"You're the best."

We split the money budgeted for a third employee between Cherie and Lucy. The right staff is everything in a small business. My life hadn't ended with Kathy's retirement. It had begun.

The cherry on top.

August. "Sorry," the detective said, closing Mora's file and centering it on his much-too-tidy desk blotter. Hubby and I looked at each other in dismay and then, as one, stared at him. We sat in two visitor chairs before his desk in his gray-walled, air-conditioned, windowless office in the basement of the police station. It was two o'clock, Thursday afternoon, a scheduled appointment.

He took in our incredulity with equanimity. "The DA dismissed the case due to insufficient evidence."

"But, but," I squeaked. "She paid herself at different rates! She doctored the time sheets. She cut three petty cash checks *and endorsed them. The money's missing*."

"The only concrete thing we have is the different hourly rates of pay and the overtime hours, but that total came to less than $200. Your former office manager couldn't, or wouldn't, say those petty cash checks were unusual. She said she whited out some of those times on the time sheets herself. Mora never changed her story that you empowered her to cut and cash those checks, that she didn't take the money, and that it was documented in the records. Those are missing." He shrugged.

Hubby and I slumped as one, defeated.

"She did this to us for three quarters of a year, stone cold, and destroyed the evidence," I said. "She's going to do it again to another trusting small business."

"She's not that smart, believe me," the detective said.

Walking out of the station into the hot humidity and hazy bright light, Hubby and I split up at the car, he going to the passenger side, I to the driver's. I powered it on, opened the windows to evacuate the heat, and turned on the air conditioning full blast. I leaned against the seatback and turned my head to Hubby. "He fell for her dewy, ingénue act."

"Yup." He rolled his eyes and rested his head on the whiplash support.

"She's an accounting major. She's only going to get better at it." We took a moment of silence for how easy it is to get around the criminal justice system.

"And Kathy threw us under the bus," I said.

"Yup." He shook his head. "She sure did."

After a moment, he sighed. "Who knows, maybe Mora had something on her," he turned to me. "Blackmail. I wouldn't put it past her."

I sighed. We sat in silence for a while. I sighed again.

"Now that I think about it, Kathy behaved true to form," I said ruefully. "I just hoped she'd come through. This mess is my fault. I asked too much of her. She as good as told me managing employees was her weak spot. I didn't listen."

"When did she tell you that?"

"After we'd hired her. She let it slip in an aside that she sold her business after a long-time employee embezzled from her. And I let it go." I sighed again and leaned forward to adjust the vent so it didn't blow straight on me. I powered the windows up and leaned back.

"I don't know," Hubby said. "After all, she only had one bad employee. That's an anomaly, not a pattern."

"I know. But really, there were lots of other clues that I ignored. There were so many times I should have held her to account and I didn't. Like, when she said Mora had talked her out of using the time clock. Like, how she wouldn't put together a procedure manual. She always had a reason. And always used a tone that said she was hurt I didn't trust her. I didn't push."

"She should have been straightforward. That was her job and her responsibility," Hubby said.

"Yes, but it's *our* business. As her boss, the buck stopped with me."

"You're being too hard on yourself."

"No," I shook my head, "just owning my piece of it."

"I wish you would have told me."

"If I'd been on top of it, believe me, I would have," I said, smiling at him. "You can be a diabolical strategist." I paused. "But I'm on top of it now. We've got procedures in place. Cherie and Lucy love it. I see now how sloppy I was with Kathy and Mora. Employees need structure. They need to know what's expected of them. The practice is clicking along like a well-oiled machine."

"That's great!" Hubby said.

"Yeah," I paused again, thinking. "You know, Mora took complete advantage of Kathy. Kathy didn't actually delegate payroll and our financials to her last July."

"What!"

"Yeah, last July, she just cut payroll without asking, and Kathy was thrilled she took the initiative. That came out a few months later and, again, I didn't like it. And again, I didn't question it either. She trusted Mora. I trusted her. She didn't check up on Mora. I didn't check up on Kathy. Mora knew that." I groaned and shook my head. "Lucky thing Kathy resigned."

"Yeah," Hubby said. "Who knows how long Mora would have run that little scam."

"I'm sorry I didn't do better." I met his eyes.

"Babe! I like that you're trusting," he said. "Besides, you're not *that* trusting. Asking Mary to do a forensic audit was a stroke of genius. What made you think to do it?"

I flashed back, looking for the triggering event. "You know, I don't remember. It's kind of a traumatic blur. I'll have to ask Mary."

Hubby shook his head. "How much did Mora get away with?"

"About $6000, between the petty cash and paying herself at her usual rate for nine months for way more hours than she worked. Thank God we can absorb the loss. Especially having beat EE." The war washed over me: composing letters at the desktop; meetings at the kitchen table; patients panicking; Cherie on the phone; Lucy stuffing envelopes; Hubby saying, "Pincer movement." The daily effort of pushing back, again and again and again. The stress and worry and fear.

"If Kathy'd been with us," I said, "she'd have wanted us to eat the fee cut, and resisted declaring war. She'd have been a reluctant soldier, dead weight, dragging every step. But Cherie and Lucy went above and beyond. Relished it, even. That freed us to be bold. To fight full throttle. Without them, we could easily have gone under."

"I would have had to take a job at the prison." Hubby met my eyes. He didn't visibly shudder, but it was there.

"What was I thinking!" I smacked my forehead. "That would have been great! Now I'm stuck running the practice. Shit!"

He leaned over and pulled me to him with the near arm, right into the cool air streaming from the central vents. "And you do it so well, O She Who Must Be Obeyed." He kissed me and whispered sweetly in my ear, "Mooooo."

Obedience to Authority by **Stanley Milgram, Ph.D.**

~A Synopsis for Your Edification
Which Will Be Referenced in the Next Chapter~

~All quoted material can be found in the original work:
Obedience to Authority by Stanley Milgram, HarperPerennial,
an imprint of HarperCollinsPublishers, 1974~

Stanley Milgram, a social scientist working out of Yale, was deeply troubled by the scale of the genocide perpetrated by the Nazi war machine during World War II. Implementation required massive numbers of workers, far too many to all be written off as sadistic monsters. In 1961, he set up an experiment that pitted two formidable human forces against each other:

> "Of all moral principles, the one that comes closest to being universally accepted is this: one should not inflict suffering on a helpless person who is neither harmful nor threatening to oneself. This principle is the counterforce we shall set in opposition to obedience."

Here is the experiment. Two men, strangers to each other, arrive at the lab and Dr. Milgram explains to both that the study is about the effects of punishment on learning. One man is designated the Learner, the other the Teacher. All three go to a room where Dr. Milgram straps the Learner's arms to a chair and attaches an electrode to his wrist while the Teacher watches. Dr. Milgram tells the Learner that he has to learn a list of word pairs, such as blue box, nice day, etc., and that whenever he makes a mistake, he will get an electric shock. With each mistake the shock will increase in intensity.

Dr. Milgram then escorts the Teacher to another room, where the Teacher takes a seat in front of a large machine called a shock generator. It has 30 switches labeled by volts, starting at 15 volts, increasing in 15-volt increments up to 450 volts. The switches are also labeled with word descriptions from the first, *Slight Shock,* to the last, *Danger-Severe Shock.*

Dr. Milgram hands the Teacher a list of word pairs and tells him it is his job to administer the test to the Learner in the other room. If the Learner answers correctly, the Teacher goes on to the next word pair. If the Learner answers incorrectly, the Teacher must push a switch that gives the Learner a shock. With each wrong answer, the Teacher must increase the shock level by one increment, 15 volts.

The Learner is actually an actor and is not receiving any shocks at all. The Teacher doesn't know this. It is the Teacher who is the subject of the experiment.

The Teacher calls out the first few items of the "learning test" and the Learner, Milgram's accomplice, unseen in the other room, soon sounds very uncomfortable. At 75 volts, the Learner grunts. At 120 volts, he shouts that the shocks are painful. At 150 volts, he demands to be released from the experiment. As the shocks grow stronger, the Learner's protests became more desperate and at 285 volts, he screams in agony.

Meanwhile, Dr. Milgram in a white lab coat, stands behind the Teacher seated at the shock generator and calmly gives a sequence of scripted prods, such as: *Please continue*. Or, *Whether the Learner likes it or not, you must go on until he has learned all the word pairs correctly. So please go on.*

This experiment has been repeated with thousands of people, men and women, from all walks of life, from different countries, and in many variations. The results are always the same.

If asked to predict at what point the Teacher will stop subjecting the Learner to shocks, most people will say the Teacher will stop, at the latest, when the Learner demands to be released from the study. But they are wrong: *63%—almost two thirds—of the total subject group pressed switches up to 450 volts, the maximum.* They sweated, they complained, they held their heads in the hands, *but they did it.* Milgram drew the following chilling conclusion.

> "A substantial proportion of people do what they are told to do, irrespective of the content of the act and without limitation of conscience, *so long as they perceive that the command comes from a legitimate authority.*"

Corollary studies and observations:

- If the Teacher did not administer the shock himself, but told someone else to do it, the number of Teachers who shocked the Learner up to 450 volts *increased* from 63% to 93%. "Predictably, subjects excused their behavior by saying the responsibility belonged to the man who actually pulled the switch."

- The only common feature of the disobedient 37% was that they tended to be highly educated. Milgram speculated that they saw themselves as equal in status to the scientist/professor, which enabled them to question the legitimacy of his authority and defy it. That was in the lab. However, disobedience is much more difficult in the community. There, the disobedient have to defy *both* the established authority *and* the 63% that accept the authority as legitimate.

- Milgram tested if modeling disobedience reduces compliance with illegitimate authority. It does. When two additional confederate teachers sitting next to the subject Teacher refused to obey (one stopping at 150 volts, the other at 210 volts), the level of obedience in the subject Teacher *dropped* from 65% to 10% for the highest 450-volt shock.

In summary:

Milgram established a dark fact of human nature: the majority of people are capable of committing atrocities if ordered to do so by a leader perceived as legitimate. Resistance requires pushing back against both the authority and the obedient community. If people are not required to directly commit acts destructive to others, their compliance with authority increases. If supported by other resisters, obedience declines.

Obedience to authority is the group default. Disobedience, to effectively induce change, requires group effort, which is difficult to build given that default. Therefore, the disempowerment of toxic authorities is possible, but hardly a given.

Talk is Cheap, Action Expensive

"You didn't!" Hubby said, putting his loaded fork back on the plate. We were home, eating supper.

" I couldn't say no."

"You hate committee work." He shook his head in disbelief. "The politics will drive you crazy. You'll have tell me all about it," he moaned. "And I'll have to listen. Please, please, think about me."

"Yeah, but it's a growth opportunity, right? Everyone says you were the voice of reason when you were on the Board. I dub thee Sir Coach," I said, tapping his head with the tip of my clean dinner knife.

The spiritual leader of our congregation had asked me to serve as an officer on the membership committee, a three-year term.

[*Aside:* If you're wondering whether we're Christian, Jewish, Muslim, or other, I'm not going to say because it would be a distraction. Instead of priest, rabbi, imam, or other, this story's spiritual leader will be known as the Heart.]

We had belonged to this congregation of less than 80 families for over fifteen years. In the last ten, I'd written the monthly[44] gossip column for the bulletin from my cozy hermit's desk and Hubby had served as a member of the Board (two terms, three years each). Hearts had come and

---

[44] No time off for vacations, illnesses, or good behavior.

gone without making an impression on me until the Heart of this story. Scholarly, spiritual, thoughtful, and psychologically astute, she actually practiced what she preached. I admired and respected her.

Dysfunctional family dynamics understates the bullying, backstabbing, rumor-mongering and hypocrisy I witnessed from the inside as an officer of membership. I was appalled to discover that the Board was making decisions affecting congregational well-being behind closed doors without congregational input, a violation of the by-laws. The president presented the Board's decisions to the congregation as a *fait accompli*.

By my third year serving on membership, I could no longer ignore that the Board wanted the Heart to go. They had no formal grounds to dismiss her. Their strategy was insidious: they talked about her behind her back and "off the record." This made congregants on the receiving end feel special while simultaneously suborning them into colluding with the Board's agenda. Using tone, gesture, and innuendo, the Board also subliminally threatened the few congregants who questioned them. "Nonsense!" The Board secretary had said to me with a frown when I pointed this out, pulling her head back in annoyed dismissal.

The Heart pushed back, but her rebuttals went unheard, or worse, were disparaged and belittled. Her frustration was demeaned as whining.

The congregation, previously satisfied, began to manifest a high level of confusion, unhappiness, and stress, the same as children experience when one parent is abusive to the other. It doesn't stretch the metaphor to think of the Board as father and the Heart as mother.

"I can't figure it out. Do *you* know what the problem is?" I'd probe congregants after services. Most people shook their heads, shrugged their shoulders, and changed the subject. A few admitted something needed to be done, but they too threw their hands up. Witnessing abuse induces fear, shuts down rational thought, and makes people avoidant.

The Heart resigned with six months' notice. I was heartbroken, the congregation shocked, and the outside community disgusted. I started hearing from friends of other faiths that they weren't surprised; it was common knowledge out in the community that the Board mistreated Hearts. In thinking about the Hearts that had passed through over the years, I realized the Board always circulated unflattering explanations about their departure: *she used us as a career stepping-stone; he didn't make the religious school a priority; she wanted too much money; etc.*

In my early days on membership, it puzzled me that the committee made no effort to connect with people of our faith out in the community. Then I met an estranged congregant—let's call her Amity—at a local classical concert. Amity had shuddered. "It's been more than twenty years since those people mauled me. And they're still running things. I'll never go back." (For decades, the same men had served as presidents and officers, in round robin, along with their wives.)

Still, I assumed that the Board, however misguided, could be shamed by congregational complaint into scheduling a meeting to resolve the tension around the

Heart's resignation. If that happened, the Heart might withdraw it. I had real hope because she'd made it clear she'd wanted to work things out. Also, Hubby and I were well-liked, had gravitas as mental health professionals, and weren't alone in wanting her to stay.

To move that reckoning along, I had to socialize extensively. Talk about a sacrifice for the greater good! I repeatedly asked the Board and allies for information: What were their concerns about the Heart? What work had they done to address them with her? I suggested an open meeting. I appealed to fairness, friendship, transparency, trust, and the institution's formal mission statement.

The president was hostile: "I don't have to explain anything to you." The vice-president was defensive: "How can you think we're holding anything back?" A third was annoyed: "We're doing our best."

Pushing congregants proved equally dismaying. Many were befuddled: *There's a problem?* Most preferred denial: *Surely not. You must be mistaken.* Others, passivity: *It'll work itself out.*

Then there were the contacts outside.

At the grocery store. "I don't get it," I said to the president— let's call her Patsy—after we'd greeted each other and stopped our carts. "Please help me understand."

She shook her head. "I can't say."

"Why not?"

"It would violate the Heart's privacy."

"Have you asked her if she'd be OK with the Board sharing what happened?"

"We're not doing that."

376

"She wants to stay!" I looked at the shelves loaded with different brands of laundry detergent. "You can't replace her like a box of soap."

"The Board has accepted her resignation," Patsy snapped, shoving her shopping cart past me.

A couple weeks later, after lunch, on the sidewalk outside the restaurant. "It makes me feel they have something to hide." I said to friend Cheryl (of Twinkle Toes infamy), president of membership, and liaison to the Board.

She stared at me for a couple beats, then shook her head. "Of course they can't say. It would violate the Heart's confidence," she said slowly, as if she couldn't believe I would be so dense.

"I think she'd be amenable."

"We can't do that to her," she repeated flatly. I looked in her eyes and no longer knew her.

"I guess we'll have to agree to disagree," I said, aggrieved. *She's no ally,* I thought. *She's a collaborator, parroting the party line.* We walked away from each other. Thunder rumbled. Big drops of rain fell heavily, drenching my hair to the scalp.

A few weeks after that. I was shopping in the co-op, turned the corner of an aisle, and there was Patsy. I acknowledged her with a nod and kept moving. She snorted and said to my back, in a whispered sneer, "Oooohhh, so you're not talking to me. Okay. Don't be nice."

Nice? *Nice?* We weren't in high school, she wasn't the popular girl, and I wasn't a groveling misfit. She needed a lesson on being a grown-up. I kept walking. I paid and waited for her outside on the sidewalk. Alarm flashed across her face, then she straightened, frowned, and attacked.

"What's your problem?" she said. "Why are you being so rude?"

I inhaled with shock. My intention to be reasonable died on the spot. "I'm not rude," I growled. "I'm furious."

"I know you're mad," she said with a shrug. "The Heart's leaving. It's a done deal. Get over it."

"Why should I?"

"You're making everyone uncomfortable being so angry."

I snorted. "*You're* the one who's uncomfortable."

"Why can't you be nice?"

"Nice!" We locked eyes. "Nice?" I opened my mouth and flamed her. "Your actions as leader of the Board have cost this congregation an outstanding Heart and robbed *ME* of my spiritual life. *That's* not nice. You're hiding what happened. *That's* corrupt. You've treated the Heart horribly. *That's* despicable. You're the president. YOU'RE responsible. *You've. Let. Me. Down.*"

She stood stricken, eyes wide and staring. I studied her for a couple beats, then stepped past her and crossed the street to the parking lot.

Another few weeks later. Patsy made eye contact from across the social hall after a well-attended holiday service and strode toward me. I frowned, obviously about-faced and left the room. She stalked me to the bathroom entrance. "You!" she said, jabbing a finger at me. I looked at the finger, silent. The person who spoke first, lost. She withdrew the finger.

"Why are you being like this?" she asked, exasperated, laying her hand on my arm. I pulled away.

"Oohhh, I *seeeee*," she said, with syrupy fake sympathy. "You're *still* mad." She rolled her eyes. "I wish you'd get over it. I'm sorry. Really, I am."

I maintained a stony silence and waited for more. But she was done. She broke eye contact, shook her head and walked away, her carriage telegraphing: *I give up.*

Behind the Scenes Diplomacy was a bust. On to Playing Hardball.

I had a decision to make. Should I formally call out the Board? Did I have the right to prioritize myself, and my personal principles, ahead of my neutral professional persona? I decided yes, I did. I was a congregant; the members of the Board were my leaders. It was their obligation to take care of me and for maintaining the standards of leadership as promised. My responsibility as a congregant was to hold them accountable when they didn't.

I wrote a letter requesting an open congregational meeting, naming names, and listing the concerns that needed addressing. I then submitted it to the office secretary, expecting she'd send it out through the institutional e-mail list. Patsy forbade it.

The poor secretary had to lie, saying it wasn't her job to forward personal email to the congregation when just last week she had sent out a artist congregant's schedule of classes at a local art center. Clearly, Patsy was controlling

379

the flow of information and felt no need to hide behind a plausible reason. I knew what I might be up against if I persisted. Still, I continued to hope for the best. (Sometimes I wonder what planet I live on.[45])

As a membership committee officer, I had a paper copy of the congregational e-mail list. It took my office assistant Lucy a few hours to input and save to a memory stick. Then I sent the letter from my home email. All hell broke loose. The Board started a misinformation campaign against me. They broke up my conversations with congregants after services with veiled threats. I was barraged with hate mail from their spouses and allies.

The congregational response was mixed. Those for holding a meeting to get answers spoke up. Those against did, too. But the majority shut down: *Gee, I don't know.... There must be some misunderstanding.... The Board wouldn't do that....*

It went on for weeks. My stomach was an acid fireball, my hair fell out in clumps, and one night I dreamt Patsy handed me a book titled *Kill Yourself, Now!*

Hubby quipped: "Was it paperback or hard cover?"

"Ha ha."

The controversy made it impossible for the Board to weasel out of calling the meeting. We ran into the Heart exiting the building as Hubby and I entered to attend it. "Aren't you coming?" I asked in surprise.

"I wasn't invited," she said.

---

[45] Planet Wishful Thinking?

"Well, I'm inviting you," I said. She nodded and joined us entering the sanctuary, where most of the pews were filled. Patsy was flustered and incensed to see her. "You shouldn't have come, Heart," she spat from the pulpit. "Since you're here, you can stay. But don't speak." Then she, the Board, and their allies proceeded to shut down all dissent. It was awful. They bullied, they shamed, and they guilted.

"How DARE you question the Board!" roared a revered patriarch— let's call him the Godfather—much feared for his temper.

A former Board member stood up. "This meeting is an insult to your hardworking Board, a slap instead of a thank you."

Another partisan said, "Yeah, how could you be so ungrateful?"

A current Board member snapped, "None of you complainers wanted the responsibility. We took it on and you voted us in. So be quiet."

"Outrageous! Disgusting! Enough of this disrespect!" thundered the Godfather before he stormed out of the sanctuary, red-faced with rage.

And the finale. Another Board ally named Snarly stood up, faced the Heart, and spewed venom: "I trusted you! You're a two-faced liar! I'm glad you resigned!" She ranted on and on. Patsy didn't stop her. Nobody did. The Heart sat motionless, without expression. When Snarly finally ran down, there was a long and horrified silence, which Patsy broke by terminating the meeting. People cleared out immediately.

"I'm sorry," I said to the Heart, as we walked through the parking lot to our cars.

She had tears in her eyes. "It's hopeless. This is what they've been doing to me behind the scenes. Only worse, no witnesses."

Hubby was incredulous. "Wow."

She nodded. "At least now the congregation has seen it for themselves."

We stopped by her car. She asked Hubby, "Did you notice how the Godfather cut down everybody who had questions?"

"Yeah." Hubby nodded, thoughtful. "What disturbed me was his wife standing up and following him out, eyes down. That's when I knew. He's abusive. She's battered." I was overcome by a tidal wave of love. I'd never liked the Godfather, for this very reason. Hubby had looked beyond his personal liking for the man, made an objective assessment, and drawn the logical conclusion. My guy.

"Snarly went off right after they left, like she'd been unleashed," he said, bringing me back.

"He's the one," the Heart said. "He's always in the shadows, controlling the Board, spreading rumors, making people doubt themselves. He's what's called a clergy-hater."

"Oh!" I said. "The anti-leader of group dynamics theory. The person in competition with the actual leader, who wants to take over."

"No, he's not in competition," she said sadly. "He eliminated the competition. Long ago. It doesn't matter who's on the Board, he's running things. He doesn't just force Hearts out either. He makes sure to hurt us, too. By

382

tarnishing our reputations and turning the congregation against us. I know, because I've been in touch with the last three."

"Wow," I said.

"They're all OK. Landed on their feet. But now he's after me. He's already written the national organization outright lies about me, to make it hard for me to get another job. Fortunately, they know me from before and they don't believe him. They've been very supportive." She paused and sighed. "They predicted it would go this way. I had hoped they were wrong."

Hubby and I looked at each other. "You're well out of it then," I said to her with sorrow. "We'll miss you."

"Thank you."

After that meeting, the Board (and allies) shunned me and anyone who'd questioned them. Non-combatants made themselves as small as possible or disappeared. Attendance at services shrank noticeably. Still, quite a few congregants, all professionals, demanded a second meeting. The Board hedged and stonewalled, scheduling it months after the first. It was held in the social hall. Attendance was sparse. Patsy stood in front and opened it with a shrug. "I was in a hurry and left my notes at home. But it doesn't matter because as far as I'm concerned, there's nothing more to say."

Cheryl stood from her folding chair and read from a scripted statement that said nothing new. No one spoke. Then one female member of the Board stood up and addressed me directly: "Frankly, you hurt my feelings with that letter." Hubby put his hand on my knee.

"The letter was a straightforward request for a congregational meeting to get questions answered," I said calmly. "Sometimes patients hurt my feelings, but I consider that my job to manage, not the patient's. You're my leader. If my asking you to do your job hurt your feelings, I'm sorry. But really, that's your problem, not mine."

Another female member of the Board stood up. "Your anger is so unfair and hurtful. We've worked really hard and done all we could!"

"You'll get over my anger soon," I said. "But you and the rest of the Board have lost us the Heart, and that's forever. Worse, questions about what happened haven't been answered. I'm entitled to be upset."

"Why didn't you talk to anyone?" a male, former president asked next.

"I did." I waited a couple of beats. "Nobody listened." He shook his head.

I waited for the attendees who had expressed their support to speak up. I waited in vain. The meeting fizzled out and so did the congregational resistance. The Board bad-mouthed the Heart till the day she left.

I resigned from membership and wrote my last gossip column for the bulletin. Cheryl emailed as chair of membership: "Please reconsider! You bring so much to the committee!" Translation: *Oh oh. We just noticed how much work you do.* Patsy emailed me as president: "Please reconsider. People love your writing." Translation: *Your column builds community feeling. You've left me holding.*

"It's time to give someone else a turn," I wrote back to both.

How did the Board handle me after their victory?

I had assumed the Board would put the needs of the institution first, dismiss my one act of defiance in a fifteen-year period, and reintegrate me in order to regain my valuable volunteer labor and cash. It wasn't an unreasonable expectation. Many a man had done far worse and been forgiven.

Instead—the needs of the institution be damned—I was marginalized in-house by the women. First, Patsy and her soldiers looked through me before, during, and after services as if I were invisible: no greeting, no acknowledgment. Most of the congregational women followed their lead. Out in the community, there were other, more dramatic rejections. One stands out.

I was at an art opening where I saw Cheryl and her husband Terence. First, I waved at him, twice, from across the room and, though he was looking straight at me, he didn't respond. Next, I was talking with an artist when Cheryl walked over without making eye contact, extended her hand to the artist, and in one smooth move stepped *directly in front of me*, physically cutting me from the conversation and the metaphoric pack. I stared at her back, astonished. The message was clear: I was out— everywhere.

Why? It seemed so…high schoolish. [46] Thinking further, I realized it was far darker than that. These people weren't kids.

---

[46] "That's just how it is with women in congregations," a couple friends said, with eye rolls. That's too bad.

Postmortem, Part I: Conformity, the Human Default Setting

Let's review what happened. First, the Board ignored my upset and requests for more information. Then the president censored my letter. I defied her and sent it from home, which caused so much discord the Board was forced to schedule the first congregational meeting. Before it was held, the core players undermined dissention through gossip and veiled social threats. While it was happening, they aggressively shut down dialogue and bullied dissenters. After, they ignored requests for a second meeting long enough to insure the Heart's departure. The evidence was undeniable: the leadership was authoritarian.

In a democracy, leadership respects the tension created by the people's disapproval and enacts policy changes to remedy that discontent. Authoritarian leaders, on the other hand, do what they want unless they are defied by the group. I was the only congregant who openly disobeyed.

Why I Was Punished

What happened validated four of Milgram's findings on obedience to authority:

(1) Virtually all people collude with authority if they aren't asked to dish out the pain.

(2) A high level of education *can* lead to widespread dissention.

(3) That didn't make any difference. This affirmed what I consider Milgram's most chilling conclusion: that in most people, disagreeing with authority *does not lead to disobedience.* They will obey, even if they don't want to, even as they complain and suffer.

(4) Authoritarians know that courage, like cowardice, is contagious. *The only thing that threatens authoritarian leadership is actual disobedience.* When I proved myself willing to defy them, the Board incited unease in congregants who spoke to me, kindling cowardice. Could congregants see that? Sure, they could. People aren't stupid, merely self-serving and easily frightened. When called to action, the first question anyone wants answered is: *What's in it for me?* Congregants answered: *Not enough.*

By formally resisting authority, I also broke gender-specific rules of conduct. The Board at the time was, unusually, all female, though they were all wives of former male presidents and officers, i.e., extensions of their men, not independent agents. Still, women are much less forgiving than men when their sisters defy gender norms.

By contrast, Hubby was actively courted (at services, with phone calls, and by emails) by former male Board members, with requests to let it go and go along to get along, no hard feelings. This, in its way, was even more shocking. Clearly they expected Hubby to align himself with the institutional patriarchy first, and his marriage second. If he had, that would have erased me as a person in my own right. I got it: my thoughts, feelings, and actions had never mattered and never would.

That I dared to publically insist otherwise—my courage—made me far too contagious for the leadership to tolerate. To consolidate their power, they had to crush me into submission with a social quarantine, of undetermined duration, controlled by the women, with the men working on Hubby to collude. But they misread us. Hubby and I terminated our membership. Talk about a shock wave!

Belonging to a pack is a powerful human need. Most people would never leave an entire social network, especially a religious one. "Belonging," even if it costs you your self, provides the illusion of protection from danger outside of the group. I'm sure many congregants took our departure as a clear message from the Board: Defy us and you're out.

But our departure also undermined the Board's authority by declaring it illegitimate. When they initiated reprisals against me, the Board assumed we'd never leave. It didn't occur to them that Hubby and I would refuse to participate in their authoritarian social club masquerading as a house of worship. As for trusting them to take care of us? Not for a New York second.

My appetite soon returned and my hair grew back. I knew I'd recovered when I dreamed I hurled a heavy hardcover titled *Live Long and Suffer* at Patsy's chest. She fumbled the catch, lost her balance, and landed on her butt.

"Are you ever coming back?" a friendly acquaintance asked when we ran into each other buying dog food. I shook my head. Why would I? Amity's shudder flashed before me. They'd mauled me, too. Well…tried to, anyway. What took me by surprise was how light and vigorous I felt. Staying in had required way too much energy, with little return—energy I now had for myself.

Postmortem, Part II: On Leadership

There has been a slow trickle of departures from the congregation since we left, all professional families. I'd be entitled to a little *schadenfreude* [47] if I didn't feel so exasperated: the Board is stupid and destructive. My former house of worship is ill, perhaps terminally.

Obedience is passive and resistance active. The disobedient must endure retaliation for their actions. Whistle-blowing by a principled individual carries a low risk of success. Even trying carries a high risk of ejection from the pack. I was pilloried by the leadership *and* the community. My solo effort to model courage failed. If only I'd been able to gather a few people around me! But I just didn't have the leadership skills.

Effective leaders need to be extroverted to get things done. To engage a group large enough to *successfully* defy institutionalized oppression, the effective leader needs even more: charisma, vision, conscience, courage, and smarts *plus* the interpersonal skills to mentor those qualities in *other* leaders, who will spread resistance in a ripple effect.

---

[47] *Schadenfreude*: (German) Taking enjoyment in the troubles of others.

And that's not all. For leaders to mobilize enough people to actual defiance against abuses of power, people's misery has to reach an unpredictable tipping point. Toxic authorities use violence of all kinds to stop that momentum Social bullying. Job loss. Police brutality. Making it difficult to register to vote and/or get to the polls, outright rigging of elections, and voter fraud. To disempower and remove resistance leaders, toxic authorities use financial ruin, slander and libel, criminalization and assassination.

That said, I believe *any* act of conscience, no matter how small, moves the world forward to a kinder, saner, more humane place, no leadership skills required. I see myself as one cell in the small organ that is my family, that is part of the larger organ of my town, and so on. By refusing to collude with congregational corruption, I did my tiny part to keep my community healthy.

I didn't personally see concrete results, but that doesn't mean there weren't any. After all, the individual neurons in my brain didn't know if their firing lead to effective action. They just fired because that's what they do. I'm a person who acts from her principles. It's what I do. I'm part of something larger than myself. A rain barrel starts out empty, but fills up, one drop at a time. I'm that drop. "We plant trees not for ourselves but for the future generations."[48]

Epilogue

---

[48] Caecilius Statius, 220-168 B.C.

What happened to the Heart? She's the Heart of a democratically run congregation in a university town much larger than ours, where she and her family are appreciated and enjoying life. Our Board gave her a gift wrapped in black paper.

Two years after we left, Hubby and I received a *pro forma*, handwritten note from the congregation's new Heart, letting us know he'd be happy to hear from us. Not a word since.

Three years after we left, Hubby and I crossed paths with three congregational power couples at a restaurant. We sat at the other end of the room. One by one, the three men, all former Board presidents, came over with big smiles to shake Hubby's hand, eyes flicking uneasily my way. The first man, Patsy's husband, greeted me, but spoke only to Hubby. The second man smiled continuously as he spoke with Hubby, while pressing his hand heavily on my shoulder. When I shrugged it off, he put it back and pressed harder. He finally removed it with a double pat, giving me a reproachful look when I didn't return his smile and goodbye. My lack of response to the third man leaning down to kiss me hello sent him on his way quickly. Message sent.

Not one woman came over. Message received.

Four years after we left, one fine July morning. Standing at the kitchen counter, I slit open a thick envelope with the congregation's return address. It was the first request in three years for annual membership dues and included a

391

typed cover letter, personally addressed to us, which opened with: "You are missed! We hope you will consider rejoining our community!" Translation: *We miss your money!*

It was signed by Cheryl, still chair of membership, with a handwritten note in blue ink beside her signature: "Your energy is missed! Hope all is well!"

"Check this out," I said to Hubby, as he poured himself a cup of coffee. He took the letter from me, read it, and curled his lip in scorn. He handed it back.

"*'Your energy is missed!'*" I mocked.

"Of course they miss it. You get things done."

"Come on!"

"Huh?"

"She's full of it. What she's *really* saying is: I don't like you, but you're too useful to ignore. 'Your energy is missed' sounds good *and* it's not a lie. But it's not true, either. Like saying something is 'interesting' when, really, you don't like it."

Hubby rolled his eyes. "Gotcha."

"Not once in the past four years has she, or anyone else, reached out," I said and shook my head. "It's too bad she sent this. I wish she hadn't."

Hubby raised his eyebrows.

"She should have kept her mouth shut," I said. "'Better to remain silent and be thought a fool than to speak and remove all doubt.'"

He chuckled in appreciation.

I tossed the mailing in the garbage can under the counter. He nodded and ambled away to read the paper and drink his coffee. I poured myself the last cup and, with a sharp tap of the basket and a brown splat, dumped the spent grounds onto all that white paper. I lightened my coffee with milk and stepped out onto the back deck.

I had let milkweed take over the garden for the monarchs. The blooms were perfectly round, each ball made up of tiny, pale pink flowers with a gentle, lilac-like perfume that drifted by on a balmy breeze. I sat down in the sun and drank my coffee. Robins foraged for worms on the lawn, a pair of nesting cardinals darted in and out of the monster forsythia, and an adolescent squirrel ran across the top the fence.

For years, I'd considered Cheryl a friend…. Her four-year silence had let me know the feeling was no longer mutual. And yet, because our end remained undeclared, a tiny ember of hope had continued to burn in my heart. Today, that hope winked out. It was over. Relief, surprisingly sweet, swept through me. I inhaled fragrant air deeply and exhaled slowly, slid down in the chair and closed my eyes, the coffee mug warm in my hands.

Visitor 1, Home 0

December

Carol and I sat opposite each other, she in the upholstered chair that matched the couch and I in my ergonomic wonder. It was four-thirty and the winter sun had set, the shaded windows dark beside our chairs. The gold light of several lamps warmed the sage walls. Carol worked as a drug rep and always came in after spending a long day driving around to physicians' offices to inform them about the latest meds launched by her company. Her territory was huge, covering two hundred square miles around our town.

She was a woman in her early thirties, chunky, rumpled, and unfortunate in her looks. Individually, her buck-teeth, lazy eye, and scoliosis wouldn't have stood out. But add to that her wrinkled blouses and ill-fitting suits, heavy black glasses, and the fact that she never, ever smiled. Somehow all these things together projected a deep unhappiness that came off as unattractive rather than sympathetic.

Yet she was smart and competent and caring. I liked her and wanted to help her shake off a little of that resignation. I wanted to see her smile, just once. It was terrible how clearly she knew she was discriminated against because of her looks. She shared one story after the other about better-looking, younger, dumber, less credentialed, less competent women with less seniority

395

getting promoted, placed at better sites, acknowledged, and given raises ahead of her.

Her co-workers made after-work social plans within hearing range, but didn't invite her. "It's like I don't exist." Her supervisors expected more work from her than from other staff. If she dared to complain, she was punished. "My boss turned down my vacation and personal time requests last year, and increased my caseload. When I pushed back about that, she assigned me all the outlying sites. With all the extra driving, I'm working twelve to fourteen hour days. Most nights, I'm not getting home in time to put my son to bed."

In the heart-breaking and stereotyped way of people who hate themselves for something they have no control over and for which they've been bullied all their lives, she had married the only man who had asked, with disastrous results.

An online gambling and gaming addict, her husband was a sociopath, parasitic type. He contributed nothing to the household, neither money nor maintenance; used her as a domestic drudge; and raged if she didn't buy him what he wanted on demand. "He knows we can't afford it. He doesn't care."

Her only joy was their three-year-old son, affectionate but a handful. Her husband and in-laws undermined her parenting, yet when the child acted up, it was her fault. "Day care costs a fortune, but I don't trust him to watch the baby. I don't know how this happened to me. I swore I wouldn't make my mother's mistake."

Of course she was depressed and emotionally battered, too. Anti-depressants—all classes, alone and in combination—hadn't helped. Counseling hadn't helped either. Three years of bi-monthly sessions later, nothing had.

Even though she groused often that the treatment wasn't working, she kept coming. As long as she did, I'd keep trying. Today might be the day my brain lit up with a flash of genius. Surprise: today was the day she fired me.

"You're not helping," she said bluntly.

We looked at each other. I nodded. "I have to agree." She looked neither surprised nor pleased at my honesty. She gazed at me impassively.

"You've told me in person I've failed you. That takes backbone. Thank you for that."

She shrugged. "It's the right thing to do."

I smiled, "That's right. That's what makes you a good worker, a good mother, and a good person." She didn't respond.

Should I make one final therapeutic comment? Was she hoping I'd pull out a last-minute reprieve?

"You took action with me right now. If you can do it with me, you can do it with your husband too."

She raised an eyebrow.

"He needs you more than you need him. You're supporting him. That gives you the power to negotiate. For example, you might say to him: If you dust and vacuum, I'll pay the cable bill. Otherwise I won't.'"

"I could never do that. He'd pitch a fit."

"So? Let him."

"I can't. You don't get it."

We gazed at each other. We were closing things down today. She wouldn't (or couldn't) acknowledge she let her husband use her. Pointing this out to her now might hurt her, the last thing I wanted. She was suffering enough.

"I'm sorry," I said, and meant it, on so many levels. She compressed her lips into a thin line and rose from her chair. I stood, too. She retrieved her coat from the couch, put it on, and said good-bye.

"The door is always open," I said. She left without a backward glance.

"There's a crack in everything. That's how the light gets in."[49]

I blew this treatment. It may have been over for Carol, but it wasn't over for me. What had gone wrong? I'd missed something. What?

As time rolled on, a trigger would remind me, and again I'd review this unsolved puzzle, shifting the pieces this way and that, looking for a new angle and not finding one. I resigned myself to not knowing, to possibly never knowing.

Ten years after the treatment ended, I handwrote the first draft of this story. I threw it in the wastebasket immediately. Why share a failure I was ashamed of? Neither Carol nor I had changed. Where was the story arc? Regardless, I retrieved it the next day and put it aside. Why did I do that? I don't know. I forgot about it for another five years.

Then two things happened. First, the Republicans swept the 2016 election, winning the House, the Senate,

---

[49] Leonard Cohen

and the presidency. The speed with which Trump and the GOP dismantled basic legislative protections for everyone not rich, white, and male shattered my sense of internal security. Until the Equal Rights Amendment passes, it is legal in this country to discriminate against women. My house of worship experience took on new meaning. There, I had the freedom to choose— stay or leave— if I didn't like how the leadership ran things. But with the elections over, I had no further choices regarding my country's leadership. For the first time in my life, I realized how vulnerable I was to institutional oppression and felt—viscerally—the helplessness that is chronic for those less privileged than myself.

Second, fear, rage, and loathing took their toll. In reaction, I signed up for a cartooning workshop. Why not? I've always admired cartoonists and the cartoon form. My need to express myself freely while it was still legal overcame my drawing inhibitions. I'd hoped that learning how to construct and draw a cartoon would blow my mind open. It didn't. What did, was a book on the recommended reading list: *Impro* by Keith Johnstone, a guide for actors learning improvisational acting. The chapter on social status relations should be required reading for all therapists.

Ingrained from birth, our place in the pack hierarchy is held in the body, like muscle memory, out of conscious awareness. Improv actors have to be able to act out, on demand and without a script, the mannerisms, diction, and attitudes of people from classes above and below their own. This is incredibly difficult to do *believably* despite rigorous training, even for as short a period of time as an improv performance.

Studying this, Johnstone observed three things. First, it is easier for the body to act authentically if the status change is close to one's own. Second, maintaining status neutrality is *not possible* because we automatically interpret each other's status. Third, our status changes in relation to whom we are with.

These last two points validated my intuitive conviction that it's futile for a therapist to maintain a neutral façade with a patient, as the training says we can and should. A therapist's status is always perceived and interpreted by the patient, and vice versa, even if only on the unconscious, physical level. Immediately, I understood how useful this would be for future work.

Meanwhile, back at the writing desk, Carol burst through five years of amnesia. I reread that first draft and relived her treatment, again. She was smart, competent, and a good person. She was no beauty queen, but she could have dressed so much better. Why didn't she? She was the family breadwinner, at the top of her family's pyramid. Why didn't she push back against her husband? For that matter, why didn't she just get rid of him?

I dropped my pen and drifted off, imagining her life as a divorcée. She would be a single mother, without the support of extended family—her parents were deceased and she had no sibs, aunts, uncles, or cousins. The in-laws would try to lure away her son while the ex would legally impoverish her with child-support payments and alimony. At work, she was already the lowest status member.

Untethered from family, her unhappiness and stress would deepen, attracting ever more social cruelty. Like a chicken locked in a coop, she'd get pecked to death.

Insight bloomed. It didn't matter that her husband was a leech. What mattered was that she was *married* and *a mother*. These rock-solid proofs of her womanly worth shielded her from the easy abuse of others and maintained her status as a viable member of the pack, at home and at work.

How wrong I'd been, and how ignorant. She needed her husband far more than he needed her. If she left him, he'd just move in with his mother. Without him, Carol's level of social vulnerability didn't bear thinking about. Better to be part of a family, no matter how low in the hierarchy. She'd never put that protection at risk. I had become dangerous to her. That's why she'd left.

I picked up my pen. The second draft wrote itself.

Assume, and make an ass of you and me.

I'm nice-looking. I had never thought about my looks except, like most women, to focus on minor deficits (big nose, short waist, pick a body part, any part). Certainly I had never considered my looks with regard to getting and keeping a job, or getting and keeping friends. My post-spat fantasy that I should trade in Hubby for a tidier, less annoying model assumed that the "better" man would not only have me, but would be happy to be chosen. (Ha. I had no idea I thought so highly of myself.)

It came as a shock to realize how much of an edge my looks gave me hierarchically and how deeply I had taken that protection for granted. That's a luxury Carol didn't have and *I hadn't seen that*, which prevented me from formulating an effective treatment strategy. Just as a chain is only as strong as its weakest link, a therapist is only as clinically effective as her blind spots.

It's always a thrill to figure out what went wrong, despite it being a blow to the ego and too late for the treatment. It matters regardless. I won't make this particular mistake again. I'll just make a new one, based on another assumption that I'm unaware of. That's the problem with assumptions. You don't know you have them. Worse, unmasking them is hardly a given.

To be open to noticing an assumption, it helps to live your life fully, learn new things, and pay attention. Sometimes, though, the discovery happens through an unpredictable aggregation of chance events. What if I hadn't retrieved that first draft from the wastebasket? What if I hadn't written it at all? What if I hadn't taken that cartoon workshop and read *Impro*? Something from all these coalesced when I drifted into the reverie that—*aha!*—revealed my unexamined operating premise, solved the mystery, and closed the case.

Excavating that assumption delighted me as much as if I'd unearthed buried treasure. Imagine my amazement on discovering its deep value, truth, and usefulness. It's a thing of beauty. Louis Pasteur famously said that chance favors only a prepared mind. Even with a prepared mind though, what are the chances? You don't have to be a genius to share Pasteur's sense of wonder: "I am on the edge of mysteries and the veil is getting thinner and thinner."

Afterword(s)

To be a good human being is to have a kind of openness to the world, an ability to trust uncertain things beyond your own control. Martha Nussbaum

He who laughs...lasts. Erma Bombeck

If you are reading this, you've finished the book. Thank you! It wasn't required reading. I wish it were, for three reasons: first, to correct misconceptions and soothe fears— about psychiatrists and therapists, those who use our services, and our treatments; second, to encourage those of you considering doing this work or already doing it; and lastly, and most importantly, to reassure everyone that flawless performance isn't required for a clinician to be genuinely helpful. A bedrock commitment to ease suffering saves the day more often than not, and drives on-going learning as well.

When I was in training and presenting clinical work to mentors, I was careful to minimize mistakes I was ashamed of in order to maximize their good opinion of me. I got away with that because few observed me in session with patients. That's too bad, twice over. I'm sure my astute teachers would have commented on things I didn't notice. I'm sure I would have improved faster for their feedback.

A therapist's treatment tool is herself. As with any tool, the skill of the person using it determines its usefulness. The more self-knowledge and self-control a therapist has, the more competent she is. The richest learning comes from studying all those ego-deflating (i.e., human) errors, limitations, and self-delusions. What we get defensive about and want to deny. For a therapist, there is no real separation between work and life. Doing therapy isn't a simile or a metaphor for life. It *is* life. An examined life.

Of course anyone, not just therapists, can live an examined life, and I highly recommend it. All you need is the interest and persistence. Yes, it's hard.[50] But if you consider the consequences, so is living on autopilot.

Had Hubby and I not gone off script and relocated to the boonies, I would still have lived an examined life. But an academic career (even an urban, non-academic job or private practice) with its demands and competition would have distracted me like a smart phone. Both take away the three key elements of discovery: boredom, uncertainty, and loneliness.[51]

---

[50] Why do we expect things to be easy? That sets the bar unreasonably high and leads to so much whining.

[51] "The phone gives us a lot, but it takes away three key elements of discovery: loneliness, uncertainty and boredom. Those have always been where creative ideas come from." Lynda Barry, from a 2016 lecture she gave at NASA's Goddard Space Flight Center.

Working out in the back forty has distinct advantages. There's not much going on intellectually and that forces me to notice small yet significant things. These jewels are everywhere— books, film, art, cartoons, snatches of overheard conversations while standing in the grocery line. I glom onto them like a magpie does shiny objects, stashing them and keeping them close. They stimulate thought and, in turn, insight. They've contributed as much to my therapy skills as the professional literature.

The appalling absence of treatment resources means I'm it for my patients and often uncertain about what to do. Regular researching, problem solving, and using my best judgment have built my confidence.

Being on my own[52] and not unduly swayed by the opinions of colleagues more forceful than myself has made it much easier to draw original conclusions. I live for the moment when disparate elements come together and— *Eureka!* Let me tell you about my best professional insight ever.

A perennial problem for therapists is a phenomenon called the Doorknob Moment. On the way out, with a hand on the doorknob, the patient drops a bombshell and falls apart. What to do? (A) end on time and send the patient out distraught? Or (B) run over and keep the next patient waiting? Nothing in my training explained *why* it was therapeutic to end on time, though that was the prevailing wisdom. When actually under pressure, I never felt

---

[52]Well, not completely. I'm blessed to have Hubby, who enjoys playing Devil's advocate without needing to win.

confident that ending on time was the right thing to do for the patient. Well, it is. Why that is, complete with science, came in a flash. That it also maintains the schedule was a door prize.

For a second or two, I was a genius. Then I did the research, fully expecting to find the article already written, by someone else. I was gobsmacked to find... nothing. I wrote it up and the paper was published.[53]

If I'd chosen to become an urban academic, publishing this paper would have met only the minimum professional expectation: publish or perish. I'd have felt only the relief of a temporary reprieve from that chronic stress. Instead, being under no such pressure, I exceeded my own professional expectations and was thrilled: *I've given back. I've moved the work forward. I can die now.*[54]

Breakthrough insights come without warning, striking like a white bolt of lightning and leaving my body filled with current. Sometimes, as with the Doorknob Moment, it's pleasurable. Other times, they show up after a crushing experience I'd rather not have gone through. (It's totally worth it.[55]) Here's an example. I got separated from Hubby and Son when we visited the Holocaust Museum in Washington, D.C., and went through most of the exhibits alone. By the end, I was overwhelmed and sickened. *If I*

---

[53] "Doorknob Moments: Handling End-of-Session Bombshells," *Psychotherapy Networker*, September/October 2018, page 17.

[54] Not!

[55] Be brave, little Piglet.

ever find myself terrified and trapped like that, I'll kill myself, I decided, *as my last act of defiance and self-control.*

Surfacing from those depths, I noticed sounds coming from somewhere out of sight. Steven Spielberg's documentary of survivor interviews was playing in an open auditorium. I took a seat, lost myself in it, and could hardly tear myself away when Hubby found me. ("We've been looking all over for you!")

My spirit was remarkably uplifted. Why? Despite the horror, each survivor had cared about someone there — *and that was enough* to keep them going. My decision to end it all assumed I would be ripped away from Hubby and Son; that I would be isolated, disconnected, and untethered; that I would be alone at the mercy of the apocalypse. But what if I was wrong about that? What if I made a friend who had my back and I theirs? Maybe then, I would choose to endure.

Insight: *Today,* none of us has access to *all* the variables that would inform action we might take in a hypothetical future. I saw myself on that future day thinking: *I can always kill myself later,* and smiled involuntarily. My decision to die had become absurd, a light and airy place compared to the claustrophobic despair that generated it. *Aha!*

Pro tip: Render your original conclusion *ridiculous* by enlarging the context you interpret it within.[56] Master this reframe and it will change your life. I promise. It just

---

[56] I panned this solid gold nugget from a talk given by David Whyte, poet and inspirational speaker, at the 2011 *Psychotherapy Networker* conference.

keeps on giving and giving. It puts things in perspective. It fosters a sense of humor. It reels you back in from the void and reconnects you to others. Even if you don't find a reframe right away, the search alone wises you up.

The human connection is a mystery. Isn't it awe-inspiring that even in the hell of a concentration camp people bond to support each other? That a suicidal person would trust me, a stranger, to help? How is that possible? Science may not have the answer yet. But it's obvious that love— the drive that connects us meaningfully with one another— is lifesaving, life enhancing, and creative. That bond contains within it all the challenges you could want and deep comfort, too. It's well worth studying and cultivating. Keep learning. Practice, practice, practice. It'll never make us perfect and that's a good thing. We all need something to complain about.

"The obstacle is the way."
Marcus Aurelius (121 AD – 180 AD)

Acknowledgments

This book would not be, if it weren't for the people I thank here, with heartfelt gratitude:

My patients, for trusting me. I would never have gotten into so much trouble otherwise, and learned so much.

My analyst therapists, for shining a light in the darkness and helping me heal, there are no words: Ralph Harris, MD and Robin Shafran, Ph.D.

My psychiatry residency mentor, Alvin Pam, Ph.D., for exceptional training and supervision, and for enduring friendship.

Lynda Barry, inspiration, professor, cartoonist, writer, and all around creative genius (validated in 2019 with a Macarthur Genius grant), for sharing the key to the creative kingdom. Her workshop, "Writing The Unthinkable," is the only course I've taken (of many) that actually teaches how to reliably and sustainably create *new* work, in any genre.

Friends— You are the best— for having my writing back:
Naomi Bradshaw, my first reader, going back more than twenty years.

Elle Garrell Berger, author and my first writing mentor, who said from the beginning, "Of course you can" and graciously allowed me to use her marvelous turn of phrase: *gift wrapped in black paper.*

Shannon Little, MD, for suggesting I submit "There's No Place Like Gnome" to a writing contest.

Susan Kemker, MD, one year ahead in the residency, for that time I demanded she accept an admission and she refused; and we're still friends, no end in sight.

Amy Guglielmo, artist and Christopher Award winning author, for saying, "Yes, it's hard." And, "Don't stop."

Terry Boyarsky, friend at first sight, for beta reading the manuscript *immediately.*

Lori B. Duff, author and wonder woman, for beta reading the manuscript *in the middle of her own book launch.*

The Erma Bombeck Humor Writers Workshop, for being a *fun*tastic writers' resource, and especially for hosting the panel that led me to my publisher.

My publishing team, for believing in and delivering this book to you— I am a *very* fortunate woman:

Donna Cavanagh, CornerOffice Books, an imprint of HOPress, publisher, for saying: "That sounds fascinating. Send me some sample chapters." And then, "Send me the whole manuscript." And then, "Let's publish it."

Kathy Taylor, editor: for her big brain, deep thinking, and gently delivered feedback, which forced me to revise against my will, and made the book so much better.

Dwayne Booth, artist and brilliant political cartoonist: for the cool cover, which repays a second look.

Kevin Gitlin, for everything.

Appendices

Ask Dr. D

Disclaimer: Answers to these FAQ's are recommendations, not prescriptions or therapy (though therapy may be required to implement). Assume we're chatting at a social event, you've just learned I'm a psychiatrist, you haven't shared any of your medical history and you're simply picking my brain out of curiosity. Bwa ha ha....Beware of what you ask for....

Hey, whatever happened to Jeb from Health Care Catch-22? Did he get a biopsy? Did he get his gum cancer treated? Did he live? I wish I knew to tell you. But sadly, I don't. He didn't keep his next appointment and didn't return my phone calls after. The End. Real life is full of non-starters, derailments and unexplained disappearances. If only life were more like fiction. I'm sorry I couldn't answer this question, but here are a few I can.

How do I pick a psychiatrist/therapist? The most important quality to look for is that feeling of connection, that the clinician wants to get to know you and help you. How do you assess that? Ask yourself these questions when you're with him or her:

Do they look at you while you're speaking?

Do they listen— really listen— to you?

Do you feel, from the questions they ask, that they want to understand *you*, as a whole person?

Do you feel safe enough to give them a chance? It may take a several sessions to figure out.

What do I do if I run into my therapist out in the community? Do I say hi, or what? By all means, if you want to say hi, do so. But—here's the good news— it's completely okay *not to*.

I always follow my patients' lead, out of respect for their vulnerability. Opening up is risky for patients, even in the safe space of the office. Outside, greeting me carries the risk that a witness might think they know me because they're in treatment. If a patient ignores me in public, I respect their need for privacy by not greeting them.

However, once a patient acknowledges me in any way, I always respond, for two reasons. First, it's simple good manners. One must always acknowledge being acknowledged. I respond in kind: a nod for a nod; a hello for a hello; a brief social conversation that doesn't touch on any clinical material or reveal the nature of our relationship.

Second, not acknowledging a patient's greeting rejects them, which hurts, arouses anxiety, and undermines trust. This is destructive to the therapeutic bond and violates the Hippocratic Oath: do no harm. Again, I always respond in kind.

That said, life being what it is, miscommunications occur. If your therapist doesn't return your greeting, it's always appropriate to give them the benefit of the doubt and ask why they didn't at the next session. How they address it with you will make a difference to your level of trust.

I'm getting forgetful. What should I do? My answer will surprise you. Stop drinking. Completely. Alcohol is a potent neurotoxin, i.e., a brain poison. The fact that alcohol damages your brain is well documented. Doubt the science at your own risk.

Not even one? Come on. One drink isn't going to hurt me. Well, no. But it's not going to help. And let's be honest. It's not just one beer, one glass of wine, or one drink. One a day adds up to seven a week to 365 a year. Multiply 365 drinks by the years you've been drinking one a day and…. The math speaks for itself.

It's hard to stop drinking. It's hard to lose your memory. You'll have to choose between hards. Maybe this will make it easier: A buzz is brief, but brain damage is forever.

Life is short, Doc, and then you die. Might as well party. You're assuming you'll be enjoying yourself right up to the point the Grim Reaper comes for you. That's not how it works (unless you're *very* lucky). There's a phase, before death but after the enjoyment, when the consequences of decades of habitual drinking, smoking, and eating junk food catch up with you. You'll be alive but sick, possibly for many long years. That's not living, is it? Of course, there's no guarantee that cleaning up will restore your health. Still, it's amazing how resilient we are and how much damage we can recover from. It's never too late. The sooner, the better.

Is there a healthy diet that's not a lot of work? I like the KIS method: Keep It Simple. Eat lots of food straight from the ground, i.e., fresh fruits, veggies, raw nuts, and grains. Avoid anything bagged, bottled, or boxed (i.e., processed). Doing that will immediately reduce your intake of sugar, preservatives, and fat. Unfortunately, that includes pasta, bread, French fries, cookies, candy, chips, and ice cream.

I hear your screams of agony. What the heck will you eat, right? Instead of canned corn, enjoy fresh corn on the cob. Instead of apple pie, eat an apple. Instead of boxed cereal, plain oatmeal with fresh fruit. Instead of chicken nuggets, a sautéed chicken breast. You may have to learn how to cook. That will serve you well when the climate apocalypse hits.

Blech. **Next, you're going to tell me to exercise regularly**. Well, sure. Why not? You may not love it but your body, and your brain, will. You'll sleep better. We can all stand to sleep more, and more restfully.

That said, sitting all day crunches your spine (leading to pain), squashes your internal organs (leading to digestive problems) and makes you flabby and lumpy in a way that even Spanx can't fix.

But exercising is so boring! Good news: you can take a daily walk on autopilot and still get the benefits. But what you really want is to go inside and *feel* your way into befriending your body. Listening to music helps a lot: the body loves to move rhythmically. I don't recommend exercising while watching television, listening to podcasts or talk radio. These keep your attention in your head rather than in your body, and you'll stay oblivious to the body's non-verbal way of communicating via sensation. If you focus on that, you might discover *it feels good* to move your bod and that it's *interesting*. You never know. Stranger things have happened.

If you think about it, the body is the most amazing tool and toy the Almighty could have given us. It's also our home for our time on Earth. Take care of it like you would your children. Don't overdo and injure yourself. Consider taking up yoga, dance, tai chi, or any activity that teaches you how to use your body as a whole and requires concentration to do well. You'll get sharper and kinder,[57] and you'll look better in your clothes, too.

This is all so hard! I know. I know. There's no escaping suffering.[58] (Why do we think we can?) Think about it this way. You'll pay now or you'll pay later. Either you suffer getting and staying healthy, or you suffer dying slowly. And speaking of paying, think of the money you're spending. Examine your pleasures. Do they hurt you and make the purveyors rich? Consider giving them up and keeping the money for yourself!

Something always comes along to derail me and I go back to my old ways. Why bother? It'll just happen again. "Being healthy" is phrased that way because health is a state of *being*. It's a process, not a goal. Because there's no defined end point, you don't have to be perfect, just persistent. Don't be afraid of working hard. The Dalai Lama said, "Improvement requires continuous effort." We're all subject to setbacks, whether random or of our own making. Think of them as an interruption in your commitment. Forgive yourself. Grieve. Then restart.

---

[57] "Love begins at home." Mother Teresa

[58] *Life is suffering. Enjoy.* Jewish Buddha (A joke. For more, Google: 'Sayings of the Jewish Buddha.')

Anything you do to support your health is always better than doing nothing.

My primary care doc isn't on my case about drinking, eating, and exercising like you, the head shrinker. Get back in your lane! Brain and body health go together, my friend. Have you forgotten you asked me what you could do to help your memory?

How can I make my husband/wife/loved one take better care of him/her self? You can't. Give up trying. You can't "make" anyone do anything, except yourself. You're the only person you have any control over. Focus on your own work. Accept your flaws and limits without letting them limit you. When you grow, there is a beneficial ripple effect on everyone around you.

I do my job to the best of my ability. But everywhere I go, people are slacking off. It's not right. It makes me so angry. Indeed. The late cartoonist Charles Schulz, creator of "Peanuts," let his character Linus shout in frustration: *I love mankind…. It's people I can't stand!* Do as Schultz did: cultivate a sense of humor. Earnestness and righteousness are deadly to getting along and enjoying life. Research suggests that reading cultivates empathy and understanding of what others go through. Read more. A lot more. Especially what makes you laugh.

Recommended Reading

Creativity

Lynda Barry, *What It Is*. An immersive, artful, and deep exploration of two questions. (1) What is an image? (2) How is an image part of the process of creating? The author, syndicated alternative cartoonist and professor at University of Wisconsin, presents in graphic form her foolproof method for consistently producing new material of any type. Testimonial: Using it, I wrote first drafts of thirteen chapters of this book in thirteen days. See also, *Syllabus: Notes from an Accidental Professor* and *Making Comics*.

Keith Johnstone, *Impro*. Even if you couldn't care less about improv acting, the chapter on social status relations has the power to pull the rug out from under everything you think you know about yourself socially.

Mind-Opening

Atul Gawande, M.D., *Checklist Manifesto*. A simple checklist has the power to organize and prevent avoidable catastrophic failures in industries of overwhelming complexity, such as medicine.

Terry Pratchett, The "Discworld" series of novels. Because we all need to laugh. More than three dozen! You're in for a treat. Social satire of the highest order, yet always affectionate.

Art Spiegelman, *Maus I: A Survivor's Tale: My Father Bleeds History* and *Maus II: A Survivor's Tale: And Here My Troubles Began*.
Spiegelman's parents "survived" WWII concentration camps. How did they make a life, after life had been rendered meaningless? Spiegelman explores this question and the consequences to his own life in these meticulously researched, deeply felt, and beautifully drawn graphic memoirs. The sections of the author working with his psychiatrist vividly reveal the healing power of a therapeutic relationship. Pairs perfectly with Van Der Kolk's *The Body Keeps The Score*.

Krista Tippett, *Becoming Wise: An Inquiry into the Mystery and Art of Living*. A compilation of essays by the journalist author based on her interviews with wise people on her public radio show, *On Being*.

David Whyte, *Consolations: The Solace, Nourishment and Underlying Meaning of Everyday Words*. These— prose-poems? meditations? prayers?— leave a transcendent afterglow that demands: *Again. Read me again.*

Ed Yong, *I Contain Multitudes*. In the beginning, there were microbes. If you collapse the Earth's entire history (4.54 billion years) into a single year, humans have existed for only *the last half hour of December 31st*. Single cell organisms emerged in March and ruled through October. So... microbes were here first. There are more bacteria in *one* person's gut than there are stars in the galaxy. If that creeps you out, remember: we wouldn't be here if microbes hadn't let us in.

The author, a science journalist, has summarized a formidable amount of research about microbes, in their huge variety, and our relationships with them. The result is seismically disruptive to anything you think you know about humanity's place in the biologic cosmos. And yet, consider this: we know next to nothing about microbes. This readable book induces awe.

Parenting

James Breakwell, *Bare Minimum Parenting: The Ultimate Guide to Not Quite Ruining Your Child*. The author, a comedian, freely admits he was just trying to be funny, which he is. There's at least one belly laugh a page, if not more. The fact that he's hit the sensible nail on the head as a happy accident in no way diminishes the usefulness of this primer for 21st century parents.

Richard Ferber, M.D., *Solve Your Child's Sleep Problems*. Practical and effective advice for parents of kids aged one to six.

Stephen H. Glenn, *Raising Self-Reliant Children in a Self-Indulgent World: Seven Building Blocks for Developing Capable Young People.* An evergreen guide for parents of school age kids.

Frances E. Jensen, MD, with Amy Ellis Nutt, *The Teenage Brain: A Neuroscientist's Survival Guide to Raising Adolescents and Young Adults.* A must read, for parents *and* teens, and anyone with a teen in their life. You'll learn how very different the teen brain is from an adult's, how amazing its capacity to learn is, how terrifyingly vulnerable it is to permanent ruination, and why teens need their parents, and adult guidance, *just as much, if not more,* than when they were younger. Read about sleep, energy drinks, alcohol, drugs, digital devices, sports and concussions, and other topics of extreme interest. Simply brilliant. Utterly useful. Don't skip this one.

Burton L. White, *The First Three Years Of Life.* I loved this book when I was a new mother. It describes the way infants morph into people as their little brains grow bigger. Each stage of development has its behaviors, which occur predictably in sequence within a reassuringly wide age range. Why does a toddler toss a toy out of the playpen for you to pick up, and then when you hand it back, throw it out again? And again? Read this book. You'll be captivated observing your baby develop into herself. People are fascinating, starting day one.

Psychiatry/Psychology/Therapy/Self Help

Daniel Amen, M.D., *Change Your Brain, Change Your Life.* Excellent, evidence-based explanations of the primary psychiatric disorders, along with sound treatment recommendations.

Susan Cain, *Quiet, The Power of Introverts in a World That Can't Stop Talking.* Superbly intelligent, deeply researched and beautifully written, this is the book to read if you, or someone you love, prefers to listen rather than talk, to work alone rather than in groups, and loathes self-promotion. Take heart, Introvert. You don't have to change yourself. The world needs you just as you are.

Mihaly Csikszentmihalyi, *Flow: The Psychology of Optimal Experience.* The psychology behind what makes an experience truly satisfying. The verbal complement to Lynda Barry's image driven *What It Is.*

Diagnostic and Statistical Manual (DSM) of Mental Disorders, published by the American Psychiatric Association. The official listing of psychiatric disorders and their diagnostic criteria.

Angela Duckworth, *Grit: The Power of Passion and Perseverance.* What is success and how do you achieve it? The secret revealed by science!

Matthew Edlund, M.D., *The Power of Rest: Why Sleep Alone Is Not Enough.* Rest more. Find out why you should and how to do so.

Sigmund Freud, *The Interpretation of Dreams.* The original. Just fascinating. Short. Readable.

Erich Fromm, *Escape from Freedom.* Written by the great social psychologist, psychoanalyst, humanist, and philosopher after World War II. What would drive people to prefer the control of a totalitarian regime to the freedoms of democracy? Pairs well with Milgram's *Obedience to Authority.*

Atul Gawande, M.D., *Being Mortal: Medicine and What Matters in the End.* Death is a fact of life, a reality that mainstream medical practice handles poorly. In this compassionate and honest book, Gawande addresses this bias, which causes so much unnecessary suffering in the dying and their loved ones. Too bad he's a surgeon. He would have made a great psychiatrist.

Jerrold Mundis, *How to Get Out of Debt, Stay Out of Debt, and Live Prosperously.* If you are carrying heavy debt, you are a slave. Free yourself.

Alvin Pam, Ph.D., and Judith Pearson, Ph.D., *Splitting Up: Enmeshment and Estrangement in the Process of Divorce.* Guess what, a legal divorce does not mean the relationship is over. Find out why here. This book is particularly useful if you're going through a divorce with kids.

Bessel Van Der Kolk, M.D., *The Body Keeps the Score: Brain, Mind, and Body in the Healing of Trauma.* An astonishing and game-changing book that pulls together over thirty years of solid research on all kinds of trauma (war, rape, domestic violence, child abuse, and more) and provides substantial evidence-based data, more than enough to update current diagnostic criteria. This in turn would allow for more targeted and effective treatment. Shamefully, this data remains mostly ignored to date by mainstream psychiatry. The extent and permanent fallout of childhood trauma— abandonment and neglect; physical and sexual abuse— is an unaddressed public health emergency.

Sociopathy

Bandy X. Lee, M.D., Editor, *The Dangerous Case of Donald Trump: 37 Psychiatrists and Mental Health Experts Assess a President.* This compelling collection of essays came out soon after Donald Trump won the 2016 presidential election. Will an equivalent compilation assessing the Republican party be forthcoming? Enquiring minds need to know.

Stanley Milgram, Ph.D., *Obedience To Authority.* A chilling must read. Milgram was deeply troubled by the scale of the WWII Nazi genocide, which required massive numbers of workers to implement, too many to write off as sadistic monsters. What would make *the majority* of regular people override personal morality to commit atrocities against innocent others? You'll find out here.

Martha Stout, Ph.D., *The Sociopath Next Door.* Another game changer. Four in one hundred people are sociopaths, people without a conscience. They are incapable of loving others or being loved, and this inability is hardwired and untreatable. They could be *anyone in your life:* child, parent, spouse, neighbor, boss. They know the rules of right and wrong— it's not rocket science— but unlike the rest of us, they use that knowledge as a tool for personal gain only. This makes the rest of us highly vulnerable to manipulation because, being normal and caring, it's almost impossible to wrap our heads around such ruthless indifference. Read this book to learn how to identify these people and protect yourself.

Glossary

AA: Alcoholics Anonymous. Leaderless support group for alcoholics, famous for its 12-step program to maintain sobriety.

ADD: Attention Deficit Disorder. A cognitive disorder characterized by inattention, distractibility, lack of follow through, lack of future planning, and impulsivity. There are several sub-types. May also be caused by traumatic brain injury, such as a car accident or football injury.

Affect: Emotional weather of the day. Affect is to mood what weather is to climate.

Agitated: A state of neurological arousal beyond mere upset, accompanied by intense negative affect.

Al-Anon: The sister group to AA, for the non-drinking loved ones of alcoholics.

Allowable (insurance): The dollar amount actually paid by a health insurance company to a clinician for service rendered. This amount is based on Medicare rates and is dictated by what the insurance company deems "allowable," independent of the clinician's actual fee or medical need. Rather, it is based on business need, i.e., profitability.

Analyst (psychoanalyst): An MD psychiatrist or Ph.D. psychologist with many extra years of training in a school of psychotherapy based on the work of a particular clinician, for example: Freud, Jung, William Alison White, Harry Stack Sullivan.

Attending: A senior teaching physician working with residents in a teaching hospital or clinic.

Burn out: A state of disengagement, boredom, and internal deadness.

Co-dependent: (adjective) Putting up with bad behavior in a partner out of unmet needs from childhood. These (often unconscious) unmet needs interfere with healthy self-esteem and independence in adulthood. As a noun, a person who does this.

Co-pay: Co-payment, i.e., the portion of the clinician's fee uncovered by insurance that is the patient's responsibility.

Consultation-Liaison: An in-hospital branch of psychiatry that specializes in the interface between psychiatry and the other medical specialties, e.g., internal medicine, surgery, and others.

Counter-transference: When the therapist unconsciously transfers personal feelings (negative, positive, or both) onto the patient that interfere with the treatment. (See **Transference.**)

CT or **CAT scan:** Computerized (Axial) Tomography. An image of the inside of the body generated by computer technology.

Defense mechanisms: Psychological strategies we *all* use, *without* conscious awareness, to protect ourselves from the anxiety triggered by unacceptable thoughts and feelings.

Delusion: A psychotic conviction that is impervious to reason and logic. There are many forms, including bizarre (you can kill others with your thoughts); grandiose (you are Jesus); suspicious (conspiracy theorists aplenty); medical (you are dying even though all tests, aka "the million dollar workup," come back within normal limits); and many more.

DSM: *Diagnostic and Statistical Manual of Mental Disorders,* published by the American Psychiatric Association. (See Recommended Reading.)

Drug rep: Pharmaceutical drug representative, i.e., salesperson for a specific medicine or group of medicines manufactured by the employer, the pharmaceutical company.

DUI: Driving Under the Influence, i.e., while intoxicated. A legal offense.

EMDR: Eye Movement Desensitization and Reprocessing therapy. A non-verbal, non-pharmacological treatment for psychiatric trauma. EMDR gives people rapid access to traumatic sensations and images and somehow helps the brain process them, which stops the flashbacks and integrates the trauma into the past. It enables patients to observe their experiences in a new way and a larger context, *without verbal give-and-take with another person.* There is evidence it can help even if the patient and therapist *do not have a trusting relationship.* This is especially interesting and useful given how trauma can destroy a person's ability to trust.

Enable: (verb) To accommodate someone in order to protect them from facing the full consequences of their choices/behaviors.

Enabler: (noun) A person who accommodates the irresponsible behavior of someone they are in relationship with.

Flashback: The unpredictable intrusion of a traumatic memory— raw, as it was first experienced— into the present, usually by a triggering sound, smell, or image.

Formaldehyde: Embalming fluid.

Gaslighting: When a perpetrator manipulates a victim with behavior or language with the intent of inducing so much self-doubt in the victim that the victim questions his/her sanity.

GPA: Grade Point Average.

GRE: Graduate Record Examination. A multiple choice, standardized exam required for admission to academic Masters and Ph.D. programs.

HIPAA: The Health Insurance Portability and Accountability Act of 1996 is a set of regulations protecting the privacy and security of certain health information.

Insight: To understand oneself with perspective.

In vivo: (of a process) Performed or taking place in a living organism, as opposed to a petri dish or glass tube.

Judgment: The ability to assess the variables and make a decision.

M & M conference: A formal medical review held by practitioners after a morbidity (illness) or mortality (death) event, both to understand what went wrong and to improve future treatment.

MCAT: Medical College Admissions Test. A standardized test used to assess medical school applicants' science knowledge, reasoning, communication, and writing skills. Required to apply to medical school.

Mood: A baseline feeling state that is persistent over time, i.e., emotional climate. (See earlier analogy with "affect.")

Morning rounds: A meeting occurring when shifts change in hospital, during which active clinical information and patient status are transferred, or signed out, by the clinicians leaving to the clinicians taking over. In teaching settings, there is also an educational component, usually done bedside, as students, residents, and the attending go *around* the ward.

MRI: Magnetic Resonance Imaging. A medical imaging technology used to assess the interior of the body, more specific (and more expensive) than CT scan (see above).

Obsession: An intrusive idea, thought, or preoccupation that cannot be shaken off with willpower. When a person loses insight that the preoccupation is irrational, the line has been crossed into delusion, i.e., psychosis.

Obsessive Compulsive Disorder (OCD): An anxiety disorder characterized by intrusive, unwanted thoughts (obsessions) and/or intrusive, unwanted behaviors (compulsions). Despite knowing these thoughts and behaviors are irrational, the patient cannot stop them.

Osmolality: The concentration, in intravenous (IV) solution, of various electrolytes or compounds the body needs (such as sodium and potassium), measured in osmoles or milliosmoles per 1000 grams of solvent. You asked.

Paranoid: A state of extreme, psychotic suspiciousness that is impervious to logic and reason.

Parentified child: A child carrying excessive responsibility for siblings or parents.

Psychotic break: This term is used when a person's mind breaks, for the first time, from the reality we, as a society, agree to function within. Usually used to describe the first psychotic episode of schizophrenia. It can include bizarre convictions (the FBI has planted a microchip in their brain and is controlling them) or auditory hallucinations (hearing voices), along with a wide range of other mental departures from the norm. It is always associated with severe distress.

Rationalization: A defense mechanism. The use of logic or intellect to mask, explain, or justify the actual, emotional reason for choices or behaviors in order to make those choices or behaviors tolerable or acceptable to oneself.

Reframe: (verb) To put a new spin on an idea from a different point of view.

Rehab: Rehabilitation. In mental health work, outpatient addiction treatment. In physical therapy, the exercise required to recover physical functioning after an injury.

Resident: A physician in training.

Sociopathy: A pervasive pattern of exploitive behavior motivated solely by self-interest, without moral conscience and without regard for the needs and rights of others. Runs the gamut of human relations, from interpersonal (bullying) to institutional (slavery).

Stalking: A pattern of harassing, intrusive and/or surveillance behavior by the perpetrator that is always frightening, and all too often dangerous to the victim because the perpetrator persists despite repeated requests to stop. Causes of the behavior include obsession, delusion (i.e. psychosis), and/or sociopathy.

Transference: When the patient unconsciously transfers childhood feelings (negative, positive, or both) about authority figures in his/her life onto the therapist. This phenomenon occurs in every treatment. A skillful therapist uses it to help the patient better understand him/herself, which moves the treatment forward. **(See also Counter-transference.)**

Unconscious: What goes on in the mind outside of conscious awareness. If conscious thought is the tip of the iceberg seen above the water, unconscious mental activity is the rest of the iceberg, unseen, under the water.

Workers Comp: Workers' Compensation Insurance. A form of state insurance whereby the state provides wage replacement and medical benefits to employees injured in the course of employment in exchange for mandatory relinquishment of the employee's right to sue their employer for negligence.

Daniela V. Gitlin, MD is a rural psychiatrist in private practice with her husband (also a psychiatrist) in upstate New York, north of the Adirondack Park. In addition to seeing patients, running the practice, empty nesting and staying married, she writes for the Psychotherapy Networker, blogs at danielagitlin.com, and has the next book under construction.

Made in the USA
Middletown, DE
07 March 2020

85569819R00249